1196x

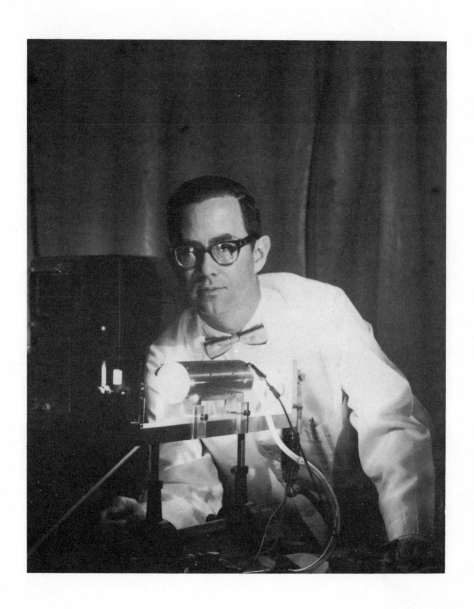

Optical Lasers in Electronics

EARL L. STEELE

Research and Engineering
Autonetics Division
North American Aviation, Inc.

John Wiley and Sons, Inc.
New York · London · Sydney

Library of Congress Catalog Card Number: 67-29008
Printed in the United States of America

I dedicate this book to:
My wife and companion, *Martha*

and to our children,
Karl Thomas, Earl Robert, Karen Lynn,
Kevin Douglas, Lisa Louise, Colleen Carol

"Though we may be learned by the help of another's knowledge, we can never be wise but by our own experience"
> ...*Montaigne*

Preface

Members of the engineering community are aware that lasers are now becoming generally available in various power, energy, and spectral ranges. For those not working in proximity to advanced laser study technical questions arise and scientific interest emerges in regard to the physical nature and potential role of the laser as it relates to their own fields.

The purpose of this book is to present an analysis and discussion of selected laser topics and is intended for those people who desire analytical and design information on laser devices. A great amount of material, spread out over the complete spectrum of technical publications, has been prepared on the laser. A certain jargon has grown out of the field, known to those working in it, but needing definition for those interested but not yet involved. This large body of literature is growing and as a consequence specific references are becoming harder to tag.

This book, then, is a collection of laser topics of interest to technical people working in electronics. The orientation is to examine the optically pumped laser as an oscillator and amplifier. The gas laser is not treated.

Optical Lasers in Electronics begins by reviewing the radiation physics and atomic principles that relate to laser action. Some particular laser configurations and special optical components, such as couplers, modulators, isolators, and detectors, are discussed in Chapter 2. In Chapter 3 the laser is considered as an oscillator and in Chapter 4, as a travelling wave amplifier. In Chapter 5 the phenomenon of *Q*-switching and the buildup of the giant laser pulse are analyzed and discussed, for they play a part in high-power systems. Semiconductor injection lasers are discussed in the sixth and final chapter.

The depth of the analysis is sufficient to permit a technically trained individual with some knowledge of differential equations and atomic physics to grasp the quantitative aspects of the topics; but the laser is treated in a manner that is understandable without extensive knowledge of quantum mechanics and without delving into quantized radiation theory. Semiclassical approaches are utilized and descriptive material is tied closely to the mathematical results. I hope that this volume will provide the mathematical insight required for one desiring a better quantitative understanding of laser phenomenon without his having to first develop a complete background in quantum theory and analysis.

This, then, constitutes the plan of presentation. Selected topics are covered by treating the physics of the laser in the language of electronics.

EARL L. STEELE

Newport Beach, California
November, 1967

Acknowledgments

"Take time for those things which are important, and not merely for those which are urgent"

I wish to acknowledge assistance from many authors, organizations, and publications for permission to use their source materials in the preparation of this book.

Among them are the following organizations:

Autonetics, a division of North American Aviation for photographs and background information

The American Telephone and Telegraph Company for material from the *Bell System Technical Journal*

International Business Machines, Inc., for data from the *IBM Journal of Research*

The Santa Barbara Research Center for data on detectors

Spectra-Physics, Inc., for data on modulators

The following trade publications:

Fairchild Publications Inc., for figures from *Electronic News*

Horizon House Publication Co. for diagrams from the *Microwave Journal* and *Solid State Design*

Iliffe Electrical Publications Ltd for drawings from *Wireless World*;

Taylor and Francis Ltd for reprints from the *Journal of Electronics and Control*

The Cahners Publishing Co. for illustrations from *EDN*

The Hayden Publishing Co. for data from *Microwaves*

In addition, data from the technical journals of the following professional societies have been used with their kind permission:

American Institute of Physics

American Physical Society

Optical Society of America
American Association of Physics Teachers
Institute of Electrical and Electronics Engineers
Institute of Physics and the Physical Society of London

Thanks are also due to Mr. C. F. O'Donnell, Vice President of Autonetics and to Dr. R. A. Gudmundsen of the Laser Research and Development Group for encouragement and permission to prepare this book while employed at Autonetics. To many authors, individually not named, whose contributions from writings and seminars vicariously contributed to this book, I also express appreciation.

Finally, to Jan Calkins, Dickey Wilkensen, and, most of all, Jean Baker goes a special note of gratitude for typing the manuscript during the long days of extensive preparation. Without their assistance and hearty cooperation the final goal would not have been achieved.

E. L. S.

Contents

Chapter 1. Laser Radiation Physics   **1**

    1-1   Classical case of wave interaction with an electron   2
    1-2   Einstein radiation coefficients   5
    1-3   Energy levels for laser materials   8
    1-4   Three-level ruby laser material   9
    1-5   Four-level laser materials   12
    1-6   Laser material test enclosures   16
    1-7   Laser rate equations   20
    1-8   Equilibrium conditions for low pump power   25
    1-9   High pump power conditions   25
    1-10 Buildup of laser action   27
    1-11 High-power laser comparison for three- and
           four-level laser systems   29
    1-12 Two-level approximations to the laser rate
           equations   33

Chapter 2. Laser Configurations and Components   **39**

    2-1 Laser cavity configurations   39
    2-2 Laser amplifier configurations   45
    2-3 The optical isolator   50
    2-4 The optical circulator   52
    2-5 Optical modulators   57
    2-6 Components using frustrated total internal reflection   77
    2-7 Laser detectors   83

Chapter 3. Laser Oscillators   **98**

    3-1 Elementary considerations   99
    3-2 Photon density for laser oscillations   101
    3-3 Laser spiking oscillations   105

3-4 Pulse reflection and pulse transmission operation   115
3-5 Laser cavity modes in oscillators   117

Chapter 4.   Laser Amplifiers   127

4-1 General discussion of reflective amplifiers   128
4-2 Simplified analytical model   132
4-3 Solution of equations   136
4-4 Pulse amplifier solution for square input pulse   141
4-5 Pulse amplifier solution for impulse-function input   153
4-6 Pulse amplifier solution for Lorenzian-shaped
     pulse input   154
4-7 Bandwidth of laser amplifier   158
4-8 Noise figure of laser amplifier   160
4-9 Experimental performance of a typical amplifier   168

Chapter 5.   Laser Q-Switching   177

5-1 Methods of Q-switching   178
5-2 Formulation of equations   185
5-3 Estimation of parameters   191
5-4 Solution for step function Q-switch   196
5-5 Solution for Q-switch variation linear in time   211
5-6 Solution for Q-switch with cosine variation in time 215
5-7 Pulse shaping considerations   219

Chapter 6.   Semiconductor Junction Diode Injection Lasers   224

6-1 Laser diode physics   227
6-2 Laser threshold conditions   236
6-3 Laser materials and output spectra   241
6-4 Effect of magnetic field on laser output   242
6-5 Effect of temperature and pressure on laser
     emission   247
6-6 Alternative schemes for pumping semiconductor
     lasers   253

Definition of Symbols   256

Index   261

Optical Lasers in Electronics

1

Laser Radiation Physics

The laser is an optical or electronic device that operates by the induced or stimulated emission of radiation. The fundamental principles are well known to modern-day physicists. A large number of solid-state electronic devices, such as photoconductor cells, photoemitting surfaces, some semiconductor elements, and, most recently, masers and lasers, depend on the emission or absorption of electromagnetic radiation by electrons bound in atoms. To achieve actual amplification at optical frequencies, considerable sophistication has been required in the preparation of materials and the application of advanced techniques.

In all of these devices the electrons must interact with an electric field; in many instances it must be an alternating electric field in the proper phase. As a consequence of this interaction the internal energy of an atomic or molecular system is altered, and energy at optical frequencies can be either emitted or absorbed.

The electric field incident on a particular atomic system can interact with an electron in a given phase relationship to take energy from it, thereby increasing the energy in the field at the expense of the electronic system; alternatively, when the electric field interacts with the electron in a different but specified phase relationship, it can also lose energy to the electron system. Thus the emission of radiation from an electronic system or the absorption can be discussed in terms of electronic interaction with the electric field under specified phase conditions.

It is important to note here that light waves, microwaves, and radio frequency waves are identical phenomena except in frequencies. The wavelengths of optical waves, however, are approximately 10,000 times shorter than those of microwaves and therefore the "circuit" techniques for measuring and controlling them are considerably different.

The fundamental nature of the induced or stimulated emission process was described by Albert Einstein and Max Planck. There is a close association between the black-body radiation equations and the detailed formulation of the quantized radiation theory. The application of these theories to the laser requires that the energy equilibrium situation in an electronic system be altered to store energy in the system composed of bound electrons and then trigger the release of this energy by interaction with a coherent light wave. This will result in stimulated or induced emission. It can thus be seen that by this process energy can be added to a light beam or electromagnetic wave incident on this electronic system and that, as a consequence, amplification can occur. Also, if the losses are small enough and feedback can be introduced, an oscillator can be constructed.

The construction and operation of practical amplifier and oscillator elements at optical frequencies is possible and has opened a completely new realm for electronic exploration.

We now discuss some of the principles and features of the radiation theory applicable to this subject.

1-1 CLASSICAL CASE OF WAVE INTERACTION WITH AN ELECTRON

The classical treatment of a bound electron as a harmonic oscillator gives a perspective that is helpful in intuitively understanding the absorption and induced emission processes. This elastically bound electron can be considered as a small antenna interacting with an incident electromagnetic wave. The electromagnetic wave provides a driving force for the electronic oscillator, and it is shown that the oscillating electron can either absorb energy from the incident wave or contribute energy to it, depending on the relative phases. We treat this simple case because of its similarity to the case of a laser.

The oscillating electron considered here is assumed to have a resonant frequency ω_0. Thus the freely vibrating oscillator with no damping has the following equation of motion, where x is the displacement from equilibrium:

$$\frac{d^2x}{dt^2} = -\omega_0^2 x. \tag{1-1}$$

We treat only vibrations in a single dimension, for it is the principle that we wish to illustrate here. The incident electric field (E) is also assumed to be sinusoidal in time:

$$E(t) = E_0 \cos (\omega t + \alpha). \tag{1-2}$$

Thus the equation of motion for an undamped oscillating electron when interacting with the electric field is given by (1-3):

$$\frac{d^2x}{dt^2} + \omega_0^2 x = \frac{eE_0}{m} \cos{(\omega t + \alpha)}. \tag{1-3}$$

It is assumed now that the electric field encounters the freely oscillating electron at $t = 0$. At that instant the vibrating oscillator has an amplitude A and a phase ϕ. Thus at $t = 0$

$$x = A \sin{\phi}. \tag{1-4}$$

The solution to the differential equation of motion from (1-3), subject to the boundary condition just noted, becomes

$$x = A \sin{(\omega_0 t + \phi)}$$
$$+ \frac{eE}{m(\omega_0^2 - \omega^2)} \left[\cos{(\omega t + \alpha)} + \frac{\omega}{\omega_0} \sin{\alpha} \sin{\omega_0 t} - \cos{\alpha} \cos{\omega_0 t} \right]. \tag{1-5}$$

This solution is composed, first, of a natural frequency term dependent on the initial amplitude and phase when the wave interacts with the oscillator; a second term, depending on the forced vibration from the electric field; and, third, two transient terms at the oscillator resonant frequency appearing as a consequence of the driving electric field. Because, however, there is no damping, they do not die away.

The power (P) or energy per second absorbed by the oscillator from the electromagnetic wave is given by (1-6) in terms of the driving force and the velocity of the elastically bound electron; thus

$$P = \frac{dW}{dt} = \left(\frac{dx}{dt} \right) \cdot e \cdot E(t)$$
$$= \left(\frac{dx}{dt} \right) e E_0 \cos{(\omega t + \alpha)}. \tag{1-6}$$

A positive value of power P represents energy absorbed by the oscillator, whereas a negative value represents energy radiated by the electron into the electromagnetic wave. By using (1-5) for the displacement, and differentiating, we obtain the velocity term

$$\frac{dx}{dt} = \omega_0 A \cos{(\omega_0 t + \phi)} + \frac{eE_0}{m(\omega_0^2 - \omega^2)} \times$$
$$\left[-\omega \sin{(\omega t + \alpha)} + \omega \sin{\alpha} \cos{\omega_0 t} + \omega_0 \cos{\alpha} \sin{\omega_0 t} \right]. \tag{1-7}$$

Inserting this expression into (1-6) for power delivered to the oscillator and integrating over one complete period (T) of oscillation of the electric wave $(T = 2\pi/\omega)$, we obtain the net energy (W) delivered to the oscillator by the electromagnetic wave:

$$W = \int_0^T eE_0\omega_0 A \cos(\omega_0 t + \phi) \cdot \cos(\omega t + \alpha) \, dt$$

$$- \int_0^T eE_0 F\omega \sin(\omega t + \alpha) \cos(\omega t + \alpha) \, dt$$

$$+ \int_0^T eE_0 F\omega \sin\alpha \cos(\omega_0 t) \cos(\omega t + \alpha) \, dt$$

$$+ \int_0^T eE_0 F\omega_0 \cos\alpha \cdot \sin(\omega_0 t) \cos(\omega t + \alpha) \, dt, \qquad (1\text{-}8)$$

where

$$F = F(\omega) = \frac{eE_0}{m(\omega_0^2 - \omega^2)}.$$

The result of this exercise reduces to the following equation for net transfer of energy over one complete cycle:

$$W = \pi(eA)E_0\left(\frac{\omega_0}{\omega}\right)\cos(\alpha - \phi) \qquad (1\text{-}9)$$

or, recognizing that the product eA is the maximum dipole moment for this oscillator (μ_m), we can write

$$\mu_m = eA$$

and

$$W = \pi\mu_m E_0\left(\frac{\omega_0}{\omega}\right)\cos(\alpha - \phi). \qquad (1\text{-}10)$$

It can be seen from this expression that the maximum absorption of energy by the oscillator occurs at resonance $(\omega = \omega_0)$ between the electric field wave and the oscillator when they are in phase ($\alpha - \phi = 0$). In this instance the energy transferred (W) is positive and the oscillator gains energy. Note also that the greater the dipole moment (μ_m), the greater the energy absorbed.

Furthermore, when the incident electric wave is out of phase with the oscillator by 180° ($\alpha - \phi = \pi$), energy is lost by the oscillator to the electric field. Thus energy can be extracted from the oscillating system when the phase difference exceeds 90°. The law of conservation of energy requires that the oscillator amplitude decrease as a consequence unless energy is supplied from an outside source. In laser terminology this outside supply of energy comes from pumping the system so as to furnish sufficient energy to the oscillator to continue the radiation to the electromagnetic wave. Energy is thus supplied to the oscillator, which in turn radiates energy to the electromagnetic wave; the effect is to amplify the electric wave as it interacts with the oscillator.

This classical description sets the stage for laser action and furnishes three important elements that must be satisfied to obtain laser action.

1. The oscillator must maintain a fixed phase relation with the incident electromagnetic field.

2. An outside source of energy must be available to the oscillator.

3. The energy radiated will be coherent with the incident wave and therefore other oscillators that are stimulated to radiate will also be "locked in" to the radiating phase of the initial oscillator. This permits coherent action between an assembly of oscillators.

In an actual atomic system, however, the radiation is governed by quantum mechanics rather than classical descriptions. This actually simplifies the description, for radiation can take place only between discrete energy states of an electron. In the quantum description oscillators radiate by a discrete change in energy between states and can radiate only when in an excited state. Thus the frequency of radiation is fixed by the energy relation between the states involved in the transition. If the upper state energy is E_2 and the lower state energy is E_1, then

$$h\nu_{21} = E_2 - E_1, \qquad (1\text{-}11)$$

where the frequency (ν_{21}) is related to the radiated energy by the Planck constant, h.

1-2 EINSTEIN RADIATION COEFFICIENTS

In the classical description radiation can occur only by the induced or stimulated emission process, which requires the presence of an electric field. In a quantized electronic system an electron can also radiate by a spontaneous process. This is characterized by a lifetime of the electron in the excited state; that is, if an electron is excited to an energy level above its normal energy state, it will remain in that excited state for some time, after which it will spontaneously return to the lower state and radiate away the energy. This can occur without the presence of an electromagnetic field and is a quantum mechanical phenomenon with no classical counterpart. It is a process similar to the spontaneous emission of nuclear particles observed in radioactive decay.

Let us now consider a two-energy-level electronic system. There will be an electron density (n_2) in the upper excited level at E_2 and, similarly, a greater electron density (n_1) at the lower energy level E_1 under thermal equilibrium conditions. There will be transitions between these two energy levels. Einstein developed a very direct proof of the relation between radiation and matter in such a system. Radiation of a proper frequency (ν_{21}) will cause transitions to occur between these two energy levels at E_2 and E_1.

Consider a system of electrons in equilibrium at temperature T. Then, by Boltzmann statistics, the electron populations at the two energy levels are related by (1-12) as follows:

$$\frac{n_2}{n_1} = \frac{g_2 \exp{(-E_2/kT)}}{g_1 \exp{(-E_1/kT)}} = \frac{g_2}{g_1} \exp{-\left(\frac{E_2 - E_1}{kT}\right)} \qquad (1\text{-}12)$$

and because $h\nu_{21} = E_2 - E_1$;

$$\frac{n_2}{n_1} = \frac{g_2}{g_1} \exp{(-h\nu_{21}/kT)}. \qquad (1\text{-}13)$$

The degeneracy factors g_2 and g_1 are the number of states available to the electrons at energy levels E_2 and E_1. Einstein then proceeded to define radiative rate coefficients. Because the system is in radiative equilibrium, the rate of emission and absorption at the photon frequency ν_{21} must be equal. To correspond to these transitions between the states of an electronic system, he then proceeded to introduce three probability coefficients, A_{21}, B_{21}, and B_{12}. They are defined as follows:

1. The coefficient A_{21} is the spontaneous emission coefficient. It is the probability per second that an electron in a state at E_2 will make a transition to a state at E_1 without any outside influence. No electromagnetic field is required.

2. The coefficients B_{21} and B_{12} are the stimulated emission coefficients. They are defined in terms of the electromagnetic energy causing transitions. Assume that an atom is in the presence of a photon cloud such that

the energy density of the photons in the frequency range dv is $\rho(v)\,dv$. Then, if the electron is in the state at E_1 (the lower state), the probability per second that it will make a transition to the upper state in E_2 with the absorption of a quantum of radiation hv_{12} is

$$B_{12}\rho(v_{12}).$$

Similarly, if it is in the upper state at E_2 in the presence of radiation, the probability per second that it will make a transition to the lower state at E_1 with the emission of a quantum of energy hv_{21} is given by

$$[A_{21}+B_{21}\rho(v_{21})].$$

Thus, when in equilibrium, the number of atoms making the transition from E_2 to E_1 equals the number making the reverse transition, we may write

$$n_2\,[A_{21}+B_{21}\rho(v_{21})] = n_1[B_{12}\rho(v_{12})]. \qquad (1\text{-}14)$$

Noting that $v_{21} = v_{12}$ and using the Boltzmann equation (1-13) for the ratio n_2/n_1, we then rewrite the above as

$$\rho(v_{21}) = \frac{(A_{21}/B_{21})}{(g_1/g_2)(B_{12}/B_{21})\exp{(hv_{21}/kT)}-1}. \qquad (1\text{-}15)$$

Now, the black-body radiation law developed by Planck gives an alternative expression for the energy density per unit frequency range in a photon cloud

$$\rho(v_{21}) = \left(\frac{8\pi hv_{21}{}^3}{c^3}\right)\left[\frac{1}{\exp{(hv_{21}/kT)}-1}\right]. \qquad (1\text{-}16)$$

Comparing these two relations, we see that

$$\frac{A_{21}}{B_{21}} = \frac{8\pi hv_{21}{}^3}{c^3} = \frac{8\pi h}{\lambda^3} \qquad (1\text{-}17)$$

and

$$g_1 B_{12} = g_2 B_{21}. \qquad (1\text{-}18)$$

For a simple electronic system with no degeneracy, that is, one in which $g_1 = g_2$, we see that $B_{21} = B_{12} = B$. This induced emission coefficient (B) can be related to the dipole moment of the transition (μ) by steps shown in standard treatments on quantized radiation theory but which are not pursued here. This relation is

$$B = \frac{8\pi^3}{3h^2}\mu^2. \qquad (1\text{-}19)$$

Furthermore, the lifetime (τ_s) for spontaneous radiation of an atom can be related to the Einstein A coefficient (A_{21}) thus

$$A_{21} = \frac{1}{\tau_s}. \qquad (1\text{-}20)$$

Note that the useful parameter for laser action is the B coefficient; the A coefficient represents a loss term and introduces into the system photons that are not phase-related to the incident photon flux or electric field. Thus the spontaneous process is a noise source in a laser. From (1-17) we note that for a given dipole moment (or B coefficient) the spontaneous coefficient is much smaller for microwaves than for optical frequencies because of the $(1/\lambda^3)$ dependence. Thus the noise from spontaneous emission in the microwave region is much less significant than at optical wavelengths.

1-3 ENERGY LEVELS FOR LASER MATERIALS

The question now is what particular atomic systems have an energy level structure that makes them acceptable candidates for laser action. Solid-state, optically pumped lasers have been successfully operated by using optical glass or crystalline host materials doped with rare earth impurities. Yttrium aluminum garnet (YAG), a crystalline laser material doped with rare earth elements, is especially promising because of the low threshold for laser action. In addition, ruby, which consists of an aluminum oxide (Al_2O_3) crystal doped with chromium ions, is an excellent laser material, as is calcium fluoride (CaF_2) doped with uranium ions. The laser action is determined by the energy level structure of the ionic impurities in the host material. The requirements on the host materials are that they be transparent to the laser radiation and the exciting radiation needed to populate the upper energy levels and of optical quality high enough that the phase of the electromagnetic wave propagating through them will not be distorted or destroyed.

Let us discuss initially the energy level structure as it relates to laser action. We consider first the three-level structure characteristic of chromium in ruby. This differs from the energy level structures of the rare earth ions in other host materials, which are characterized by a four-level system. Suffice it to say at this point that the differences are significant in terms of laser action; these differences are delineated in later discussion.

1-4 THREE-LEVEL RUBY LASER MATERIAL

The three-level energy diagram is shown in Figure 1-1. The steps leading to laser action in this system can be illustrated as follows:

1. The laser material, in the shape of a long rod, is subjected to radiation from an extremely intense light source which causes interatomic transitions from level 1 to level 3. At the same time transitions occur between level 1 and level 2. This is called optical pumping.

2. If the nonradiating transition between level 3 and level 2 is sufficiently fast, the electrons in the pump band at level 3 will transfer to level 2 rather than return directly to level 1.

3. The population of electrons in level 2 now increases as a result of the direct transition as well as the pump action and subsequent transfer from level 3.

4. Radiation of light quanta occurs when electrons make the transition from level 2 to level 1. This can be by spontaneous or stimulated emission. As long as the electron population in level 2 is less than that in level 1, however, there will be a net absorption of radiation at the frequency $\nu_{12} = \nu_{21}$ and any photons emitted will be quickly reabsorbed.

5. When the pumping action is sufficiently large and fast, the population at level 2 can be made larger than that at level 1 and a net emission of radiation at frequency ν_{21} will occur. This is called population inversion. It must happen fast compared with the spontaneous decay.

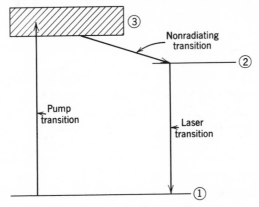

Figure 1-1 Three-level energy diagram.

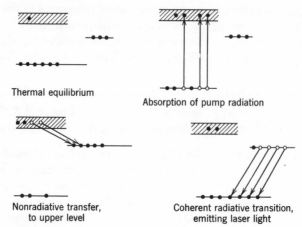

Thermal equilibrium

Absorption of pump radiation

Nonradiative transfer,
to upper level

Coherent radiative transition,
emitting laser light

Figure 1-2 Schematic diagram illustrating the sequence of events occuring in laser action.

6. By placing reflectors at the ends of the laser and forcing the radiation to be reflected back and forth to maintain the high photon density, stimulated emission will increase and exceed the spontaneous emission rate.

7. The emission at frequency ν_{21} now stimulates surrounding atoms to radiate because of the large photon density buildup, and an avalanche of photons develops at the frequency ν_{21}.

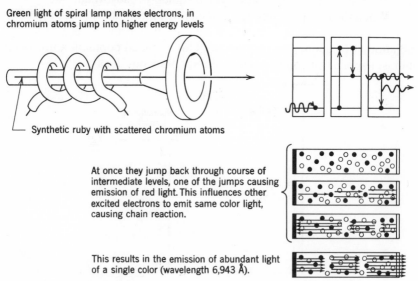

Green light of spiral lamp makes electrons, in chromium atoms jump into higher energy levels

Synthetic ruby with scattered chromium atoms

At once they jump back through course of intermediate levels, one of the jumps causing emission of red light. This influences other excited electrons to emit same color light, causing chain reaction.

This results in the emission of abundant light of a single color (wavelength 6,943 Å).

Figure 1-3 Schematic representation of the total laser process.

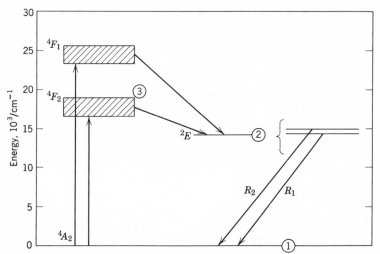

Figure 1-4 Energy level diagram for chromium ruby. Adapted from Maiman et al., *Phys. Rev.*, (1961).

8. The result is an intense light beam emerging from the end of the laser rod in an extremely narrow frequency band with a high degree of directionality. The wavefront is highly coherent, and therefore the (angular) divergence of the beam as it emerges from the laser rod is small compared with conventional light sources.

A schematic diagram of these processes is shown in Figure 1-2, in which the steps are illustrated by starting with the electrons in thermal equilibrium and proceeding through the final laser action. This is further

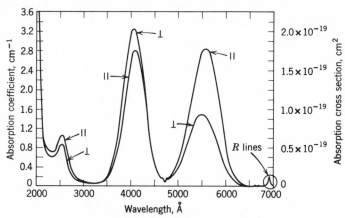

Figure 1-5 Absorption spectra of ruby for light incident parallel (‖) to the *C* axis and perpendicular (⊥) to the *C* axis. The *R* lines are the laser radiation wavelengths. After Maiman et al., *Phys. Rev.* (1961)

illustrated for a schematic laser structure by showing the location of the flash pump lamp (Figure 1-3). The actual three-level energy diagram for chromium is given in Figure 1-4.

The excited laser level 2 is actually a double level, closely spaced, with the largest contribution to laser action coming from the R_1 line. This occurs because the dipole moment for the R_1 radiation process is larger than that for the R_2 line and, in addition, the spontaneous lifetime for the R_1 line exceeds the thermal relaxation time for energy transfer between the R_2 and R_1 levels. Therefore most of the radiation appears in the R_1 line. The two levels together, because of the thermal intermixing, perform the role of level 2 in the three-energy level system.

The absorption spectra for ruby is shown in Figure 1-5, in which the large absorption peaks correspond to transitions between level 1 and the two upper pump bands identified as $^4F_1$ and $^4F_2$ at level 3. Note that a characteristic of the three-level laser material is that the laser transition takes place between the excited laser level 2 and the final ground state 1, the lowest energy level of the system. This differs from the four-level system, which is now discussed.

1-5 FOUR-LEVEL LASER MATERIALS

The four-level laser system, which is characteristic of the rare earth ions in glass or crystalline host materials, is illustrated in Figure 1-6. In any examination of this figure it will be noted that just as in the three-level system, pump transitions occur between the ground level 1 and the pump band (now at level 4); rapid nonradiative relaxation is required between the pump band and the excited laser level (now at level 3). The laser transition now occurs between level 3 and level 2, but the lower

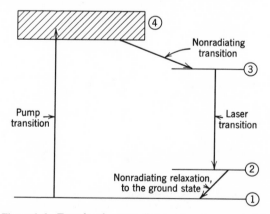

Figure 1-6   Four-level energy diagram for a laser material.

level 2 is no longer the ground state. Thus it can be seen that if the relaxation rate from level 2 to level 1 is rapid the lower laser level 2 can be kept essentially empty. In the four-level system population inversion $(n_3 > n_2)$ is maintained until the excited laser level (level 3 in the four-level system) is completely empty. Conversely, in the three-level system population inversion exists only until the population in the excited level (level 2 in the three-level system) equals the ground state population. Thus a quick examination indicates that the four-level system should be

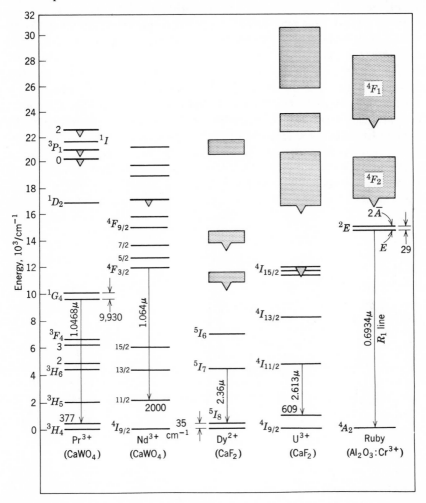

Figure 1-7 Energy level diagrams of $CaWO_4$: Pr^{3+}, $CaWO_4$: Nd^{3+}, CaF_2: Dy^{3+}, CaF_2: U^{3+}, and Al_2O_3: Cr^{3+}. The dark triangles indicate useful absorption bands or levels. After Yariv and Gordon, *Proc. IEEE* (1963).

more efficient and have a lower threshold; that is, it should be possible to extract a greater fraction of the energy from the four-level system as well as to start laser action at a lower threshold of absorption. Figure 1-7 is an energy-level diagram showing the useful absorption levels for some laser crystalline materials. The absorption spectra for Nd^{3+} in a calcium tungstate ($CaWo_4$) crystalline host material is shown in Figure 1-8. This absorption spectra does not change appreciably when Nd is used with other host materials since the absorption is characteristic of the ion and not of the host. Note that the absorption bands for this ion are much narrower than in the ruby spectrum and therefore the amount of useful light from a broad spectra flash lamp available for pumping is reduced over that for ruby; from this perspective the efficiency of using the energy put into the flash lamp is reduced. This can also be seen by reference to the relative width of the absorption bands shown in Figure 1-7.

The efficiency of energy transfer from the pump lamp to the active laser ion has been a subject of extensive study. It has been found that the addition of manganese ions (Mn^{2+}) to the glass host doped with Nd^{3+} as the active impurity greatly improves the energy transfer between the pump lamp and excited laser level. This occurs because the Mn^{2+} ion increases the absorption and subsequently transfers the energy to the Nd^{3+} ion, which in turn radiates the energy in the laser transition. The increased

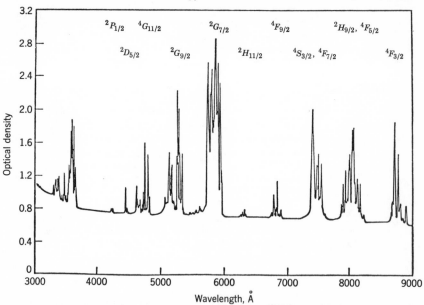

Figure 1-8 Absorption spectra for Nd^{3+} in crystalline $CaWO_4$: Nd^{3+} host laser material. The Nd^{3+} sample is 0.4 cm thick. Measurements made at 73°K. After Johnson, *J. Appl. Phys.*, (1963).

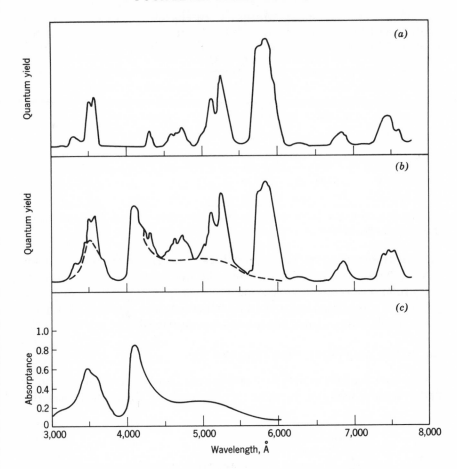

Figure 1-9 Excitation Spectra for the 1.06 μ fluorescence transition of Nd^{3+}. *a*. Nd^{3+} in unsensitized glass of composition $Mg(PO_3)_2$. *b*. Nd^{3+} in Mn^{2+} sensitized glass of composition $(Mg_{0.5}, Mn_{0.5})(PO_3)_2$. The dashed curve is the approximate residue when curve (*a*) is subtracted out. *c*. Absorptance of Mn^{2+} in $(Mg_{0.5}, Mn_{0.5})(PO_3)_2$ glass 0.6 cm thick containing no Nd^{3+}. After Melamed et al., *Appl. Phys. Lett.*(1965).

absorption and its effect on the output laser radiation at 1.06 μ are illustrated by reference to Figure 1-9, in which the effect of the manganese absorption is immediately obvious.

A similar phenomenon has been observed by adding a supplementary impurity to YAG doped with various rare earth ions. Here, again, the supplementary ions improve the efficiency of energy conversion by transferring a large part of their absorbed energy to the active ion. Table 1-1 illustrates this improvement in efficiency as noted by the reduction in the threshold for laser action when supplementary ions are added.

TABLE 1-1 EFFECT ON EFFICIENCY OF ENERGY TRANSFER FROM PUMP LAMP TO LASER RADIATION AS OBSERVED BY CHANGE IN LASER THRESHOLD WHEN SUPPLEMENTARY IMPURITIES ARE ADDED TO YAG

	Pulse Threshold of Laser (joules)			
	Active Ion: Tm^{3+}		Active Ion: Ho^{3+}	
Host Material	$\lambda = 1.884\,\mu$	$\lambda = 2.014\,\mu$	$\lambda = 2.097\,\mu$	$\lambda = 2.091\,\mu$
$YAG(Y_3Al_5O_{12})$	590	208	44	1760
$Er_{1.48}Y_{1.5}Al_5O_{12}$	180	170	11	390
$YAG + 5\%\ Cr^{3+}$		30	25	25

Data taken at 77°K with an FT 524 helical flash xenon lamp. Courtesy of Johnson et al., *Appl. Phys. Letters* (1965).

A chart summarizing some properties of laser materials other than YAG is presented in Table 1-2. Here the wavelength of laser emission, the strong absorption regions, and reported laser threshold values are given for various laser host materials and doping ions. Further references are available in the original paper and are very extensive.

1-6 LASER MATERIAL TEST ENCLOSURES

One laser configuration typical of those used for laser crystal evaluation under pulse conditions is shown in Figure 1-10. This illustrates the

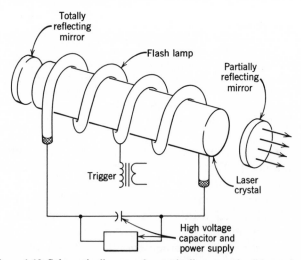

Figure 1-10 Schematic diagram of an optically pumped solid state laser.

relations among the various elements that constitute a solid state, optically pumped laser. Energy is stored in the capacitor bank, which is charged from the d-c high voltage power supply. For smaller laser crystals this voltage is probably in the range between 2000 and 5000 V. The flash tube is filled with xenon and does not conduct until the gas is ionized by a high voltage pulse from an external trigger. When it is pulsed by the trigger the stored energy is released, causing the xenon to emit very intense radiation, which then is absorbed by the laser crystal by the pumping action. Laser action then occurs in the optical resonant cavity formed by the reflecting mirrors at the ends of the laser rod, and the laser beam emerges through one of the partly transmitting mirrors.

In order to increase the effective optical coupling between the flash lamp and the laser rod, the complete assembly must be surrounded by reflecting walls. This complete ruby laser configuration is shown in Figure 1-11 for a system that uses a helical flash lamp enclosed in a cylinder with the rod centered in the enclosure.

Another configuration that has been employed extensively and with greater efficiency than the helical flash lamp design is shown in Figure 1-12. Here a linear flash lamp is placed parallel to the laser rod in an enclosure of elliptical cross section. The pump lamp is placed at one focus and the laser rod at the other.

Figure 1-13 is a photograph showing an actual laser double-ellipse enclosure designed for two flash lamps. More details on laser cavity designs and configurations are presented in the following chapter and additional variations and features are discussed there.

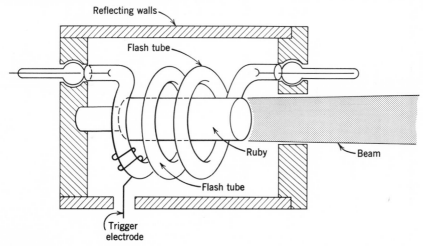

Figure 1-11 Sketch of complete ruby laser assembly, including outside enclosure.

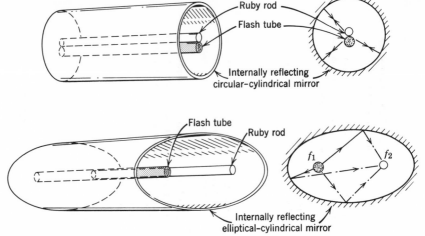

Figure 1-12 Cylindrical and elliptical cavity designs for more efficient coupling of the pump lamp to the laser rod. After Harris, *Wireless World* (1963).

1-7 LASER RATE EQUATIONS

We now discuss the underlying differences between the three- and four-level laser systems on a quantitative basis. This is done by reference to the rate equations that describe the photon and electron population densities in the various energy levels. As already noted, the operation of the laser depends on a material with narrow energy levels between which electrons can make transitions. Usually these levels are due to impurity atoms in a host crystal and are characterized by the energy level schemes shown in Figure 1-14 for the three-level case and Figure 1-15 for the four-level case. It must be noticed that the pump levels in these figures are broad.

In general the laser operates as follows. Light impinges on the laser material and causes electrons to make a transition from the ground (or lowest) state to one of the higher states. This is shown by an arrow in Figure 1-14 between the level marked E_1 and the broad level E_3. In Figure 1-15 this is shown between E_1 and E_4. Because of the width of E_3 (or E_4), also called the pump level, a large number of electrons may be caused to make this transition. In fact, the percentage of the total number of electrons excited in the ground state may be shown to depend directly on the breadth of E_3 (or E_4). The electron then loses energy by various means to E_2. This transition may be made directly or by decaying to the bottom of the pump band, E_3, and then decaying to E_2. In this process the energy lost by the electron is transferred to the lattice.

Figure 1-13 Photograph of laser cavity open to show the flash lamps and laser rod in place.

Finally, the electron returns to the ground state (or to E_2 in Figure 1-15) by the emission of a photon. It is this last transition that is responsible for the laser action. When sufficient electrons are in the upper state the radiation emitted can stimulate further emission, much like fission in

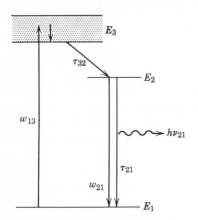

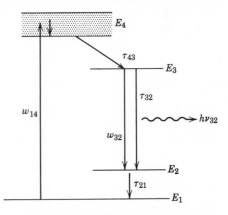

Figure 1-14 Energy level diagram for the model of a three-level laser, with rate terms identified.

Figure 1-15 Energy level diagram for the model demonstrating four-level laser operation, with rate terms identified.

atomic reactions. In an operating laser this feedback from emission is increased by placing the material in an interferometer cavity such that the emission is passed many times through the material. In the four-level scheme the electron must further decay to the ground state either by relaxation to the lattice or by emission of another photon. In principle the two schemes seem quite similar.

In detail, however, there are some striking differences. We are interested in knowing how much power is necessary to cause oscillations, what the maximum amount of power available is, and what the relative efficiencies of the two systems are. The answers to these questions lie in the dynamic set of equations for the population of each of the energy levels plus the equation for the energy density due to photons at the laser frequency in the interferometer.

The electron densities in the various energy levels (E_i) are given by n_i; the induced emission or absorption rate between two levels (i,j) is given by w_{ij}. We assert that $w_{ij} = w_{ji}$ for these examples. The time constants (τ_{ij}) represent the spontaneous relaxation times between levels.

In the following equation (1-21a–c) the first terms arise from stimulated emission and the last two from material relaxation processes. From the diagram of Figure 1-14 we obtain the following set of equations:

Three-Level

$$\frac{dn_3}{dt} = w_{13}(n_1 - n_3) - \frac{n_3}{\tau_{32}} - \frac{n_3}{\tau_{31}} \tag{1-21a}$$

$$\frac{dn_2}{dt} = w_{12}(n_1 - n_2) - \frac{n_2}{\tau_{21}} + \frac{n_3}{\tau_{32}} \tag{1-21b}$$

$$\frac{dn_1}{dt} = w_{12}(n_2 - n_1) + w_{13}(n_3 - n_1) + \frac{n_3}{\tau_{31}} + \frac{n_2}{\tau_{21}}, \tag{1-21c}$$

where w_{13} is the pump rate between the ground state and the pump band and w_{12} is the stimulated rate between laser levels. It is to be noticed that because we have a constant number of electrons (N) in the system

$$n_1 + n_2 + n_3 = N, \tag{1-22}$$

and therefore it follows that

$$\frac{dn_1}{dt} + \frac{dn_2}{dt} + \frac{dn_3}{dt} = 0 \tag{1-23}$$

The equation governing the quantum energy density (ρ) of photons in the interferometer cavity is simply

$$\frac{d\rho}{dt} = w_{12}(n_2 - n_1) + \kappa \frac{n_2}{\tau_{21}} - \frac{\rho}{\tau_c}. \tag{1-24}$$

The first term is the number of quanta received from the stimulated emission of electrons from E_2 to E_1. The second term comes from the fluorescent emission from state 2, and the third term is the loss from all sources in the interferometer. The optical laser cavity has a decay time constant of τ_c. This loss includes mirror scattering, and power output losses through the partly silvered output mirror. The constant, $\kappa = c^3/8\pi\nu^2\Delta\nu V$, is included as a number, much less than 1, which is the fraction of the fluorescence radiated into the coherent mode of the interferometer of volume V. We can similarly write down the differential equations for a four-level scheme:

Four-Level

$$\frac{dn_4}{dt} = w_{14}(n_1 - n_4) - \frac{n_4}{\tau_{43}} - \frac{n_4}{\tau_{42}} - \frac{n_4}{\tau_{41}} \tag{1-25a}$$

$$\frac{dn_3}{dt} = \frac{n_4}{\tau_{43}} - \frac{n_3}{\tau_{32}} - w_{32}(n_3 - n_2) - \frac{n_3}{\tau_{31}} \tag{1-25b}$$

$$\frac{dn_2}{dt} = w_{32}(n_3 - n_2) + \frac{n_3}{\tau_{32}} - \frac{n_2}{\tau_{21}} + \frac{n_4}{\tau_{42}} \tag{1-25c}$$

$$\frac{dn_1}{dt} = w_{14}(n_4 - n_1) + \frac{n_4}{\tau_{41}} + \frac{n_3}{\tau_{31}} + \frac{n_2}{\tau_{21}} \tag{1-25d}$$

$$\frac{d\rho}{dt} = w_{32}(n_3 - n_2) + \kappa \frac{n_3}{\tau_{32}} - \frac{\rho}{\tau_c}. \tag{1-25e}$$

Of course, many of the relaxation times are so large that the terms involving them may be neglected. Those found experimentally to be in this category in the three-level case are τ_{31}, and in the four-level case, τ_{42} and τ_{31}; also the fluorescent lifetimes are longer than the radiating lifetimes. In addition, it is obvious that κ must be of the order of the solid angle of the output laser beam, or about 10^{-5}.

The solution to these equations is complicated by the fact that the stimulated emission coefficients are dependent on the intensity of radiation present. Thus w_{12} (w_{32} in the four-level scheme) is related to the intensity of radiation (I), the speed of light (c), and the Einstein stimulated emission coefficient (B):

$$w_{12} = B\left(\frac{\rho}{\Delta \nu}\right) = B\left(\frac{I}{c\,\Delta \nu}\right) = B_s \rho. \qquad (1\text{-}26)$$

Note again that ($\rho/\Delta\nu$) is the photon energy density per unit frequency interval as originally defined in the Einstein radiation rate coefficients.

The sets of equations for the three- and four-level lasers may now be written as follows:

Three-Level

$$\frac{dn_3}{dt} = w_{13}(n_1 - n_3) - \frac{n_3}{\tau_{32}} \qquad (1\text{-}27a)$$

$$\frac{dn_2}{dt} = B_s\rho(n_1 - n_2) + \frac{n_3}{\tau_{32}} - \frac{n_2}{\tau_{21}} \qquad (1\text{-}27b)$$

$$n_1 + n_2 + n_3 = N \qquad (1\text{-}27c)$$

$$\frac{d\rho}{dt} = B_s\rho(n_2 - n_1) + \kappa\frac{n_2}{\tau_{21}} - \frac{\rho}{\tau_c}. \qquad (1\text{-}27d)$$

Four-Level

$$\frac{dn_4}{dt} = w_{14}(n_1 - n_4) - \frac{n_4}{\tau_{43}} \qquad (1\text{-}28a)$$

$$\frac{dn_3}{dt} = B_s\rho(n_2 - n_3) + \frac{n_4}{\tau_{43}} - \frac{n_3}{\tau_{32}} \qquad (1\text{-}28b)$$

$$\frac{dn_2}{dt} = B_s\rho(n_3 - n_2) + \frac{n_3}{\tau_{32}} - \frac{n_2}{\tau_{21}} \qquad (1\text{-}28c)$$

$$n_1 + n_2 + n_3 + n_4 = N$$

$$\frac{d\rho}{dt} = B_s\rho(n_3 - n_2) + \kappa\frac{n_3}{\tau_{32}} - \frac{\rho}{\tau_c}. \qquad (1\text{-}28d)$$

In both cases a set of nonlinear differential equations is based on the products of n and ρ. These equations are treated analytically and numerically in later portions of this volume by making different approximations. Although no attempt is made to solve these equations here, they are used to compare the laser action in the two energy level schemes.

1-8 EQUILIBRIUM CONDITIONS FOR LOW PUMP POWER

First consider the situation for low pump power, where the power is considerably below that required for threshold. In this case ρ is quite low and the nonlinear term can be neglected. At equilibrium, such that

$$\frac{dn_1}{dt} = \frac{dn_2}{dt} = \frac{dn_3}{dt} = \frac{dn_4}{dt} = \frac{d\rho}{dt} = 0,$$

the populations of the various states are solved:

Three-Level

$$\frac{n_3}{N} = \frac{\tau_{32}}{2\tau_{32} + (1/w_{13}) + \tau_{21}} \tag{1-29a}$$

$$\frac{n_2}{N} = \frac{\tau_{21}}{2\tau_{32} + \tau_{21} + (1/w_{13})} \tag{1-29b}$$

$$\frac{n_1}{N} = \frac{\tau_{32} + (1/w_{13})}{2\tau_{32} + \tau_{21} + (1/w_{13})} \tag{1-29c}$$

$$\rho = \frac{\kappa(n_2/\tau_{21})}{(1/\tau_c) - B_s(n_2 - n_1)}. \tag{1-29d}$$

Four-Level

$$\frac{n_4}{N} = \frac{\tau_{43}}{2\tau_{43} + \tau_{32} + \tau_{21} + (1/w_{14})} \tag{1-30a}$$

$$\frac{n_3}{N} = \frac{\tau_{32}}{2\tau_{43} + \tau_{32} + \tau_{21} + (1/w_{14})} \tag{1-30b}$$

$$\frac{n_2}{N} = \frac{\tau_{21}}{2\tau_{43} + \tau_{32} + \tau_{21} + (1/w_{14})} \tag{1-30c}$$

$$\frac{n_1}{N} = \frac{\tau_{43} + (1/w_{14})}{2\tau_{43} + \tau_{32} + \tau_{21} + (1/w_{14})} \tag{1-30d}$$

$$\rho = \frac{\kappa(n_3/\tau_{32})}{(1/\tau_c) - B_s(n_3 - n_2)}. \tag{1-30e}$$

1-9 HIGH PUMP POWER CONDITIONS

This gives the solution for very low values of photon density (ρ) in the cavity. From the differential equations it is obvious that if we solve the equilibrium conditions without neglecting the stimulated emission term there will be two equilibrium values for the photon density because of the quadratic terms developing in the cross multiplication of ρn_2, ρn_3, and ρN.

The second solution may be found by assuming that ρ is large; thus in the three-level case we let $\rho/\tau_c > \kappa\,(n_3/\tau_{32})$. Again setting the time derivatives equal to zero and noting from the equation for $d\rho/dt$ that

$$\frac{\Delta n}{N} = \frac{1}{NB_s\tau_c}, \tag{1-31}$$

where $\Delta n = n_2 - n_1$ in the three-level case and $n_3 - n_2$ in the four-level case, we may easily obtain the following equations:

Three-Level

$$\frac{n_1}{N} = \frac{[1-(1/NB_s\tau_c)]\,(1+w_{13}\tau_{32})}{3w_{13}\tau_{32}+2} \tag{1-32a}$$

$$\frac{n_2}{N} = \frac{(1+w_{13}\tau_{32}) + (1/NB_s\tau_c)\,(2w_{13}\tau_{32}+1)}{3w_{13}\tau_{32}+2} \tag{1-32b}$$

$$\frac{n_3}{N} = w_{13}\tau_{32}\left[\frac{1-(1/NB_s\tau_c)}{3w_{13}\tau_{32}+2}\right] \tag{1-32c}$$

$$\frac{\rho}{N}\!\left(\frac{\tau_{21}}{\tau_c}\right) = \frac{[w_{13}(\tau_{21}-\tau_{32})-1]-(1/NB_s\tau_c)\,[w_{13}(\tau_{21}+2\tau_{32})+1]}{3w_{13}\tau_{32}+2}. \tag{1-32d}$$

Four-Level

$$\frac{n_1}{N} = \frac{[1-(1/NB_s\tau_c)]\,(w_{14}\tau_{43}+1)}{2w_{14}(\tau_{43}+\tau_{21})+1} \tag{1-33a}$$

$$\frac{n_2}{N} = \frac{\tau_{21}w_{14}[1-(1/NB_s\tau_c)]}{2w_{14}(\tau_{43}+\tau_{21})+1} \tag{1-33b}$$

$$\frac{n_3}{N} = \frac{\tau_{21}w_{14}+(1/NB_s\tau_c)\,[w_{14}(2\tau_{43}+\tau_{21})+1]}{2w_{14}(\tau_{43}+\tau_{21})+1} \tag{1-33c}$$

$$\frac{n_4}{N} = \frac{\tau_{43}w_{14}[1-(1/NB_s\tau_c)]}{2w_{14}(\tau_{43}+\tau_{21})+1} \tag{1-33d}$$

$$\frac{\rho}{N}\!\left(\frac{\tau_{32}}{\tau_c}\right) = \frac{w_{14}(\tau_{32}-\tau_{21})-(1/NB_s\tau_c)\,[w_{14}(2\tau_{43}+\tau_{32}+\tau_{21})+1]}{2w_{14}(\tau_{43}+\tau_{21})+1}. \tag{1-33e}$$

From these equations we can calculate minimum values of w_{13} (or w_{14} in the four-level case), always assuming that the fluorescent laser level has the longest lifetime.

Three-Level

$$w_{13}\tau_{21} \geqslant \frac{NB_s\tau_c + 1}{NB_s\tau_c - 1}. \tag{1-34}$$

Four-Level

$$w_{14}\tau_{32} \geqslant \frac{1}{NB_s\tau_c - 1}. \tag{1-35}$$

For usual values, say, $N = 10^{18}$, $B_s = 10^{-7}$, and $\tau_c \simeq 10^{-9}$, respectively, the quantity $NB_s\tau_c = 10^2$. *Substitution of this result in the above equations demonstrates that for equilibrium conditions sustained oscillations may be reached at a much lower threshold in the four-level scheme than in the three-level, assuming equal relaxation times.*

1-10 BUILDUP OF LASER ACTION

The operation of the laser may be seen from the differential equation for the photon densities (ρ). For the three-level system, for instance, neglecting the spontaneous emission term,

$$\frac{1}{\rho}\frac{d\rho}{dt} = \frac{1}{\tau_c}\left[\frac{n_2 - n_1}{(n_2 - n_1)_t} - 1\right] = \frac{1}{\tau_c}\left(\frac{\Delta n}{\Delta n_t} - 1\right), \tag{1-36}$$

where we have written $(n_2 - n_1)_t = 1/B_s\tau_c$ as the threshold value of $n_2 - n_1$. If $n_2 - n_1$ is greater than this threshold value, ρ will increase exponentially in time; that is,

$$\frac{\rho}{\rho_0} = \exp + \int \frac{dt}{\tau_c}\left[\frac{n_2 - n_1}{(n_2 - n_1)_t} - 1\right]. \tag{1-37}$$

Of course, the total number of atoms that must be pumped is greatly different in the three-level and four-level schemes. The lower laser level in the three-level case is almost totally populated, and in the four-level case it may be almost totally unpopulated, depending on the energy difference between the laser levels and the temperature of the crystal.

This equation cannot be integrated because the time dependence of $n_2 - n_1$ is not known. We know, however, that it will increase to a maximum at a point at which the exponent is zero and then will decrease. Although the time dependence of this behavior is complicated, we may calculate, approximately, the value of ρ at the maximum. Let us assume that the rise is rapid enough that only a minor change may occur in the population of the upper states. Under this restriction n_3/τ_{32} in the three-level case and n_4/τ_{43} in the four-level case may be neglected. Also assume that the natural depopulation is slow compared with the laser action; thus $w_{13}(n_1 - n_3)$ in the three-level case and n_2/τ_{21} in the four-level case may also be neglected. Hence we consider only the laser action.

We may write the following two equations:

$$\frac{1}{\rho}\frac{d\rho}{dt} = (n_2 - n_1)B_s - \frac{1}{\tau_c} = \frac{1}{\tau_c}\left(\frac{\Delta n}{\Delta n_t} - 1\right) \tag{1-38}$$

and

$$\frac{1}{\rho}\frac{d}{dt}\left(\frac{n_2 - n_1}{N}\right) = -\beta\frac{(n_2 - n_1)}{N}B_s = -\left(\frac{\beta}{N}\right)\left(\frac{1}{\tau_c}\right)\left(\frac{\Delta n}{\Delta n_t}\right), \tag{1-39}$$

where $\Delta n = n_2 - n_1$. The β comes from the fact that depopulating n_2 populates n_1 and so, for every unit change in ρ, there may be two unit changes in Δn. This depends, however, on the depopulation of the lower state, so that if the pump rate (w_{13}) in the three-level case is strong enough or the relaxation rate from the lower laser level (τ_{21}) in the four-level case is short enough β is equal to 1. Thus β ranges between 1 and 2.

$$\frac{d\rho}{d(\Delta n)} = -\frac{1}{\beta}\left(\frac{\Delta n - \Delta n_t}{\Delta n}\right) \tag{1-40}$$

and therefore

$$\rho - \rho_0 = -\frac{1}{\beta}(\Delta n - \Delta n_0) + \frac{1}{\beta}\Delta n_t \ln\frac{\Delta n}{\Delta n_0}, \tag{1-41}$$

where ρ_0 and Δn_0 are the initial conditions of ρ and Δn. The maximum value of ρ occurs when $d\rho/dt = 0$ or when $\Delta n = \Delta n_t$.

$$(\rho_{\max} - \rho_0)\beta = -\Delta n_t + \Delta n_0 + \Delta n_t \ln\frac{\Delta n_t}{\Delta n_0}. \tag{1-42}$$

$$\frac{\beta(\rho_{\max} - \rho_0)}{\Delta n_0} = 1 - \frac{\Delta n_t}{\Delta n_0}\left(1 + \ln\frac{\Delta n_0}{\Delta n_t}\right). \tag{1-43}$$

This is seen to agree at threshold; when $\Delta n_0 = \Delta n_t$, then $\rho_{\max} = \rho_0$ and ρ_0 is the value just at threshold. As mentioned above, if the lower state is depopulated rapidly enough, β becomes unity and we may exchange every inverted atom for a stored light quantum, for very high $\Delta n/\Delta n_t$. The terms on the right represent the power lost in the interferometer cavity while the stored light (ρ) is building up. Thus if $\Delta n_0/\Delta n_t$ is large enough only small amounts of energy are lost during the buildup, whereas if $\Delta n_0/\Delta n_t$ is near unity the buildup is slow and nearly all ρ is lost during buildup. If $\Delta n = \Delta n_t$, no buildup can be made, for light quanta are lost as fast as they are generated.

1-11   HIGH-POWER LASER COMPARISON FOR THREE- AND FOUR-LEVEL SYSTEMS

High-power laser output implies that large amounts of energy are stored in the laser rod and that this energy is discharged in a very short time. In the laser we are limited in the amount of energy that flows by the number of atoms present; the total amount of energy per unit volume that is possible is $N\,h\nu$, which is the order of 1 joule/cm^3 for ruby. To obtain high powers, then, we are forced to release this amount of energy very rapidly. These two aspects of high power are discussed below.

From the three-level and four-level equilibrium equations without stimulated emission, we obtain the maximum population inversion as follows, provided that the nonradiating relaxation rate from the pump band is short.

Three-Level

$$\left(\frac{n_2 - n_1}{N}\right)_{\text{max}} = 1. \tag{1-44}$$

Four-Level

$$\left(\frac{n_3 - n_2}{N}\right)_{\text{max}} = 1. \tag{1-45}$$

Thus, if we pump hard enough, all the electrons will end up at the level with the slowest relaxation time. This is not the complete story for laser operation, however, for we must know how difficult it is to reach this limit. Again, using the equations without stimulated emission, we obtain the following relations:

Three-Level

$$w_{13}\tau_{21} = \frac{1 + [(n_2 - n_1)/N]}{1 - [(n_2 - n_1)/N]}. \tag{1-46}$$

Four-Level

$$w_{14}\tau_{32} = \frac{(n_3 - n_2)/N}{1 - [(n_3 - n_2)/N]}. \tag{1-47}$$

From the original definitions of w_{13} or w_{14} in (1-26) it is seen that they are proportional to the pumping intensity. Assuming equal relaxation times, for small inversions

Three-Level

$$\frac{n_2 - n_1}{N} \ll 1.$$

Four-Level

$$\frac{n_3 - n_2}{N} \ll 1.$$

The four-level inversion is proportional to the power, whereas the three level inversion is roughly constant. For large inversions, however, $(n_2 - n_1)/N \sim 1$, and $(n_3 - n_2)/N \sim 1$, the four-level system needs roughly one half the pump power to achieve the same inversion.

From the equations of steady state while laser action is occurring (ρ large), we may calculate the maximum value of ρ. Assume that all relaxation times are short compared with the laser decay and that the pump rate is large, $w_{13}\tau_{21} \gg 1$ in the three-level case and $w_{14}\tau_{32} \gg 1$ in the four-level case. Then

Three-Level

$$\frac{\rho}{\tau_c} = \frac{N[1 - (1/NB_s\tau_c)]w_{13}}{3w_{13}\tau_{32} + 2}. \tag{1-48}$$

Four-Level

$$\frac{\rho}{\tau_c} = \frac{N[1 - (1/NB_s\tau_c)]w_{14}}{2w_{14}(\tau_{43} + \tau_{21}) + 1}. \tag{1-49}$$

Thus in the three-level case, if $3w_{13}\tau_{32} \ll 2$, ρ is proportional to w_{13}, and in the four-level case, when $2w_{14}(\tau_{43} + \tau_{21}) \ll 1$, ρ is proportional to w_{14}. If the reverse case is true as in the case of saturation, (ρ/τ_c) is the following:

Three-Level

$$\frac{\rho}{\tau_c} = \frac{N[1 - (1/NB_s\tau_c)]}{3\tau_{32}}. \tag{1-50}$$

Four-Level

$$\frac{\rho}{\tau_c} = \frac{N[1 - (1/NB_s\tau_c)]}{2(\tau_{43} + \tau_{21})}. \tag{1-51}$$

Thus not only is it more difficult to pump with the three-level case, but the ultimate power out is greater in the four-level case.

We now wish to know how much light output this inversion will produce in a laser beam. We notice that the output power, P_{out}, is given by

$$P_{out} = \frac{\rho h \nu}{\tau_0},\qquad(1\text{-}52)$$

where τ_0 is the relaxation time due to output power and ρ is the number of stored photons of frequency, ν. If we lump all other losses in the cavity into another relaxation time, τ_2, we have the relation

$$\frac{1}{\tau_c} = \frac{1}{\tau_0} + \frac{1}{\tau_2},\qquad(1\text{-}53)$$

where τ_c is the total relaxation time of the optical cavity. If the window is sufficiently transparent, the majority of light is lost through it and $\tau_c \sim \tau_0$.

In the preceding section we calculated the value of ρ/τ_c for various conditions. The highest peak conditions occur when a large number of electrons can be stored in the upper state and kept from lasering by increasing the threshold. They are then suddenly "dumped" into a laser mode by reducing the threshold. From the preceding section (1-43) the number of photons getting into the laser mode is approximated by

$$\beta\left(\frac{\rho_{max} - \rho_0}{\Delta n_0}\right) = 1 - \frac{\Delta n_t}{\Delta n_0}\left(1 + \ln \frac{\Delta n_0}{\Delta n_t}\right).\qquad(1\text{-}54)$$

The value of β ranges from 1 to 2, depending on the depletion rate of the lower state. In the three-level case it will probably be near 2, and for the four-level case it will be near 1 if the relaxation of the lower state is rapid; in our discussion we assume that it is unity.

The values of ρ_0 and Δn_0 are those at the time when the threshold is reduced and laser action begins. The value of ρ_0 is then quite small and can be neglected, and the value of Δn_0 is dependent on the pumping rate according to (1-54).

As already stated, if Δn_t is close to Δn_0, then the peak value of ρ_{max} is only a small fraction of the total inversion. This points out the value of a small threshold. When $\Delta n_t/\Delta n_0$ is small, we get essentially all the emitted light into the interferometer. Figure 1-16 shows the variation of photon flux in the cavity with inversion over threshold. When $\Delta n_t/\Delta n_0 = 0.05$, a large amount over threshold, $\rho/\Delta n_0 = 0.8$ and a large fraction of the

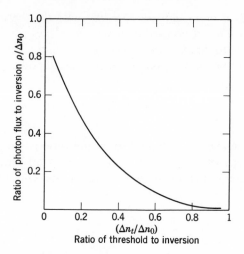

Figure 1-16 Photon density developed in the laser cavity as determined by the amount of electron inversion over the threshold value.

stored energy is converted to photon laser flux. If we are over threshold by a large amount, it is seen that nearly all the electrons will be converted into light in the interferometer cavity independent of threshold. Thus $\rho_{max} \approx \Delta n_0$, and therefore

$$(P_{out})_{max} = \frac{\Delta n_0 h\nu}{\tau_c}. \tag{1-55}$$

The conversion efficiency is then found to be proportional to the following ratios:

Three-Level

$$\frac{(P_{out})_{max}}{w_{14}\tau_{32}} = \frac{\Delta n_0 h\nu}{\tau_c} \frac{1 - (\Delta n/N)}{1 + (\Delta n/N)}. \tag{1-56}$$

Four-Level

$$\frac{(P_{out})_{max}}{w_{14}\tau_{32}} = \frac{\Delta n_0 h\nu}{\tau_c} \frac{1 - (\Delta n/N)}{\Delta n/N}. \tag{1-57}$$

Thus we see that the conversion efficiency is also much larger in the four-level system than in the three-level case. Another advantage in the four-level system, then, is this efficiency factor.

1-12 TWO-LEVEL APPROXIMATIONS TO THE LASER RATE EQUATIONS

As we have seen in the preceding discussions, two levels are of prime importance in laser action: the excited laser level (E_2 in the three-level system and E_3 in the four-level) and the lower laser level (E_1 in the three-level and E_2 in the four-level). Thus for many analyses of laser action an approximation of the three- and four-level systems to a two-level representation would be useful if accurate. This section will discuss the conditions that must exist if the two-level approximation is valid.

A diagram shows the energy levels and the radiation rates involved (Figure 1-17). We examine the rate equations to see how they can be restated to conform to this system.

In this two-level system w_p represents the rate of pumping electrons from the lower level l to the excited upper level u. The induced or stimulated emission or absorption rate (w_i) between the two levels results from the actual photon-induced laser transition caused by photons at frequency ν_{ul}; the relaxation time (τ_s) represents the spontaneous emission losses from the excited upper level u.

Thus the rate equations for the two-level system just described are as follows:

$$\frac{dn_u}{dt} = w_p n_l - w_i(n_u - n_l) - \frac{n_u}{\tau_s} \tag{1-58a}$$

$$\frac{dn_l}{dt} = -w_p n_l + w_i(n_u - n_l) + \frac{n_u}{\tau_s} \tag{1-58b}$$

where the first term on the right is due to pumping from the lower level to the upper level; the second term is that due to stimulated emission transitions between levels; the final term arises from spontaneous emission from the upper state. It should be noted that the stimulated

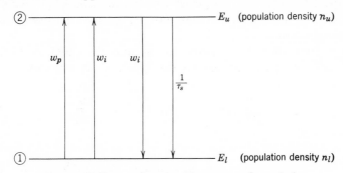

Figure 1-17 Proposed two-level laser system for analysis.

emission rate (w_i) depends on the photon density in the laser. For this treatment, however, I do not explicitly bring in the photon density, for it is not required to make the comparison intended here.

Three-Level Case

The three-level rate equations (1-21) are now examined to determine the conditions necessary to permit a valid approximation to a two-level system. Assume that the spontaneous loss rate from the pump band of the three-level system is small compared with other rates and also that the nonradiating decay time (τ_{32}) between the pump band and the upper laser level is short. Then the rate equation (1-21a) for the population density in level 3 can be written as

$$\frac{dn_3}{dt} = w_{13}(n_1 - n_3) - \frac{n_3}{\tau_{32}}. \tag{1-59}$$

If τ_{32} is short compared with the time intervals involved in laser action, the electron density (n_3) will not have time to become large because it starts from zero. If we integrate (1-59) over a time period that is small compared with the time over which the lower state density (n_1) will change appreciably and thereby also make note of the fact that $n_3 \ll n_1$, we obtain

$$n_3 \simeq n_1(w_{13}\tau_{32})[1 - \exp(-t/\tau_{32})]. \tag{1-60}$$

Now for τ_{32} very short compared with other rate constants as postulated, we see that, because equilibrium is quickly established,

$$n_3 \simeq n_1(w_{13}\tau_{32}). \tag{1-61}$$

The significance of this result is simply to state that the electrons that make the transition into the pump band are immediately transferred out to the excited laser level and therefore the electron density in the pump band remains low.

If we substitute this relation for n_3 into the other rate equations (1-21b, c) for n_2 and n_1 and observe that $\tau_{32}/\tau_{31} \ll 1$, we obtain

$$\frac{dn_2}{dt} = w_{13}n_1 - w_{12}(n_2 - n_1) - \frac{n_2}{\tau_{21}} \tag{1-62a}$$

and

$$\frac{dn_1}{dt} = -w_{13}n_1 + w_{12}(n_2 - n_1) + \frac{n_2}{\tau_{21}}. \tag{1-62b}$$

These are the rate equations for the levels directly involved in the laser transitions in the three-level system.

Thus a direct comparison between the two-level equations (1-58) and (1-62) for the three-level case illustrates that the two-level approximation can be made if we let

$$w_p = w_{13}$$

$$\tau_s = \tau_{21}$$

$$w_i = w_{12}. \tag{1-63}$$

This result further highlights the fact that the transfer of electrons from the ground state (E_1) to the upper laser level (E_2) is limited by the transition rate to the pump band (w_{13}) and not by the nonradiating relaxation rate out of the pump band (τ_{32}) to the excited laser level (E_2).

To recapitulate, the three-level laser system can be adequately represented by the two-level approximation if the following two conditions are met:

1. The nonradiating transition between the pump level and the upper laser level occurs more rapidly than other transition processes.

2. Spontaneous losses from the pump band to the ground state are negligible.

These conditions are met by ruby, and therefore laser analysis of the ruby system can proceed on the basis of a two-level approximation to a high degree of accuracy.

Four-Level Case

The four-level rate equations (1-25) are now examined to ascertain under what conditions the two-level approximation can be used.

Ignoring the insignificant direct transitions between the pump band and the lower laser level and assuming spontaneous emission losses from the pump band to be small, we can write (1-25a) for the electron population in the pump band (n_4) as

$$\frac{dn_4}{dt} = w_{14}(n_1 - n_4) - \frac{n_4}{\tau_{43}}. \tag{1-64}$$

If we assume in this case, as in the three-level example, that the relaxation rate $(1/\tau_{43})$ between the pump band and the upper laser level occurs more rapidly than the pump rate (w_{14}), we observe that $n_4 \ll n_1$ especially for $(t < \tau_{43})$, and we may further write

$$\frac{dn_4}{dt} = w_{14}n_1 - \frac{n_4}{\tau_{43}}. \tag{1-65}$$

Now, subject to the above conditions, which also imply that the ground state population (n_1) does not change appreciably for $\tau \sim \tau_{43}$, and applying the boundary condition that $n_4 = 0$ at $t = 0$, we integrate (1-65) to obtain the following result:

$$n_4 = n_1(w_{14}\tau_{43})[1-\exp(-t/\tau_{43})]. \tag{1-66}$$

At equilibrium we see that

$$n_4 \simeq n(w_{13}\tau_{43}). \tag{1-67}$$

Again, the significance of this relation in the laser system is to indicate that the electrons are transferred out of the pump level (E_4) to the excited laser level (E_3) as fast as they are pumped in from the ground state (E_1) Here, however, it is important to note that the ground state is *not* the lower laser level. The lower laser level is at E_2 and not at E_1 in the four-level system being discussed.

Because an equilibrium value of n_4 is quickly established after pumping starts, we may use this equilibrium value given by (1-67) in the rate equation for the electron populations in the other levels. Thus we write

$$\frac{dn_3}{dt} = w_{14}n_1 - w_{32}(n_3 - n_2) - \frac{n_3}{\tau_{32}} \tag{1-67a}$$

$$\frac{dn_2}{dt} = w_{32}(n_3 - n_2) + \frac{n_3}{\tau_{32}} - \frac{n_2}{\tau_{21}} \tag{1-67b}$$

$$\frac{dn_1}{dt} = -w_{14}n_1 + \frac{n_2}{\tau_{21}}. \tag{1-67c}$$

For the four-level laser to maximize its intrinsic advantage, the lower laser level population (n_2) should be kept as low as possible. As shown earlier, this minimizes the amount of pumping needed to achieve a given inversion and allows more power to be coupled out. To achieve these objectives it is necessary that the nonradiative relaxation time (τ_{21}) from the lower laser level to the ground state be very fast. When pumping action starts we note that

$$\frac{dn_1}{dt} = -w_{14}n_1,$$

and because we assumed that the transition rate $(1/\tau_{21})$ out of the lower laser level (E_2) is rapid, it might be possible with a very large pump rate (w_{14}) to empty the ground state completely and fill the excited laser level. In this case the two-level laser approximation would not be valid. If, however, the rate processes are such that an equilibrium condition develops $(dn_1/dt = 0)$ before laser action really gets under way, then the two-level approximation is valid.

Thus let $dn_1/dt = 0$; then

$$n_1 = \frac{n_2}{w_{14}\tau_{21}}. \tag{1-68}$$

Using this in (1-67) we see that

$$\frac{dn_3}{dt} = \frac{n_2}{\tau_{21}} - w_{32}(n_3 - n_2) - \frac{n_3}{\tau_{32}}. \tag{1-69a}$$

$$\frac{dn_2}{dt} = \frac{n_2}{\tau_{21}} + w_{32}(n_3 - n_2) + \frac{n_3}{\tau_{32}}. \tag{1-69b}$$

Again, by a direct comparison with (1-58), we see that the two-level approximation holds where

$$w_p = \frac{1}{\tau_{21}}$$

$$w_i = w_{32}$$

$$\tau_s = \tau_{32}. \tag{1-70}$$

It will be noted, however, that the equivalent pumping rate is not governed by the transition rate between the ground state (E_1) and the pump band (E_4), but rather by the relaxation rate out of the lower laser level $(1/\tau_{21})$. This simply states that the rate of transfer of electrons between the lower and upper laser levels via the pump band is limited by the relaxation time (τ_{21}) and not by the transfer steps to the pump band and subsequent relaxation to the upper laser level. In this instance the four-level system takes on many of the characteristics of the three-level system since the pumping limitation is on the removal of electrons from the lower laser level and not on the pump rate from the ground state.

To recapitulate, the conditions that must be satisfied in order to approximate the four-level laser system validly with a two-level scheme are the following:

1. The nonradiating relaxation rate out of the pump band to the upper laser level must be rapid when compared to pump rate from the ground level.

2. The electron density in the ground state (not the lower laser level) must reach some low equilibrium value rapidly. This then causes the four-level system to assume some of the limitations of the three-level systems, since the bottom laser level can never be considered as empty.

Thus the advantages of the four-level system are preserved when the pump action is limited by w_{14}, since the system will appear to be pumping from a large source of electrons that is independent of the lower laser level.

Rapid relaxation out of the lower laser level is also important, however, to make the effectiveness and efficiency of the pumping action on the inversion ratio more pronounced.

REFERENCES

Haun, R. D., "Laser Materials and Devices, A Research Report," *Electrotech.*, **72**, 63–71 (September 1963).

Johnson, L. F., "Optical Maser Characteristics of Rare Earth Ions in Crystals," *J. Appl. Phys.*, **34**, 897–909 (April 1963).

Johnson, L. F., J. E. Geusic, and L. G. Van Uitert, "Coherent Oscillations from Tm^{3+}, Ho^{3+}, Yb^{3+}, Er^{3+} Ions in Yttrium Aluminum Garnet," *Appl. Phys. Letters*, **7**, 127–129 (September 1, 1965).

Lamb, W. E., Jr., "Theory of an Optical Maser," *Phys. Rev.*, **134**, A1429–1450 (June 15, 1964).

Ludman, J. E., "Analysis of Transients and Stability in an Idealized Two-Level Laser System," *Appl. Opt.*, **2**, 862–863 (August 1963).

Maiman, T. H., "Stimulated Optical Emission in Fluorescent Solids. I. Theoretical Considerations," *Phys. Rev.*, **123**, 1145–1150 (August 15, 1961).

Maiman, T. H., R. H. Hoskins, I. J. D'Haenens, C. K. Asawa, and V. Eutuhov, "Stimulated Optical Emission in Fluorescent Solids: II, Spectroscopy and Stimulated Emission in Ruby," *Phys. Rev.*, **123**, 1151–1157 (August 15, 1961).

Melamed, N. T., C. Hirayama, and E. K. Davis, "Laser Action in Nd-Doped Glass Produced through Energy Transfer," *Appl. Phys. Letters*, **7**, 170–172 (September 15, 1965).

Schawlow, A. L., "Advances in Optical Masers," *Sci. Am.*, **209**, 34–45 (July 1963).

Sukheeja, B. D., and M. L. Narchal, "Stability of an Idealized Two Level Laser," *Appl. Optics* **5**, 1464–1465 (September 1966).

Yariv, A., and E. I. Gordon, "The Laser," *Proc. IEEE*, **51**, 4–29 (January 1963).

2

Laser Configurations
and Components

There are many possible physical arrangements available for the construction and assembly of an operating, optically pumped laser. The actual arrangements of the location of the pump lamps, laser rod, and reflecting surfaces are varied, and many excellent variations have been achieved. It is the purpose of this chapter to illustrate some practical configurations that have worked well and to describe some of the auxiliary components developed and tested for use with the laser. It is not intended to be an exhaustive catalog of all designs available or attempted but rather a sampling to provide the reader with information on which way to proceed for actual laser construction.

2-1 LASER CAVITY CONFIGURATIONS

The design of the laser cavity is of considerable significance because it determines the degree to which the light from the pumping lamp will be coupled into the laser rod. It also determines the ease of permissible adjustments or alignments of the mirrors constituting the ends of the optical cavity.

Two categories of reflecting surfaces concern us in the laser.

1. One set is constituted by the mirrors at the end of the laser rod, which determine the optical Q of the cavity. In some configurations these mirrors are attached or coated directly to the end surface of the laser rod; in other arrangements the mirrors may be deteached and removed a considerable distance away. They may be plane mirrors or concave or convex surfaces or combinations. One of these mirrors will very likely be only partly reflecting, for it will serve as the laser output port. We refer to them as the end mirrors.

2. The second category of reflectors is concerned with reflecting light flux from the flash lamps back to the laser rod to increase the efficiency of energy transfer. These reflectors surround the flash lamps and the rod; the reflector surfaces should be highly polished, not diffuse, especially at the absorption bands of the laser rod. Much of the radiation from the flash lamps does not impinge directly on the laser rod, and it is the purpose of the reflectors to focus the stray radiation from the lamps into the rod for greater efficiency of operation. In many instances the characteristics of the reflectors may well determine whether laser action can actually be achieved. They are generally referred to as pump reflectors and, in essence, constitute the sides of the laser cavity.

Our prime discussion here concerns the side reflectors, those concerned with the reflection of pump light into the laser rod.

Two common laser reflector designs for illuminating the laser crystal are illustrated in Figure 2-1. Both use linear flash lamps in a cylindrical reflector; one design has a circular cross section, whereas the second design has an elliptical contour. The cross sections are shown on the right in this figure. In the circular cross section reflector (Fig. 2-1a) the crystal and flash lamp should be mounted as close together as possible, with their long axes parallel to one another and to the axes of the reflecting cylinder. Because the radiation is emitted from the flash lamp, which is slightly off the cylinder axis, it will be reflected back to the laser rod which is also slightly off axis, but symmetrically so. Thus, if the diameter, of the rod and flash lamp is small compared with the cylinder

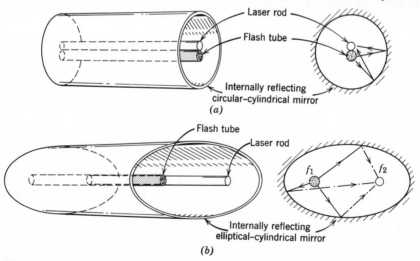

Figure 2-1 Two laser cavity configurations for coupling pump lamp radiation into the laser rod.

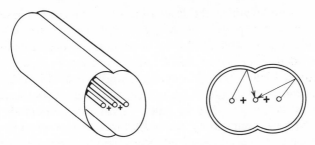

Figure 2-2 Laser cavity design for using two flash lamps to pump one rod. This is composed of two intersecting cylinders. The flash lamps are located off center but symmetrical with the rod. The center axes of the circular cylinders are indicated by plus signs. The laser rod is in the middle.

diameter, the light will be focused on the rod after reflecting off the cylinder wall.

The elliptical cavity (Fig. 2-1b) is more difficult to construct but provides somewhat greater efficiency. In this case the flash lamp is placed at one focus of the reflector and the laser crystal at the other; it is, of course, necessary that all the axes be parallel. It will be recalled that in the case of an elliptical reflector light radiated from one focus is reflected from the surface and passed back through the other focus. Thus virtually all light transmitted radially from the flash lamp is reflected onto the rod. The internal surfaces of these reflectors should have a high optical polish and perhaps be coated with a metal of high reflectivity, such as gold.

The greatest efficiency of these designs is achieved when the pump

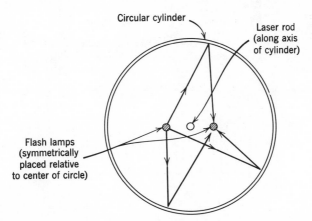

Figure 2-3 Cross section of poor cavity design for the two-flash-lamp laser cavity. The light from one flash lamp, when reflected from the wall, is focused on the other lamp and not on the laser rod.

lamp is the same length as the laser rod, for no excess radiation is lost. When, however, the power or energy output level of the laser is not sufficient with one flash lamp driven to its limit, a second lamp may be added, provided some cavity modifications are made. A cross section is illustrated in Figure 2-2. This configuration is a double cylinder with a laser rod common to both. This cavity, however, lacks the efficiency of the others. Although twice as much energy can be pumped into the cavity by the flash lamps, only about 1.6 times as much can be coupled into the laser rod. This loss of efficiency results from the removal of part of the cylinder walls to allow for the common placement of the laser rod, and thus the coupling is reduced. More power can be obtained, however, from this double-lamp configuration than from the single-lamp design.

It should be noted here that the use of two lamps symmetrically placed in the simple circular cylinder cavity, with the laser rod then on the axis of the cylinder, will degrade the efficiency to a great extent. A cross section of this configuration is shown in Figure 2-3. The reason for the poor performance of the design is that the radiation from the two lamps

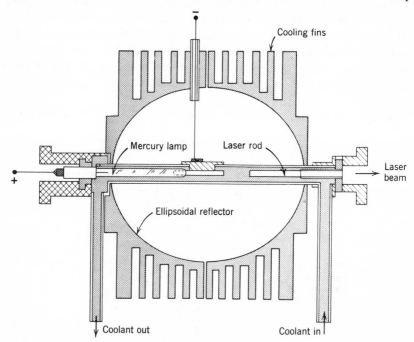

Figure 2-4 Diagram of a highly efficient, single-pump laser cavity. It is an ellipsoid of revolution, with the laser rod and the pump lamp symmetrically placed along the major axis of the ellipse.

is focused one on the other and *not* on the laser rod. Therefore this cavity configuration is to be avoided, for the coupling is poor and the laser threshold will be high. It can be made to work, however.

Another laser cavity design with high coupling efficiency is shown in Figure 2-4. This design extends the principle of focusing in an elliptical geometry to a total ellipsoid of revolution. Here the laser rod and the pump lamp are at opposite ends of the major axis of the ellipse; the laser mirrors in this design are coated directly on the laser rod. This design takes advantage of a very interesting property of the ellipse illustrated in Figure 2-5. Any light ray passing through the major axis at a point between the end of the ellipse (A) and the focus (f_1) is reflected by the surface of the ellipse to a point on the major axis between the opposite focus (f_2) and the opposite end of the ellipse (B). Thus all the radiation emitted by the flash lamp on the axis of the ellipse, if properly placed, passes through the laser rod. The coupling is greatly enhanced.

Two problems exist with this geometry:

1. Radiation emitted uniformly per unit length from the pump lamp is not focused uniformly per unit length on the rod; some portions of the rod receive more photons than others.

2. The cavity is useful only with one flash lamp; it is not possible to extend the design to multiple lamp systems.

Even with these problems, however, this cavity design is useful and works extremely well. The design lends itself to effective cooling measures as illustrated in Figure 2-4, where a coolant can circulate over both lamp and rod in a simple flow system. The cooling fins permit a high thermal loss rate to the surrounding atmosphere, and the complete configuration is extremely compact.

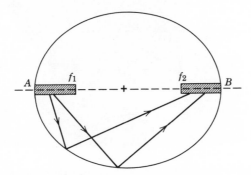

Figure 2-5 Optical paths of radiation in an ellipsoid of revolution. All rays from the left of the focal point (f_1) are focused to the right of focal point f_2 after reflection.

A photograph of one such cavity is shown in Figure 2-6, in which all the critical parts may be easily seen.

Figure 2-6 Photograph of an elliptical cavity of revolution, showing cooling fins on the structure for improved heat transfer. Courtesy of Autonetics, a division of North American Aviation.

This elliptical geometry has been utilized in a continuously emitting (CW) solid state laser system using a mercury lamp for the pumping source and either ruby or neodymium-doped calcium tungstate ($CaWO_4$) as the laser rod. Extreme care has to be exercised when operating to ensure adequate cooling of the laser rod, because a great amount of thermal radiation is absorbed in laser action. Of course, longer laser rods and corresponding longer pump lamps can be used in a larger cavity to increase the power output. The elliptical geometry allows many interesting variations and, optically, is as close to an ideal geometry as possible.

2-2 LASER AMPLIFIER CONFIGURATIONS

Some typical laser amplifier arrangements, along with their properties and features, are discussed in this section. The purpose here is to point out the essential elements required and to note the manner in which they are used.

The laser amplifier assembly normally contains at least two parts. One is the oscillator laser device, and the second is the amplifier section itself. As in conventional electronics, the use of an amplifier section after an oscillator often permits a lower power oscillator to be more critically designed, but high-power output is then made available by following the oscillator with an amplifier section. So it is with lasers.

An additional element is sometimes used between multistage amplifier elements, especially where high gain is required. This device is called an optical isolator and fulfills the role of preventing feedback between the amplifier sections. The isolator is not normally a laser itself but an optical device that permits only one-way transmission of radiation. When

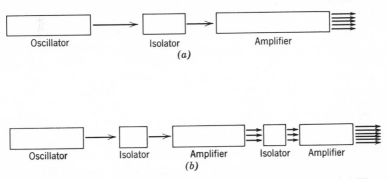

Figure 2-7 Schematic representation of a laser oscillator-amplifier configuration. The upper figure (*a*) illustrates a single amplifier stage, whereas the lower figure (*b*) represents multistage amplifiers, where the isolation between stages becomes more critical to the operation.

multistage amplifiers are used the isolator element is especially important to preclude internal feedback between the amplifier stages, which will thus prevent internal oscillations from breaking out at the high-gain levels. The laser oscillator-amplifier system might then be represented schematically as shown in Figure 2-7. The upper portion of the figure (2-7a) represents a simple one-stage amplifier system following an oscillator where we have indicated isolation between the two laser elements; the lower portion (2-7b) represents a multistage amplifier arrangement.

Figure 2-8 is a diagram that represents a straightforward, optically pumped laser amplifier system which uses neodymium-doped laser material. Here the oscillator section is a solid-state laser with mirrors on both ends of the rod. The amplifier section has no mirrors because feedback is not desired in this stage; it is intended that the radiation from the oscillator enter the amplifier, stimulate emission in the material, gain energy, and then emerge as an amplified beam. For optimal operation, the flash lamp for the amplifier stage has to be synchronized with that of the oscillator. This must be timed so that there is a maximum population inversion in the amplifier when the beam from the oscillator enters it. The firing of the flash lamps for the oscillator, then, is usually delayed relative to the amplifier lamp flash. The amount of this delay depends on the exact circuit used and the particular flash lamp, but ordinarily it is of the order of 50–100 μsec. A variation on this configuration, which can reduce radiation loss from reflections at the ends, is to cut the ends of the amplifier rod at a Brewster angle and thereby eliminate reflections at the surface for the proper polarized beam. A photograph of a ruby oscillator-amplifier combination with the Brewster

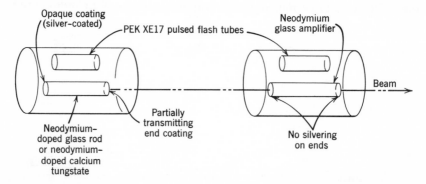

Figure 2-8   Schematic diagram of a neodymium-doped laser oscillator-amplifier system. At the ends of the oscillator rod there are mirrors, whereas there are none in the amplifier. In operation the oscillator pump lamp is delayed relative to the amplifier flash lamp. Courtesy of Gessell, *Electronic News* (October 1964).

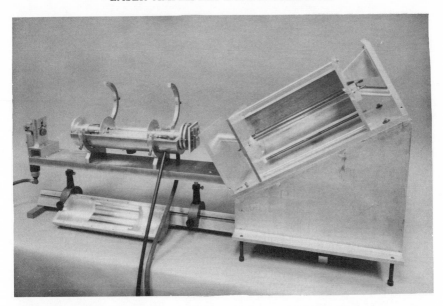

Figure 2-9 Photograph of a ruby oscillator-amplifier combination. Shown on the left is the Q-switched laser oscillator using a 6-in. rod. On the right is an amplifier using a 12-in.-long ruby rod cut with Brewster angle faces. Courtesy of Autonetics, a division of North American Aviation.

faces cut on the amplifier rod is shown in Figure 2-9. In this case the light from the ruby oscillator is already properly polarized by choosing the proper axis of the ruby; the amplifier is placed at an angle with the oscillator axis in order to permit the light to be incident on the input face of the amplifier at the Brewster angle.

Some experiments which use the oscillator-amplifier as an image intensity amplifier have been successfully performed with a ruby laser configuration. The experimental set-up is shown in Figure 2-10. Here

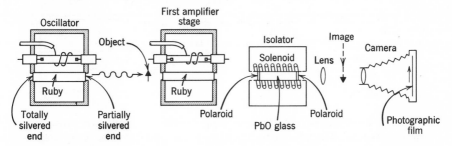

Figure 2-10 Schematic description of an image amplification experiment using a ruby amplifier. The higher power optical beam obtained by using an amplifier stage increases the contrast of the image. After Geusic and Scovil, *Bell System Tech. J.* (1962).

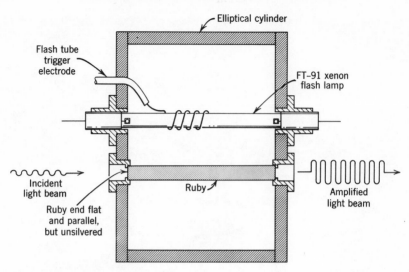

Figure 2-11 A ruby optical amplifier used in laser amplification measurements. After Geusic and Scovil, *Bell. System. Tech. J.* (1962).

the light from an oscillator impinges on a transparent object (in this case a figure on a film). The laser light from this object then passes through the amplifier and is recorded on film in the camera. It has been found that there is considerable increase in the contrast when the amplifier stage is used. Thus the image amplification properties have been demonstrated. A diagram of the actual laser amplifier used is shown in Figure 2-11.

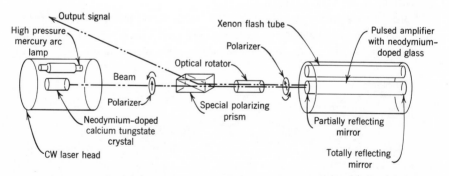

Figure 2-12 Regenerative feedback neodymium amplifier using reflective surfaces on the amplifier laser rod. The radiation is coupled out of the system by using optical rotation of the polarization and a special polarizing prism. The wave makes several passes through the amplifier section because of the total reflection at the right end and partial reflection at the other end. After Gessell, *Electronic News* (October 1964).

A variation on the laser amplifier design is achieved by adding reflective surfaces to the amplifier in the single-stage arrangement shown in Figure 2-12. With reflecting mirrors on the amplifier stage, multiple passes of the light wave are permitted and the effect of a longer laser or higher total gain is achieved. In this instance it is practical to run the oscillator as a continuously emitting laser (CW) with isolation between oscillator and amplifier provided by the special polarizing prism and the polarizers, and a pulsed output occuring when the amplifier is triggered. The amplifier plays the role of a regenerative amplifier subject to similar problems of breaking into oscillation when the gain is too great or the input power excessive.

A final configuration to be discussed consists of a traveling wave amplifier, which serves as its own oscillator. This design utilizes an isolator to eliminate standing waves in the system since it permits radiation to traverse the optical path in only a clockwise direction, as shown in Figure 2-13. In many respects this may be treated as a traveling wave oscillator and works in the following way.

The optical cavity consists of the laser rod, which emits in only one direction because the radiation is allowed to travel only one way by the isolator. Every time the radiation passes through the laser rod it is amplified. Each time the photons pass the partly transmitting mirror

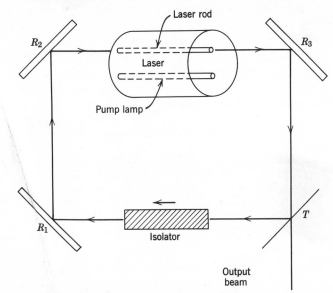

Figure 2-13 Traveling wave oscillator configuration. Mirror T is partially transmitting while mirrors R_1, R_2, and R_3 are totally reflecting. The isolator permits light to travel in one direction with low loss, but in the opposite direction the attenuation is high.

(*T*) energy is extracted. A greater fraction of the total energy can thus be extracted from the laser rod with this structure, for standing waves are not allowed; thus the total inverted population can be used more effectively.

2-3 THE OPTICAL ISOLATOR

The purpose of an optical isolator is to allow a light beam to be transmitted in one direction through it, with low loss but with high attenuation of the beam when traveling in the opposite direction. In the optical case this nonreciprocal element works by using the Faraday effect; a material, such as a glass, with heavy lead content can be used. The material must have a suitable Verdet constant, so as to permit rotation of the plane of polarization of a light beam passing through it. The construction of one such nonreciprocal element is shown in Figure 2-14. Here, a wave enters from the left-hand side with its polarization defined by the polarizer as shown in the end view. The plane of polarization is rotated by 45° in the clockwise direction by the Faraday medium and passes through the right-hand polarizer. A wave entering the right-hand polarizer, however, has its plane rotated 45° in the clockwise direction and hits the left-hand polarizer with its plane of polarization in the low transmittance or absorbing direction of the polarizer. The direction of the axially applied magnetic field with respect to the forward direction must be chosen in accordance with the sign of the Verdet constant of the Faraday medium used. The polarizers can be dichroic materials, a Glan-Thompson prism, or crystalline polarizers such as calcite.

The optical isolator is shown in Figure 2-15 as the interstage coupling between two power-amplifier laser stages. Isolation is achieved by the

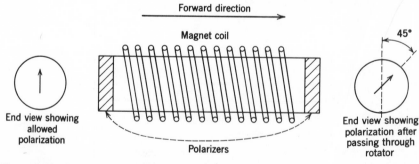

Figure 2-14 Schematic diagram of an optical Faraday rotation isolator. The polarized radiation passing from left to right is rotated by 45°. Any back-reflection that enters the rotator from the right is rotated an additional 45°. This radiation will then be extinguished at the left end because the polarizer is now aligned at 90° to the back reflection.

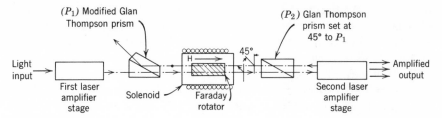

Figure 2-15 Schematic diagram of an optical isolator. Light is polarized by passing through P_1. The plane of polarization is then rotated 45° by the Faraday rotator and passed through the second polarizer (P_2) to the second amplifier. Any reflected light will be rotated an additional 45° upon traversing the rotator and thus cannot enter the first amplifier through polarizer P_1.

rotation of the plane of polarization of the incident light. The optimum condition for operation is that the outputs of both lasers be plane-polarized. This is not always true, however, and it may be necessary to tolerate considerable light loss if the polarization is circular or random. The function of the polarizing prism (P_1) is to ensure that light from the first amplifier stage is plane-polarized in the proper orientation.

The essential element of the optical isolator is the Faraday rotator. The Faraday effect is the rotation of the plane of polarization by a magnetic field parallel to the light path and is described by the equation

$$\theta = K_v LB, \tag{2-1}$$

where $\theta =$ the angle of rotation
$L =$ The path length in the material
$B =$ the component of the magnetic field in the direction of the light path
$K_v =$ constant of proportionality, called the Verdet constant.

The Faraday effect is reversible; if the light is reflected back through the material after the first traversal, the rotation is doubled.

As shown in Figure 2-15, light passing from left to right is polarized in the vertical plane by the polarizing prism (P_1) and then through the Faraday rotator, in which the path length and magnetic field are adjusted to produce rotation of the plane of polarization by 45°. The light then passes through the polarizing prism (P_2) at the right, which is rotated 45° with respect to the initial polarizing prism in order to pass the light beam emerging from the rotator.

Any reflected light traveling from right to left is polarized at 45° to the vertical plane by polarizer (P_2), but after passing through the rotator it is polarized in the horizontal plane by the additional 45° rotation. This plane of polarization is reflected at the interface of the initial polarizing prism and passes out of the surface indicated at 45° to the main axis of the system. Thus no feedback occurs and isolation is achieved.

The Faraday effect is small; it is wavelength-dependent and largest near an absorption resonance for any given material. For this reason it is necessary to choose different materials for different wavelength intervals, similar to the microwave analogy. The Verdet constants for some typical materials are given in Table 2-1.

TABLE 2-1   VERDET CONSTANT OF
SOME MATERIALS

Material	Verdet Constant (K_v) (radians/cm-gauss)
Diamond	3.72×10^{-6}
Quartz	4.82
Barium crown glass	6.40
Dense flint glass	25.60
KCl	8.35
CaF	2.54
ZnS	65.20

Verdet constant measured as the rotation in radians of polarized beam by transmission through 1-cm thickness of material with 1-gauss magnetic field at room temperature and $\lambda = 5893$ (sodium D-line).

2-4   THE OPTICAL CIRCULATOR

The fact that optical radiation can be isolated from a given device by use of an isolator is useful in many applications. In microwave radar, the role of the circulator has been well discussed as an element for isolating certain segments of a circuit from unwanted signals. The optical circulator performs the same role in potential laser applications, but at optical frequencies, by combining the polarization rotation features of the isolator into a more intricate device. This, too, as in the case of the single isolator, has applications in the isolation of laser amplifier stages.

Let us first define the mission of the circulator. It is commonly conceived as a four-port device in which some of the ports are isolated from others. A schematic design of this element is shown in Figure 2-16. It operates as follows. An input signal (S_1) entering the circulator at port 1

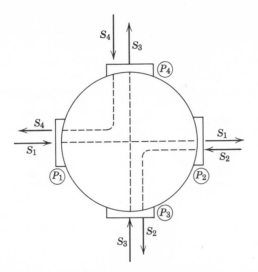

Figure 2-16 Schematic diagram of an optical circulator. A suitably polarized light beam entering port P_1 is transmitted to port P_2 but does not appear at either port P_3 or P_4. A reflection back into port P_2 is transmitted to port P_3 but not to either the input port (P_1) or port P_4. Similar conditions hold for signals incident on other ports.

is transmitted to port 2 and does not appear in either port 3 or 4. A signal (S_2) entering port 2 is transmitted to port 3 and is isolated from ports 1 and 4. Similarly, a signal (S_3) entering port 3 is transmitted to port 4 and does not appear at either port 1 or 2; finally, a signal (S_4) incident on port 4 is transmitted to port 1 and is isolated from ports 2 and 3. Its advantage for optical isolation can be seen immediately. An optical signal (S_1) which passed through the circulator might suffer some reflection at the output port 2. This reflection (S_2), however, would not be fed back to the input port 1 but rather would be transmitted out of the system through port 3. Thus in a transmit-receive system the high-powered transmitted radiation would be sent from port 1 through 2, whereas the weaker return signal would be sent through port 3 to port 4, where the sensitive detector would be located. Thus the high-power transmission branch would be isolated from the high-sensitivity detection branch of the system.

The actual construction of a circulator element would make use of four Faraday isolator elements and a selective reflector. This is shown schematically in Figure 2-17. The selective reflector element has the property that it transmits without loss one component of polarized radiation, whereas it totally reflects radiation with the other component of polarization. Such an element is a Nicol prism or calcite prism, which exhibits a different index of refraction (and reflectivity) for the two planes

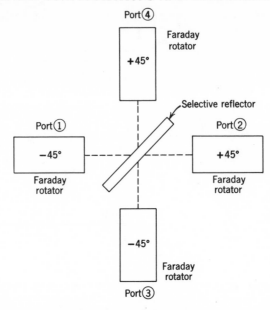

Figure 2-17 Schematic construction of an optical circulator. The selective reflector transmits, without loss, one polarization component and totally reflects the other. The Faraday rotators shift the component of polarization by the angle indicated.

of polarization. For illustrative purposes in our example we assume that the polarization component of 0° will be transmitted and the 90° polarization component will be reflected. The Faraday isolator elements rotate the plane of polarization by ±45° in a manner already described. Assume that the input signal (S_1) at port 1 is polarized at +45°. The Faraday rotator in the path at port 1 is then arranged to give a −45° rotation for radiation passing through it, whereas port 2 gives +45°. The input beam (S_1) then has 0° polarization on approaching the selective reflector and is transmitted through it because of the 0° polarization, and, after passing through the output rotator at port 2, will have +45° polarization. This is demonstrated in Figure 2-18a. No signal appears at either port 3 or 4.

Suppose, instead, that the signal enters the circulator at port 2, polarized again at +45°. Then, as can be seen in Figure 2-18b, the rotator in the port 2 arm will add +45° rotation, giving a total of 90° polarization, and the radiation will then be selectively reflected into port 3 rather than transmitted to port 1, because of the 90° polarization. It will emerge from port 3 with a polarization of +45° after passing through the final rotator.

In a similar manner it can be shown that a +45° polarization beam incident on port 3 will be transmitted through port 4 and a signal input polarized at $+45°$ at port 4 will be transmitted to port 1, and the other ports will still be isolated from the signals.

There are, of course, two important physical parameters of the circulator that determine its ultimate usefulness. The first is the degree of isolation of one port from the others, and the second is the insertion loss between the input and output port. Using materials now available, circulators have been made with insertion loss of the order of 1 db and

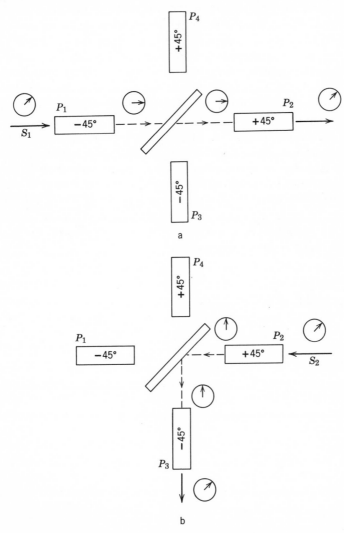

Figure 2-18 Diagram showing exit port for two input signals. In *a* the input at port P_1 emerges from port P_2; in *b* the input at port P_2 emerges from port P_3.

isolation between adjacent ports of −40 db. In the optical case this requires using Brewster angle faces accurately aligned to the order of 0.5°, which is perfectly reasonable in view of present-day optical techniques.

A modification of the circulator for use as an oscillator-amplifier isolation section is shown in Figure 2–19. Here there are two reflector elements and one rotator. The selective reflectors could reasonably be calcite prisms in this case. The proper input polarization from the oscillator must be chosen so as to transmit through the calcite prism (*a*) along path 1. The unwanted polarization would be deflected along path *A* and out of the optical system. The beam is then rotated by 45° by the Faraday rotator and subsequently transmitted through the second calcite prism (*b*) to the amplifier along path 2. At the second prism any unwanted reflection from the amplifier face will be passed back through the rotator and out of the system along path 3. An improper polarization reflected from the amplifier will also be reflected out of the system at prism (*b*) along path *B*. It should further be noted that an incorrect polarization that might still exist in the beam when it emerges from the rotator toward the amplifier will also be deflected out of the system along path 4. The basic performance and efficiency of this system then center around the ability of the Faraday rotator to give a uniform rotation of 45° to the incoming radiation and the ability of the prisms to provide polarization separation.

The paths noted (1, 2, 3, and 4) would then correspond to the four ports of the circulator in this configuration.

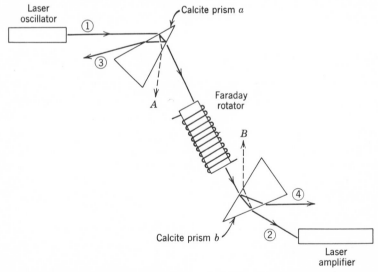

Figure 2-19 Oscillator-amplifier configuration using the Faraday rotator as an isolation section. The improper polarizations are deflected out of the system by the calcite prisms.

Optical circulators, then, can be constructed and effectively utilized in laser applications of extensive interest.

2-5 OPTICAL MODULATORS

Because of the increasing availability of lasers for experimental applications, the ability to control and vary the properties of the light beams becomes important. To this end, we present some discussion on the techniques of modulating laser beams and the devices that have been found useful.

An optical carrier beam can be modulated by several methods, which are essentially extensions of low-frequency techniques. They include a modulation of the drive of the signal generator or oscillator, modulation by variable reactance, and modulation by variable absorption. An example of modulation by variation of the oscillator drive would be to vary the length of the resonant cavity, which amounts to putting a frequency-modulated component on the output carrier wave. The modulation by variable reactance is performed primarily by the use of retardation-type, electro-optical devices using the Kerr effect or the Pockels effect. The variable absorber modulation can most effectively be done by placing a variable absorber inside the resonant cavity to enhance the mode locking and thus provide frequency modulation. A simple alternative is to place the variable absorber outside the cavity and simply vary the intensity of the external beam in a chosen manner.

Our discussion here centers around the electro-optical type of modulators, for they are capable of performing at microwave frequencies and thus modulation is practical in a range that can be useful for advanced communications.

A look at the modulators available today shows that mechanical modulators are merely mirrors that vibrate at the information rate and change the path length of the beam. This in turn changes the beam's phase with respect to an unaffected beam, but the mirrors cannot respond to a driving rate much above a few megacycles.

There are two kinds of electrical modulator: electroacoustical and electro-optical. In the first case acoustical waves are set up in certain materials. These waves interfere with the incident laser beam and deflect it. The deflection also yields a small amount of frequency shift, but because the frequency shift is small applications are limited. A Debye-Sears modulator is an example of this type, which uses ultrasonic waves in liquids or solids.

Electro-optical modulators, on the other hand, offer wide dynamic ranges and can follow rapid variations in applied voltage. In this method the crystals change their refractive index with the applied electric field. The incident beam is split in two and each portion travels at a different velocity in the crystal, which results in a phase difference between the two parts at the output. Electro-optical modulators are most suitable for applications in electronics.

The electro-optical effect is expressed as a function of the applied electric field (E) by an expression such as given by (2-2):

$$\Delta\frac{1}{\mu^2} = rE + PE^2, \tag{2-2}$$

where μ is the refractive index, r is the linear electro-optical coefficient,

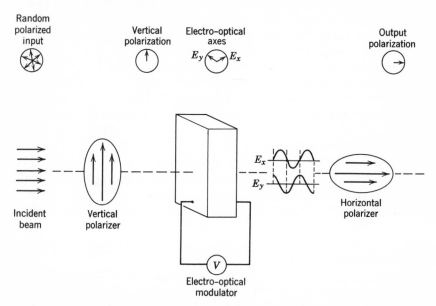

Figure 2-20 Schematic diagram of an electro-optical modulator using the Pockels effect. A time-varying voltage (V) applied to the electro-optic crystal varies the output intensity of one polarized component of the beam.

and P is the coefficient associated with the quadratic effect. In solids the linear variation of the index term rE is known as the Pockels effect while the variation arising from the quadratic term is called the Kerr effect. In the Pockels effect the polarization axis along which the retardation occurs is perpendicular to the applied electric field, whereas in the Kerr effect the axis and electric field are parallel.

A crystal that undergoes an index of refraction change with the application of a field is called birefringent and can be used in what is called a retardation type of modulator. Its operation is based on two factors: (a) the introduction of interference between two polarized portions of an incident wave, and (b) the accomplishment of a phase retardation between them. The retardation or path difference for the two waves occurs because the two components of a polarized beam see different indices of refraction and therefore travel at different velocities in the crystal.

In Figure 2-20 the basic elements of an electro-optical modulator are shown. The analysis of this element is made for the linear electro-optical or Pockels effect, and the dependence of the output intensity from such a modulator on the phase retardation is described.

Assume that an electromagnetic wave is traveling along the z-axis and that the electro-optical crystal exhibits birefringence in the $xy =$ plane

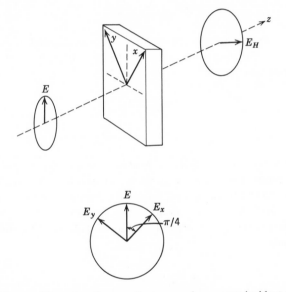

Figure 2-21 Diagram illustrating the coordinate axes for a wave incident on an electro-optic crystal. The electro-optic axes of the crystal are shown as x and y and are at 45° to the polarization of the incident beam. These coordinates are used in the accompanying analysis.

when the electric field is applied along the z-axis; assume further that the electro-optical axes are along the x- and y-coordinates as shown in Figure 2-21 and are at an angle of $\pi/4$ to the vertical polarization. The incident beam is assumed to be polarized in the vertical plane by the polarizer at the input to the modulator. Thus the wave incident on the electro-optical crystal is given by

$$E = E_0 \cos \omega t \qquad (2\text{-}3)$$

and the polarized components along the electro-optical axes are then

$$E_x = \frac{E_0}{\sqrt{2}} \cos \omega t \qquad (2\text{-}4a)$$

$$E_y = \frac{E_0}{\sqrt{2}} \cos \omega t. \qquad (2\text{-}4b)$$

Now, when an electric field is applied axially along the crystal, and the crystal orientation is proper, the index of refraction change can be obtained from (2-2). Thus, using only the linear term for the Pockels effect, we see that

$$\mu - \mu_0 = \pm \tfrac{1}{2} r \mu_0{}^3 E_z, \qquad (2\text{-}5)$$

where μ_0 is the index of refraction with no applied field. When the crystal axes are properly chosen, the index along the two optical axes can be written as

$$\mu_x = \mu_0 + \tfrac{1}{2} r \mu_0{}^3 E_z \qquad (2\text{-}6a)$$

$$\mu_y = \mu_0 - \tfrac{1}{2} r \mu_0{}^3 E_z. \qquad (2\text{-}6b)$$

In other words, the velocity of propagation of a wave polarized along the x-axis differs from that of a wave polarized along the y-axis. Thus after traversing the thickness (L) of the modulator a phase change occurs. The phase shift of the two polarization components can be written as follows, where λ is the wavelength and μ_x and μ_y are the indices along the respective optic axes:

$$\phi_x = 2\pi \mu_x \frac{L}{\lambda} \qquad (2\text{-}7a)$$

$$\phi_y = 2\pi \mu_y \frac{L}{\lambda} \qquad (2\text{-}7b)$$

$$\phi_z = 2\pi \mu_0 \frac{L}{\lambda}. \qquad (2\text{-}7c)$$

There is no change of index with applied voltage in the z-axis.

The equation for the polarized electric fields must also reflect this phase shift in traversing the crystal and, therefore, from (2-4) we write the following relations for the electric field after passing through the electro-optical material:

$$E_x = \frac{E_0}{\sqrt{2}} \cos (\omega t + \phi_x) \qquad\qquad (2\text{-}8a)$$

$$E_y = \frac{E_0}{\sqrt{2}} \cos (\omega t + \phi_y). \qquad\qquad (2\text{-}8b)$$

Now, using the equations (2-6) that relate the index of refraction to the applied electric field, we see that

$$\phi_x = 2\pi \mu_x \frac{L}{\lambda} = \left(2\pi \mu_0 \frac{L}{\lambda}\right)(1 + \tfrac{1}{2} r \mu_0{}^2 E_z) \qquad\qquad (2\text{-}9a)$$

$$= \phi_0 + \Delta \phi$$

$$\phi_y = 2\pi \mu_y \frac{L}{\lambda} = \left(\frac{2\pi \mu_0 L}{\lambda}\right)(1 - \tfrac{1}{2} r \mu_0{}^2 E_z) \qquad\qquad (2\text{-}9b)$$

$$= \phi_0 - \Delta \phi.$$

The net phase shift or total retardation between the two waves (ϕ) is seen to be

$$\phi = \phi_x - \phi_y = 2\Delta \phi = \left(\frac{2\pi L}{\lambda}\right)(r \mu_0{}^3 E_z) \qquad\qquad (2\text{-}10)$$

$$= \left(\frac{2\pi}{\lambda}\right)(r \mu_0{}^3 V).$$

The components of the electric wave emerging from the electro-optical crystal of length L then can be written as

$$E_x = \left(\frac{E_0}{\sqrt{2}}\right) \cos (\omega + \phi_0 + \Delta \phi) \qquad\qquad (2\text{-}11a)$$

$$E_y = \left(\frac{E_0}{\sqrt{2}}\right) \cos (\omega t + \phi_0 - \Delta \phi). \qquad\qquad (2\text{-}11b)$$

It is seen that the phase shift ($\Delta \phi$) for each component depends directly on the voltage (V) applied to the electro-optical crystal, for $E_z = V/L$.

At the output port of the electro-optical modulator we now insert a horizontally polarized analyzer element. This transmits only the horizontal components of the electric field.

Because the orientation of the electro-optical axes are at an angle of $\pi/4$ to the vertical, these components (E_x and E_y) are also at $\pi/4$ with the

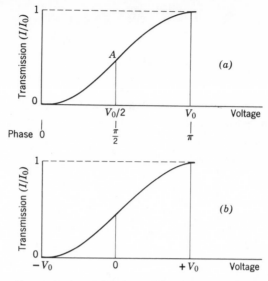

Figure 2-22 Transmission versus voltage applied to an electro-optic crystal using the Pockels effect. *a* represents the transmission through the crystal; *b* represents the same configuration but with the addition of a λ/4 bias for shifting the polarization of the incident wave.

horizontal. Thus the transmitted electric (E_H) field at the output have contributions from both E_x and E_y, and we write

$$E_H = \frac{E_x}{\sqrt{2}} + \frac{E_y}{\sqrt{2}}$$

$$= \frac{E_0}{2}\left[\cos(\omega t + \phi_0 + \Delta\phi) + \cos(\omega t + \phi_0 - \Delta\phi)\right]. \quad (2\text{-}12)$$

This reduces to

$$E_H = E_0 \sin(\Delta\phi) \cos(\omega t + \phi_0). \quad (2\text{-}13)$$

The output light beam intensity is therefore given by integrating the square of the electric field over a complete period. Thus

$$I = \frac{\omega}{2\pi} \int_0^{2\pi/\omega} E_H^2 dt$$

$$I = I_0 \sin^2(\Delta\phi) = I_0 \sin^2(\phi/2), \quad (2\text{-}14)$$

where I_0 is the incident intensity and ϕ is the total phase retardation between the two polarized waves traversing the electro-optical crystal.

Because the phase retardation in the linear case (Pockels effect) is proportional to the voltage, we may plot a curve of transmission versus voltage for such a system. This is illustrated in Figure 2-22. The equation of this curve is

$$\frac{I}{I_0} = \sin^2\left(\frac{\pi}{2}\frac{V}{V_0}\right),\qquad(2\text{-}15)$$

where V_0 is the voltage required for maximum transmission ($I/I_0 = 100\%$). We thus see that the transmission of such an element can be altered by the application of a voltage along the axis.

The effectiveness and ease of operation of such a modulator can be enhanced by the addition of one extra element. This is called a quarterwave plate and placed in the optical path as noted in Figure 2-23. This permits a phase shift of $\pi/4$ between the two polarized electric waves to occur before entering the voltage-sensitive modulator element; therefore a bias is introduced into the transmission curve so that the transmission can be shifted around point A on the transmission rather than about zero, and the change of transmission is more nearly linear with a voltage change than when starting at the origin. A smaller voltage is required for modulation as seen by observing (2-16).

With a quarter-wave plate bias we see that

$$\frac{I}{I_0} = \sin^2\left(\frac{\pi}{4}+\frac{\pi}{4}\frac{V}{V_0}\right)$$

$$= \tfrac{1}{2}\left[1 + \sin\left(\frac{\pi}{2}\frac{V}{V_0}\right)\right].\qquad(2\text{-}16)$$

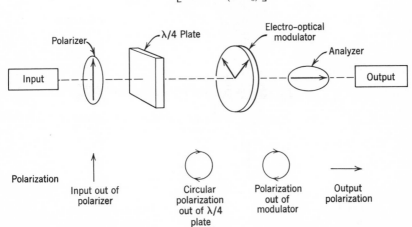

Figure 2-23 Schematic representation of an electro-optical modulator employing the $\lambda/4$ bias in order to obtain linear operation.

This transmission curve is given in Figure 2-22*b*, where the voltage (V) now varies around a bias point in the linear portion of the curve.

The linear nature of the modulation of transmission or intensity with voltage can be observed by assuming a small perturbing voltage on the crystal. Then (2-16) can be expanded to yield the following for the case in which $V/V_0 \ll 1$:

$$\frac{I}{I_0} \simeq 0.5 + \left(\frac{\pi}{4}\right)\left(\frac{V}{V_0}\right). \tag{2-17}$$

If we now apply a *small*, sinusoidally varying voltage signal to the modulator, we see that the intensity of the transmitted radiation is also modulated. Thus, with a modulating frequency ω_m and a depth of modulation m, and when $m \ll 1$, so that the modulating voltage is

$$\frac{V}{V_0} = m \sin \omega_m t,$$

we see that

$$\frac{I}{I_0} \simeq 0.5 + \left(\frac{\pi m}{4}\right) \sin \omega_m t \tag{2-18}$$

and amplitude modulation of the emitted radiation occurs.

Some of the most promising materials for a Pockels effect modulator are potassium dihydrogen phosphate (KDP), a deuterated version of KDP in which the hydrogen is replaced by deuterium, and ammonium

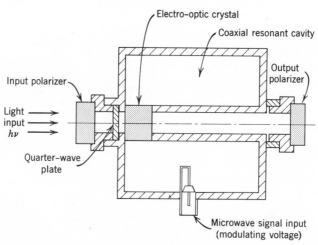

Figure 2-24 Diagram of a microwave cavity configuration capable of driving an electro-optical light modulator at microwave frequencies.

dihydrogen phosphate (ADP). The electro-optical coefficient (r) for KDP is about 10^{-10} m per v, whereas for ADP it is approximately 8.5×10^{-12} m per v. At modulation frequencies above 50 kc, however, which is above the resonance point for these crystals, the value of the Pockels electro-optical coefficient drops to about 60% of the above value. For microwave modulation, therefore, the coefficient is reduced over the quoted values. A schematic representation of a modulator enclosed in a cavity for operation at microwave frequencies is shown in Figure 2-24. The cavity is a coaxial design, with the electro-optical crystal providing capacitative loading; the optical ports and polarizers are also shown.

Transverse Mode Operation

The modulator described so far is called a longitudinal effect device. A similar device operating in a transverse mode imposes the incident electric field along an optical birefringent (x) axis. The wave propagates along the other optical axis (y), but still the voltage is in the z-direction, as shown in Figure 2-25. The electric field would then appear *across* the other optical axis (y), but still the voltage is in the z-direction, as shown in Figure 2-25. The electric field would then appear *across* the material. The effect of this on the operation can be seen from reference to 2-8, where

$$E_y = 0$$

$$E_x = \frac{E_0}{\sqrt{2}} \cos (\omega t + \phi_y). \tag{2-19}$$

In this case there will occur pure phase modulation because of the effect of the field (E_z) on the index and, therefore, the phase factor (ϕ_y). A further advantage is that the electrodes do not have to be placed on the surfaces through which the beam passes; A longer crystal, however, is needed to acquire a given phase shift.

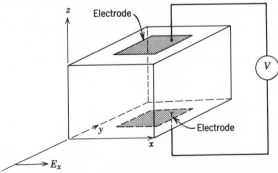

Figure 2-25 Schematic representation of an electro-optic crystal being used as a modulator in the transverse bias mode of operation.

The longitudinal modulator when used at microwave frequencies is subject to some limitations on length. If the length of the crystal is of the order of a half wavelength of the modulating signal, the radio frequency (RF) field changes sign in the sample, thereby canceling out some of the modulation. A variation of this device, therefore, makes use of a traveling wave configuration in which the RF field travels down the electro-optical material with the light wave. Unfortunately, in most instances the light velocity and the RF wave velocity do not agree and, therefore, do not propagate together.

The speed of the light is $v = c/\mu$, and the velocity of the modulating wave is $v = c/\sqrt{\epsilon}$, where ϵ is the dielectric constant. Therefore, if μ can be made equal to $\sqrt{\epsilon}$, the two waves will travel at equal velocities and the length of the modulator may be made arbitrarily long. The difficulty with this seemingly simple approach is that μ in most cases is not equal to $\sqrt{\epsilon}$. The exception is GaAs, where both μ and $\sqrt{\epsilon}$ are about equal to 3.2. There is no optical cement, however, with the same μ that will glue the crystals together to achieve a sufficiently long sample. All optical cements

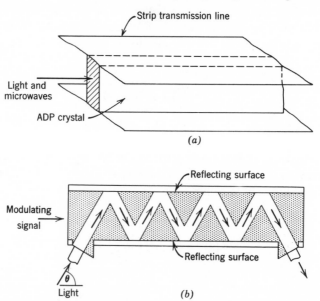

Figure 2-26 *a.* Colinear traveling wave modulator using a strip line partially filled with the electro-optic material. The TEM mode velocity synchronization can occur over a bandwidth greater than 1000 mc by appropriately choosing the relative width of the strip line and the material. *b.* Zigzag traveling wave modulator, where the modulating signal is assumed to travel as a TEM wave along the axis of the structure. The modulating electric field can be either parallel or perpendicular to the plane of the figure by choosing a suitable crystal orientation. After Anderson, *Microwaves* (1965).

have an index of about 1.7; therefore only crystals with an index of 1.7 could be used in order to avoid losses due to mismatches at the glue-to-crystal interfaces. Nevertheless, the velocities may be matched with a dielectrically loaded wave guide structure, in which the dielectric constants of the air gaps and of the crystal yield the proper ϵ.

Several ways, however, have been proposed for obtaining the advantage of a traveling wave structure without the synchronization of light and RF waves. The advantage of this is that broad band performance also can only be achieved by a continuous interaction in a substantially dispersionless structure where both the modulating and optical signals can propagate as TEM waves with equal phase velocities. The requirement that must be met is that

$$\frac{V_P}{\cos \theta} = \frac{c}{\mu_0}, \tag{2-20}$$

where V_P is the phase velocity of the RF wave, or microwave, and the angle θ is between the light propagation direction and the traveling RF wave direction.

One structure in which this is realized is shown in Figure 2-26a. Light propagates along the axis of the structure as a plane wave with velocity c/μ_0. The relative widths of the strip transmission line and electro-optical material are chosen so that the modulating signal propagates as a TEM wave with the same velocity. Velocity synchronization can then by attained at all frequencies for which the electrical width of the electro-optical material is less than half a wavelength.

Alternatively, a strip transmission line may be completely filled with the electro-optical material as shown in Figure 2-26b, and the light allowed to zigzag between reflecting planes at an angle θ determined by (2-20). The advantages of this configuration, relative to the straight-through arrangement, are the following:

1. The increased optical path substantially reduces the crystal length required for a given modulation with a given input power.

2. Upper frequency limit, hence the bandwidth, is extended, for there is no abrupt change in the microwave propagation constant at the frequency for which the electro-optical material is a half-wavelength wide or at the wave guide cutoff.

The major disadvantage of this configuration is that, at least for a polarization modulator, the modulating medium must be isotropic, for the optical path does not maintain a constant orientation relative to the crystalline axes. Thus the active medium must be a cubic crystal, such as

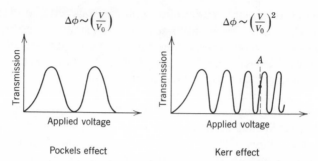

Figure 2-27 Comparison of the transmission of a Kerr cell and a Pockels cell with applied voltage. The curves show the quadratic variation of the electro-optic effect in the Kerr cell. The Pockels cell has a linear response. The phase in the Kerr cell varies as the square of the voltage, whereas the phase in the Pockels cell is linear with voltage. The a-c modulating voltage for the Kerr cell may be reduced if the cell is biased to point A with a d-c potential.

zinc sulfide or cuprous chloride. One practical advantage of using cuprous chloride stems from its relatively high optical index of refraction. This means that all light inside the crystal that hits the surface at the matching angle θ is reflected. The reflectors shown in Figure 2-26b, with their inevitable optical loss, thus can be eliminated, for total internal reflection will occur.

Kerr Modulator

To use the quadratic electro-optical or Kerr effect in modulation we again are interested in the relative phase retardation of polarized waves traversing the crystal, but here the retardation varies with the square of the modulation voltage rather than linearly with it. A comparison of the transmission or retardation in the Pockels effect and Kerr effects with modulation voltage is shown in Figure 2-27. As noted in the Kerr effect, the retardation depends on the square of the applied voltage and its axis is along the electric field. This quadratic effect may, however, be made linear if the electric field is large enough. Thus, because the electric field may be written as a d-c term ($E_{d\text{-}c}$) plus an RF term, we obtain

$$E = E_{d\text{-}c} + E_{\text{RF}}$$

and

$$E^2 = E_{d\text{-}c}{}^2 + E_{\text{RF}}{}^2 + 2E_{d\text{-}c}E_{\text{RF}}. \qquad (2\text{-}21)$$

Now, because $E_{\text{RF}} \ll E_{d\text{-}c}$, this may be reduced to

$$E^2 \simeq E_{d\text{-}c}{}^2 + 2E_{d\text{-}c}E_{\text{RF}}, \qquad (2\text{-}22)$$

which gives a variation that again is a phase retardation linearly proportional to the applied modulating voltage.

All of the materials showing promise for use in electro-optical modulators can be classified as ferroelectrics, a term that originated in the similarity of these materials to ferromagnetic materials. Explicitly, these materials exhibit, in certain temperature ranges, an induced polarization that may be orders of magnitdue larger than in normal materials when an external field is applied.

A typical curve of dielectric constant versus temperature is shown in Figure 2-28. At temperatures above the Curie point the dielectric constant for many materials can be well approximated by a Curie-Weiss type of dependence:

$$\epsilon = \epsilon_0 + \frac{C}{T - T_0}, \tag{2-23}$$

where ϵ_0 is the temperature-independent portion of the dielectric constant, C is the Curie constant, and T_0 is the Curie-Weiss, or simply Curie, temperature.

Because the electro-optical effect in a given material is roughly proportional to the induced polarization, greatly enhanced effects can be produced if the temperature of the material is maintained slightly above its Curie point. Table 2-2 shows the Curie points of some typical electro-optical materials.

TABLE 2-2 CURIE TEMPERATURES OF VARIOUS
FERROELECTRIC MATERIALS OF INTEREST FOR
ELECTRO-OPTICAL MODULATORS*

Material	Curie Point (°C)
Potassium dihydrogen phosphate (KDP), KH_2PO_4	−150
Potassium dideuterium phosphate (KD*P), KD_2PO_4	−60
Potassium niobate, $KNbO_3$	435
Potassium tantalate, $KTaO_3$	−260
Barium titanate, $BaTiO_3$	120
Potassium tantalate niobate (KTN), $KTa_{.65}Nb_{.35}O_3$	≈10

*Courtesy of *Spectra Physics Technical Memorandum* (1966).

Although liquid Kerr cells using nitrobenzene have been used extensively for a number of years, their application to CW modulation is difficult because of the large power/bandwidth quotient. A much more promising approach based on the Kerr effect uses mixed crystals near

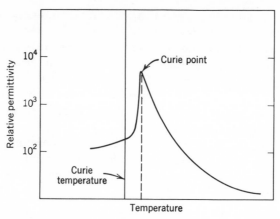

Figure 2-28 Dielectric constant versus temperature of a representative ferroelectric of interest in electro-optical modulation.

their Curie point. Potassium tantalate niobate (KTN), which uses the Kerr effect, is a mixture of two crystals with high and low Curie points. The Curie point of the mixture, being near room temperature, is in a convenient range for a practical device.

In addition to the large electro-optical effect obtained by operating near the Curie point, the a-c voltage required for 100% modulation can be reduced by applying a large static bias voltage to the material for linear operation.

The KTN crystals are small; they require only small operating voltages, ranging from 20 to 60 v peak with a 300-v d-c bias. A 3-mm cube crystal can modulate a 10 mc. The amount of bias is usually limited only by the

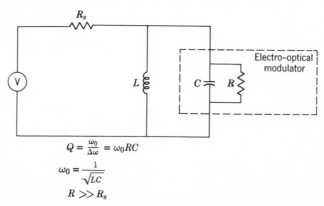

$$Q = \frac{\omega_0}{\Delta\omega} = \omega_0 RC$$

$$\omega_0 = \frac{1}{\sqrt{LC}}$$

$$R \gg R_s$$

Figure 2-29 Schematic diagram illustrating the equivalent circuit for an electro-optical modulator. The modulator appears as a highly capacitive load to the driving circuit.

breakdown point of the crystal. Besides reducing the drive voltage, the bias also increases the linear electro-optical effect by moving the operating region to the steeper slope of the response curve.

A further item of interest for the users of such devices is the power requirements for achieving modulation.

The electro-optical modulators discussed may be considered to be capacitive loads to the driving voltage modulation source. The desirable characteristics for modulators, in general, may be stated as low driving power, high optical transmission, and a large dynamic range.

The capacitive load assumption allows the required driving power to be estimated in terms of the center resonant frequency (ω_0), the quality factor (Q) of the elements, and the voltage (V) required to attain a specific depth of modulation. The simple equivalent circuit of such a modulator is given in Figure 2-29.

Here the series resistance (R_s) and the inductance (L) can be associated with the leads and contacts to the electro-optical crystal. The impedance of this modulator can be written as

$$Z = R_s + \left(\frac{1}{R\omega_0{}^2C^2}\right)\left(\frac{\omega}{\omega_0}\right)^2 \left\{\frac{1 + jRC(\omega/\omega_0)[1 - (\omega/\omega_0)^2]}{[1 - (\omega/\omega_0)^2] + (\omega/\omega_0{}^2RC)^2}\right\}, \quad (2\text{-}24)$$

which, near resonance, since $R \gg R_s$, becomes

$$Z \simeq R_s + R \simeq R. \quad (2\text{-}25)$$

In other terms we may relate the resistance (R) to the quality factor (Q) and capacitance of the modulator by noting

$$Q = \omega_0 RC. \quad (2\text{-}26)$$

Thus

$$R = \frac{Q}{\omega_0 C}, \quad (2\text{-}27)$$

leading to

$$Z = \frac{Q}{\omega_0 C}. \quad (2\text{-}28)$$

The power to drive the modulator may now be written in terms of the the voltage and impedance:

$$P = \frac{V^2}{Z} \simeq \frac{\omega_0 CV^2}{Q}. \quad (2\text{-}29)$$

Note that ω_0 is the center frequency of the resonance of the modulator. It can be further noted from the definition of quality factor Q that

$$Q = \frac{\omega_0}{\Delta\omega}, \qquad (2\text{-}30)$$

where $\Delta\omega$ represents the frequency range between half-maximum points on the resonance curve and thereby also signifies the effective bandwidth. Thus the driving power may also be written as

$$P = CV^2\Delta\omega.$$

To minimize the driving power it is necessary to reduce the driving voltage as well as the simultaneous minimization of capacitance for a given bandwidth.

In the longitudinal mode of operation of the Pockels cell we can see the advantage of using longer crystals, for they will reduce capacitance. It also becomes advantageous to use a material such as KTN because the driving voltage can be reduced by such an enormous factor.

Some properties of electro-optical materials for use in the microwave modulation of light at $\lambda = 1\mu$ are given in Table 2-3. Here we can note the extreme ranges over which the driving voltages are required for these applications.

TABLE 2-3   PROPERTIES OF ELECTRO-OPTICAL MATERIALS*

Material	Class	Optical Index of Refraction (μ_0)	Half-Wave Retardation Voltage (kV)	Microwave Dielectric Constant (ϵ)	Quality Factor (Q)
KDP	Uniaxial	1.468	8.4	20	120
CuCl	Cubic	1.93	6.2	8	1,000
ZnS	Cubic	2.368	10.4	10	500
$N_4(CH_2)_6$	Cubic	1.591	9.2	—	—
ZnSe	Cubic	2.660	7.1	—	—
KTN	Cubic	2.287	38 v	10^4	150

KTN evaluated by assuming a biasing electric field of 10^4 V/cm on the material.
*Courtesy of Anderson, *Microwaves* (1965).

Absorption Modulators

The electro-optical modulators discussed so far rely on the change of index of refraction with applied electric field. As such, they are reactive; no optical energy is actually dissipated in the material. As mentioned

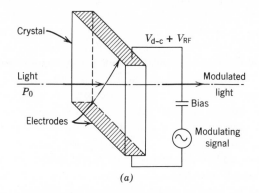

(a)

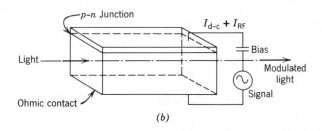

(b)

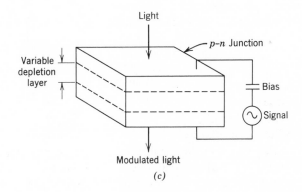

(c)

Figure 2-30 a. The absorption edge modulator. By properly varying the absorption edge of the semiconductor with d-c bias, the incident photon flux is absorbed in synchronism with the microwave modulating signal. b. Modulation by free carrier absorption. The incident photons are absorbed in the material by free carriers whose density is controlled by the voltage applied across the p-n junction. This is limited to relatively low modulation frequencies. c. A free carrier absorption modulator based on the variable depletion layer at the p-n junction. The modulating signal varies the width of the depletion layer and thus the absorption of the incident photon flux is varied. After Anderson, *Microwaves* (1965).

73

earlier, modulation by optical absorption is also possible particularly by using semiconductors such as silicon, germanium, or gallium arsenide. Two potentially useful methods at microwave frequencies are (1) the shift of optical absorption edge with an applied electric field and (2) the modulation of free carrier absorption by injected carriers.

The first method is based on the fact that in many crystals the optical absorption varies rapidly with photon energies in the vicinity of the band gap, near the absorption edge, and that the spectral position of this edge can be varied by an applied electric field. One possible configuration is shown in Figure 2-30a. A major problem of this modulation method is that the optical absorption induces photoconductivity and this results in considerable power dissipation, for large electric fields are required to shift the absorption edge appreciably.

The second modulation method is based on control of the density of absorbing carriers by injection at a p-n junction. The optical absorption coefficient can be written as

$$\alpha = \frac{Z_0}{\rho_0 \mu}\left[\frac{1}{1 + (\lambda_c/\lambda)^2}\right], \tag{2-32}$$

where $Z_0 = 377$ (impedance of free space)
  $\rho_0 = $ d-c resistivity of the semiconductor
  $\mu = $ index of refraction
  $\lambda = $ optical wavelength.
The term λ_c is a characteristic wavelength, related to the observed d-c resistivity by

$$\lambda_c = \frac{2\pi \text{cm}_c}{\rho_0 n_c q^2}, \tag{2-33}$$

where $m_c = $ carrier mass
  $n_c = $ carrier density
  $q = $ electronic charge
Because λ_c is generally in the far infrared, modulators using free carrier absorption will be most effective at longer wavelengths.

One experimental arrangement is shown in Figure 2-30b. In this operation the carriers are injected into the bulk of the material by a shallow, forward-biased p-n junction, across which the modulating voltage is also applied. Here the highest modulating frequency is determined by the carrier lifetime. Using germanium with a carrier lifetime in the range of 1 μsec, the 3-db modulation frequency would be about 1 mc.

Higher frequency operation could be obtained with a reverse-biased junction in which the absorption is controlled by varying the thickness of the depletion layer, as in Figure 2-30c. Sufficient free carrier absorption over an optical path as short as the width of a depletion layer, however, will require very heavy doping as well as operation at long wavelengths.

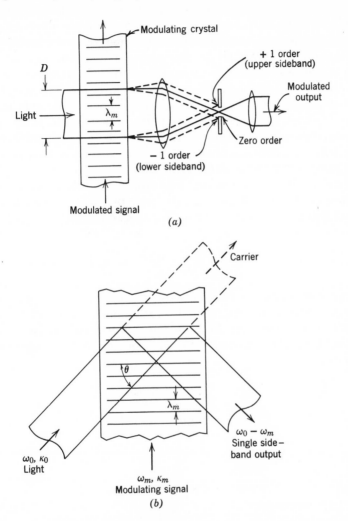

Figure 2-31 *a.* Transmission-type diffraction grating modulator. A diffraction grating with sufficiently wide grating spacings, λ_m, is produced by an acoustical wave or a microwave beam in a medium with a high dielectric constant. With a given spacing, λ_m, the amount of energy diffracted out of the beam into the sidebands, and therefore the amount of modulation, is determined by the amplitude of the modulating signal. *b.* Bragg angle reflection-type diffraction grating modulator. The light diffracted out of the beam at the Bragg angle (Θ) has a single Doppler-shifted frequency of $\omega_1 = \omega_0 \pm \omega_m$. After Anderson, *Microwaves* (1965).

Electroacoustic Modulation

At high frequencies ultrasonic waves propagating through a material can also interact with the radiation passing through, and thus modulation can occur under the proper conditions. In effect, a diffraction grating is set up in the modulator material by the moving ultrasonic wave. This wave propagates through the material, and, when the grating spaces are proper, energy in the optical beam can be diffracted out into sidebands.

One way in which this effect can be used to modulate light is shown in Figure 2-31. Here the modulating signal produces a grating that diffracts energy out of the main optical beam, thus decreasing its intensity. The amount of energy removed depends on the "ruling depth" of the grating, which corresponds here to the amplitude of the microwave modulating signal. Thus amplitude variations of a microwave carrier are transformed into intensity variations of an optical beam.

Similarly, a diffraction grating modulator can also be made to work by reflection, as shown in Figure 2-31b. Reflection occurs when the optical and modulating wave vectors satisfy the Bragg criterion:

$$\frac{k_m}{k_0} = 2 \sin \theta. \tag{2-34}$$

The light is then reflected from the moving grating, with a Doppler-shifted frequency given by $\omega_1 = \omega_0 \pm \omega_m$. This system is a single-sideband, suppressed carrier modulator, because the reflected light is spatially well separated from the incident beam and contains only a single, shifted optical frequency.

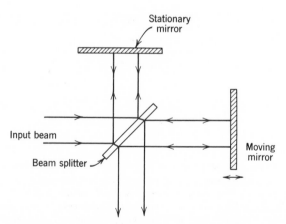

Figure 2-32 A modulator using a moving mirror in a Twyman-Green interferometer. The variable interference in the interferometer causes the output beam to be modulated.

Interferometer Modulator

This modulator is a retardation model that does not depend on an induced birefringence in an electro-optical crystal caused by a modulation voltage. It is mechanical in nature and is illustrated by describing the Twyman-Green interferometer structure operated as a modulator.

The approach is shown in Figure 2-32, in which we see the Twyman-Green interferometer with one of the mirrors driven by a piezoelectric element to modulate the output. The two light beams are spatially separated, and the retardation is accomplished by a physical change in actual path length. When adjusted to show a single fringe over the output aperture, the device is in principle capable of 100% modulation.

The frequency response or bandwidth of this device is determined by the upper frequency at which the driven mirror can be made to follow the applied electric signal. By driving both mirrors and modifying the interferometer to focus on the driven element to limit the aperture it has been possible to extend the bandwidth into the megacycle region. Imperfections in the optics and the achievable alignment have limited the maximum transmission to the order of 30–50%.

2-6 COMPONENTS USING FRUSTRATED TOTAL INTERNAL REFLECTION

Present-day optically pumped lasers require end reflectors or mirrors having varying degrees of transmission for operation. Because the laser output radiation is highly monochromatic, the selectively reflecting, narrow band, coated type of optical mirror has found wide application. As laser development has proceeded, however, and the output power level has increased into the megawatt range, it has been found that the coated mirrors, as well as other optically coated optical parts, are damaged by the intense light beam.

Because these high-power lasers were pulse systems, repeated optical bursts were possible only by replacing the mirrors between pulses. This, clearly, was not only cumbersome because of the exacting optical alignment required but also led to inaccuracies in measurements because of the change in optical cavity Q after each adjustment. Nondestructible optical elements were needed to extend high power laser measurements in an orderly fashion. Therefore elements employing frustrated total internal reflection (FTIR), such as the optical coupler and modulator described in this section, are useful because they are fabricated without any optical coatings whatsoever.

The principle of operation of an element employing FTIR can be seen schematically in Figure 2-33. Assume that a light beam is incident from the left on the face of a 90° prism and that the index of refraction (μ) of

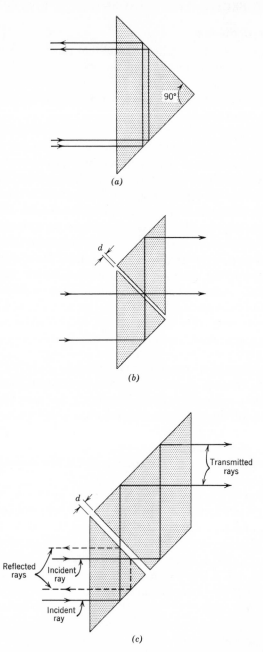

Figure 2-33 *a.* Total internal reflection in a prism. *b.* Frustrated total internal reflection, allowing partial transmission. *c.* Modification to retain an accurate image transmission through unit. After Steele et al., *Applied Optics* (1966).

78

the prism material is high enough that the critical angle for internal reflection is less than 45° (i.e., $\mu > 1.414$). Then, as shown in Figure 2-33a, the light beam will be totally internally reflected at the prism sides when the radiation is incident normal to the face; the result is a 100% reflector. This type of prism has been used extensively as the high reflectivity mirror in many laser structures.

Now, if a second prism is brought near one side of the initial prism as shown in Figure 2-33b and the spacing (d) is less than the wavelength (λ) of the incident radiation, a transmission of electromagnetic energy will take place from one prism to the other; the total internal reflection will be frustrated. By varying the spacing, the percentage transmission (or reflection) can be changed to almost any degree desired. If the spacing is reduced to zero, the transmission will be total except for reflections at the front and rear surface; if the second prism is removed and the spacing is large, the transmission will be reduced to zero. Thus by setting the spacing properly a reflector can be constructed to yield any desired value of reflectivity. If the spacing is varied with time, the output beam will be modulated in intensity because of the variation in transmission.

A useful device with a fixed value of reflectivity is illustrated schematically in Figure 2-33c. This variation in structure has been introduced because the simple design shown in Figure 2-33b yields a transmitted image that is split and inverted; this is bothersome in the optical alignment of a laser. Thus the modification Figure 2-33c is instituted, wherein all the rays experience an identical number of reflections in passing through the coupler; the output beam pattern then is an accurate reconstruction of the cross section of the input beam.

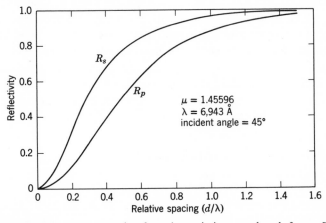

Figure 2-34 Reflectivity versus spacing for ruby emission wavelength for an FTIR gap using fused silica.

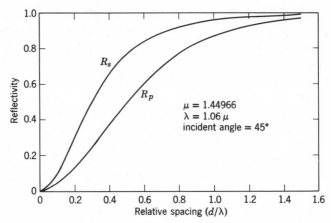

Figure 2-35 Reflectivity versus spacing for Nd^{3+} emission wavelength for an FTIR gap using fused silica.

The variation of reflectivity (R) as a fraction of the air gap spacing (d) for two pieces of fused silica is shown in Figures 2-34 and 2-35 for an incident angle of 45°. Because the reflectivity depends on the plane of polarization of the incident radiation, two curves are shown; one curve is for the case in which the electric vector is parallel to the plane of incidence (R_p) and the second is for the electric vector normal to the plane of incidence (R_s). The respective values of transmissivity are (T_p) and (T_s) for the two planes of polarization. The curves in Figure 2-34 were calculated by assuming the index of refraction of the silica at the ruby emission wavelength ($\mu = 1.45596$). The curves in Figure 2-35 are similar except that the index used was calculated for the emission wavelength of Nd^{3+} in a glass host matrix ($\mu = 1.44966$). The equations from which the reflectivity plot was determined are given as follows (2-35). They have been evaluated for the coupler geometry used, in which the angle of incidence is 45°.

For polarization parallel to the plane of incidence,

$$\frac{R_p}{T_p} = \frac{(\mu^2 - 1)^4}{4\mu^2(\mu^2 - 2)} \sinh^2\left[2\pi\frac{d}{\lambda}\left(\frac{\mu^2 - 2}{2}\right)^{1/2}\right]. \qquad (2\text{-}35a)$$

For polarization normal to the plane of incidence,

$$\frac{R_s}{T_s} = \frac{(\mu^2 - 1)^2}{\mu^2(\mu^2 - 2)} \sinh^2\left[2\pi\frac{d}{\lambda}\left(\frac{\mu^2 - 2}{2}\right)^{1/2}\right]. \qquad (2\text{-}35b)$$

In addition, it is assumed that $R + T = 1$.

It should be noted that the strong dependence of the reflectivity on the air gap spacing is determined by the exponential term. In this term there is a factor involving $(\mu^2 - 2)^{1/2}$ which is sensitive to the exact value of the index of refraction (μ).

A schematic of the actual structure of such a unit as finally designed is shown in Figure 2-36. The cover plates are required in order to protect the FTIR interface from dust and contamination. In addition, there must be an air gap maintained between the cover plate and the prisms to preserve the total internal reflection.

The fact that the reflectivity of an FTIR element can be altered by changing the critical spacing leads to the possibility of fabricating variable couplers. One such optical switch or modulation cell was constructed of germanium for use at 10μ wavelength radiation. The structure is shown in Figure 2-38. The beam from a laser enters the input window. When the FTIR air gap is open the incident beam is totally reflected at the FTIR interface along path A and is eventually absorbed at the edge. Thus no radiation emerges in the output beam. If the gap is now greatly reduced there is considerable transmission across the interface as shown by path B, and the output beam intensity increases. This variable FTIR unit can then be used as an external modulator for a light beam. Figure 2-39 is a photograph of such a cell, and the transmission of this cell for various wavelengths is given in Figure 2-40.

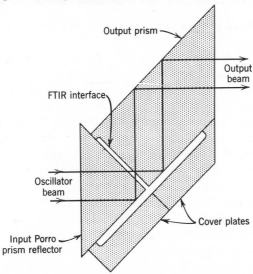

Figure 2-36 Schematic representation of an actual FTIR output coupler. It operates without degradation under very large power pulses from a laser. After Steele et al., *Applied Optics* (1966).

Figure 2-37 Photograph of an operating coupler, showing size relative to coin and $\frac{1}{2}$-in. reflector.

Another variation of the variable FTIR cell is shown in Figure 2-41, in which the device can be used as a variable output coupler at the exit port of a laser. The armature is anchored to the piezoelectric driver at one end. The other end is one surface of the FTIR gap. A voltage applied to the piezoelectric driver will change the gap spacing. When the FTIR interface gap is large, the radiation in the laser is incident, as shown from the left, reflected at the interface, and reflected back into the laser cavity from the mirror surface on the outer surface of the cell. By varying the voltage on the piezoelectric driver to reduce the FTIR gap the reflectivity is reduced and a fraction of the beam can be coupled out; or by continuously varying the voltage the output beam can be modulated. This cell can also be used as a Q-switch by keeping the gap closed while the laser is being pumped, then opening it to a predetermined reflectivity to permit the reflective feedback to occur and thereby develop laser oscillations. The principles of Q-switching are discussed in greater detail in a later chapter; the critical element in this particular operation is that the reflectivity can be varied in a controlled manner in a short time.

2-7 LASER DETECTORS

To one interested in measuring the properties of optical lasers, in evaluating the light pulse characteristics, or in using the laser in various applications, the role of available detectors is pertinent. We present here some descriptive data for detectors that have been found to be suitable in laser experimentation. Some characteristic curves are given which may be used for the rapid evaluation of detector properties for specific purposes.

Optical detectors may be generally classified as photon effect devices or thermal effect detectors. The discussion here primarily concerns the photon effect devices, for the thermal effect detectors are generally too slow for the required measurements.

A further delineation of the photon effect devices can be made according to three categories: (a) photoemissive, (b) photoconductive, and (c) photovoltaic detectors. Other devices have a photoelectromagnetic (PEM) effect, but their use is so limited that we devote no attention to them. Some of these devices also have internal gain or amplification associated with their action and these features are also discussed briefly. The actual circuit configurations in which these detectors can be used are characterized by either direct photodetection or a photomixing detector system. The photomixing system requires a local oscillator, generally constituted by a laser with a high stability of both frequency and phase, whereas the direct photodetector variety does not. We turn first to the devices operating by direct photodetection.

Let us discuss the *photoemissive type of detectors*, which are generally

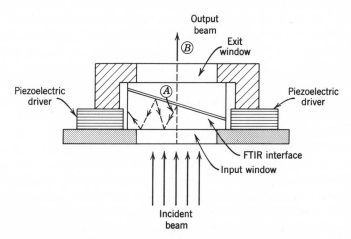

Figure 2-38 Schematic diagram of optical switch or modulator.

Figure 2-39 Photograph of optical modulation cell. Courtesy of Astheimer et al., *Appl. Opt.* (1966).

characterized by a vacuum diode structure with the photoemissive material coated on a cathode and a voltage bias applied to a nearby anode. These devices can be used in the wavelength region between the visible and near infrared. The effectiveness of the photoemissive surfaces decreases by a factor of at least 20 in going from the ruby laser emission wavelength (about 7,000 A) to the neodymium-doped laser emission (about 1.06 μ). A comparison of various photoemissive surfaces of interest in the optical laser region is shown in Figure 2-42. Note that the S-20 surface is to be preferred for ruby laser radiation, whereas the S-1 is more sensitive in the near infrared range—out to 1.1 μ. As long as the light beams are of high intensity these photoemissive diodes work very well. When the intensity levels are low, however, photoemissive devices such as photomultipliers become of interest because of the internal multiplication or gain that is built in and gives a greater quantum efficiency. The quantum efficiency of a photodetector is defined as the average number of electrons emitted per incident photon on the photo-surface. For photodetectors without gain this yield generally ranges between 10^{-2} and 10^{-5}, depending on the wavelength and material. In a photomultiplier the electrons emitted or ejected from the photosurface hit a secondary emission surface, which causes many electrons to be ejected for each incoming electron. These secondary electrons are in turn multiplied at the emission surface of the next stage. The multiplier output becomes $M = S^n$, where M is the multiplication factor, S is the secondary emission ratio, and n is the number of stages. The factor S may have values up to 10, and the number of stages may be of the same order; thus M may become quite high. Current gains of more than 60 db are common, but the multiplier frequency response has been limited because of transit time effects to a bandwidth of about 100 mc.

The dispersion of the electron cloud as it leaves each multiplier electrode causes the ultimate limitation on useful bandwidth.

In the case of *photoconductive detectors* the important physical phenomenon that governs the performance is a change in electrical resistance caused by the absorption of photons.

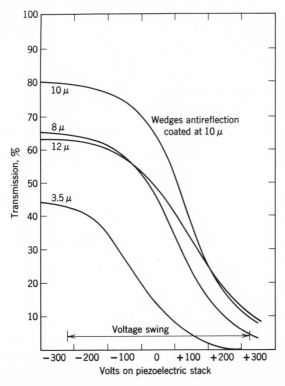

Figure 2-40 Transmission of modulation cell as a function of voltage on piezoelectric transducer and wavelength of incident radiation. After Astheimer et al., *Appl. Opt.* (1966).

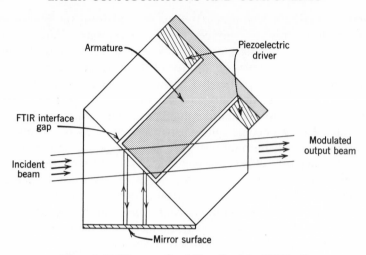

Figure 2-41 Diagram of variable reflectivity FTIR cell.

Essentially, photoconductivity causes a decrease in electrical resistance, which increases the current through the device. This process involves the absorption of energy from photons, the excitation of charge carriers to a high energy state in which they are free to contribute to the electric conductivity, and the return of charge carriers from the conducting state to the ground state. Photoconductor response extends into the infrared region, where photoemissive devices do not function. Semiconductor detectors (Ge, PbS, InSb) have relatively high dark currents

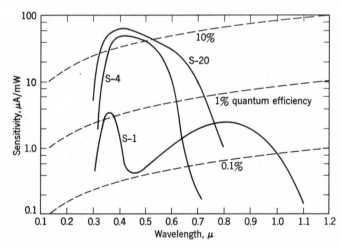

Figure 2-42 Typical spectral response curves for phomemissive surfaces of S-1, S-4, and S-20 cathodes.

at room temperature and approximately miscrosecond response times, whereas silicon has a low dark current. Insulator cells (CdS, CdSe) have low dark currents at room temperature but much slower response times.

Detectors using the photovoltaic effect operate because of the action of photons which produce a voltage, which can then be detected without need for bias supply or a load resistor. This effect occurs as the result of absorption of ionizing radiation in the vicinity of a potential barrier, such as in a *p-n* junction. Photovoltaic effect photodiodes in the visible region include selenium, selenium oxide, and gallium arsenide types. Indium antimonide is used in the 4- to 5.5-μ region. Silicon and germanium are effective in the visible and near infrared range. A number of materials can be used to build detectors in both the photoconductive and photovoltaic modes. Microwave response photodiodes have recently been built and extend the frequency range of solid state detectors to several gc. The best of these have been constructed of silicon epitaxial and germanium *p-i-n* junction diodes.

A *photovoltaic device* can be operated as a photodiode by applying a bias voltage and a load resistance in series with the photosensitive *p-n* junction layer. In darkness the device is simply a rectifier. As the light intensity increases the reverse current increases sharply and photodiode action occurs. Combining two photodiodes back to back gives a phototransistor that can have a gain factor exceeding unity.

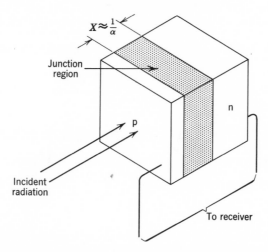

Figure 2-43 Schematic diagram illustrating the use of a semiconductor p-n junction as a photodiode. The signal is incident on the left face, and the photocurrent is then measured by the receiver. The effective collecting volume is determined by a thickness dictated by the inverse of the absorption constant (α).

Silicon photodiodes have a sensitivity and frequency response adequate for many applications, for they have a peak response at about 8500–9000 A.

A schematic example of such a photodiode structure is shown in Figure 2-43. Here the radiation is absorbed in the *p-n* junction region, creating electron hole pairs separated by the built-in barrier voltage, which then causes the photocurrent to appear. This current is then measured by the circuit as indicated. The ultimate frequency limitation of such a device will be governed by the *p-n* junction capacitance across the barrier thickness (*x*) and the series resistance of bulk semiconductor material.

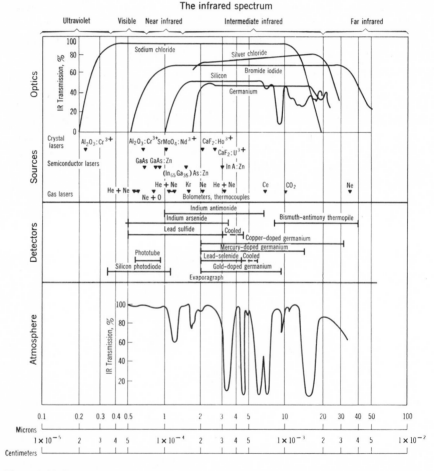

Figure 2-44 Comparison chart showing wavelength properties of lasers and related materials and devices.

TABLE 2-4 HIGH FREQUENCY CUTOFF CHARACTERISTICS OF SEVERAL SOLID STATE DEVICES

Material	Wavelength Region (μm)	Area (cm^2)	R_s (ohms)	C_b (pF)	f_{RC} (gc/sec)	Transport Distance (μm)	f_{TR} (gc/sec)
Si, p-i-n	0.65–0.75	6×10^{-5}	5	0.5(−6 v)	45	2.5	15
	0.65–0.75	2×10^{-4}	5	1.5(−10 v)	12	2.5	15
	0.5–0.95	3.5×10^{-2}	65	5.0(−100 v)	0.5	75.0	0.5
Ge, n-p	0.5–1.5	4×10^{-4}	6	5.6(−6 v)	17	0.4	8
GaAs, p-n	0.4–0.8	1.3×10^{-4}	3.0	7.0(−4.5 v)	7.5	1.0	8
		7×10^{-4}	2.5	32(−4.5 v)	2	1.0	8
InAs, p-n	0.5–3.5	3.2×10^{-1}	12	3.0(−5 v)	4.5	2.0	10
		2×10^{-3}	8	30(−2 v)	0.65	2.0	10
InSb, p-n (77°K)	0.5–5.2	5×10^{-4}	18	7.1(−0.2 v)	1.2	2.0	10

Data courtesy of Lasser, *IEEE Spectrum* (1966).

An example of this resistance-capacitance (RC) time constant as it relates to several devices is given in Table 2-4, with the bias voltage on the photodiode indicated. Another inherent frequency limitation can arise from the transit time of the carriers across the junction region. This frequency limitation is also given in Table 2-4 and is identified by f_{TR}.

A chart illustrating some general properties of lasers, materials, and devices related to the infrared spectrum is given in Figure 2-44. The transmission bands in the atmosphere are shown here for convenience as well as some data on typical optical materials used in the intermediate and far infrared ranges. Typical detector devices, including some of the thermal effect detectors mentioned earlier as being slow in frequency response, are noted here. The photoemissive detectors described earlier are gathered together here under the single designation of phototubes. Of course, the sensitivity of various detectors varies with wavelength, and this variation is indicated by the data given in Figure 2-45, where the parameter D^*, called the detectivity, is plotted versus wavelength. The detectivity of an infrared detector is a direct measure of its ability to detect an optical signal at a given wavelength out of the surrounding noise. The higher the detectivity, the better the detector at that wavelength. Because the internal noise and, thus, the detector performance are temperature-sensitive, data are also given for some units at different temperatures.

It was mentioned earlier that a photomixing detector system can be utilized to achieve greater sensitivity at low signal levels. In the case of lasers this amounts to employing a superheterodyne technique at optical frequencies by mixing two coherent light beams together.

The operation of a superheterodyne detector is based on the well-known empirical fact that all optical detectors measure the intensity, rather than the amplitude, of an incident electromagnetic wave. If we assume that two electromagnetic light waves of different frequencies fall on the same area of a detector, the amplitude of the resultant wave is given by

$$E_1 = E_S \cos \omega_S t + E_L \cos \omega_L t, \tag{2-36}$$

where E_S and E_L are the amplitudes and ω_S and ω_L are the angular frequencies of the two incident waves. We are implicitly assuming that the two waves are parallel when incident on the surface of the detector.

To detect the presence of the signal we measure the photointensity, which is given by the square of (2-36).

$$E_1{}^2 = E_S{}^2 \cos^2 \omega_S t + E_L{}^2 \cos^2 \omega_L t + E_S E_L \cos (\omega_S + \omega_L)t$$
$$+ E_S E_L \cos (\omega_S - \omega_L)t. \tag{2-37}$$

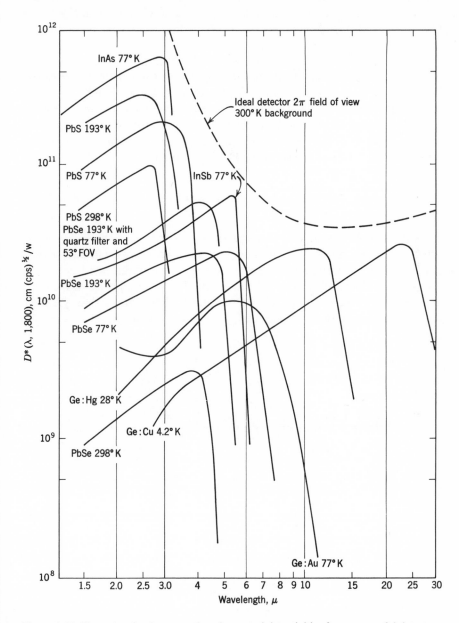

Figure 2-45 Chart showing long wavelength spectral detectivities for some useful detectors of interest in laser studies. *Note.* FOV means "field of view" of detector. Data courtesy of Santa Barbara Research Center.

Assume that the detector has a high frequency cutoff above the difference frequency ($\omega_S - \omega_L$). Because of this cutoff, we cannot assume that the detector will respond to signals at the frequencies given by the first three terms of (2-37).

There is a minimum time required for the generation of electron hole pairs, known as the electron-photon correlation time. It is of the order of 3×10^{-14} sec. The detector, therefore, will not respond to signals at optical frequencies exceeding 10^{-14} sec. Under these conditions we can only detect the average power in these high frequency terms. The average of $\cos^2 \omega t$ is one half, whereas the average of the linear cosine term, $\cos (\omega_S + \omega_L)t$, is clearly zero. The result then is

$$E_1^2 = \frac{E_S^2}{2} + \frac{E_L^2}{2} + E_S E_L \cos (\omega_S - \omega_L)t. \tag{2-38}$$

Thus, if two coherent electromagnetic waves are superimposed on each other in space, the vector amplitudes of the two waves will add, giving rise to a single amplitude-modulated wave at the difference frequency. An optical detector placed in the path of this composite wave will detect simply the envelope of the modulated light wave, thus yielding an electrical signal that is modulated at the beat frequency.

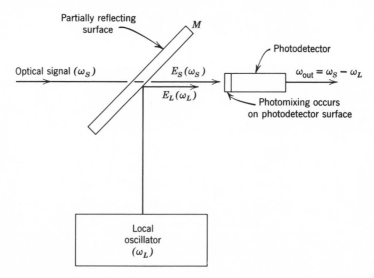

Figure 2-46 Schematic diagram of a photomixing optical system. The optical signal passes through the partial reflector and mixes with the beam from the local oscillator, which is reflected by the reflector. The combined signal is then incident on the detector.

The frequency $(\omega_S - \omega_L)$ has been found to fall in the microwave range for lasers operated to date.

If we now look at the schematic of a photomixing optical system shown in Figure 2-46, we see the essential features of the scheme. The signal from the local oscillator laser (E_L) at frequency ω_L is reflected toward the detector by the partly reflecting surface (M), whereas the optical signal (E_S) at frequency ω_S is incident on this same surface but is partly transmitted through it. When the resulting electromagnetic wave composed of the electric field from both the oscillator and signal beam is incident on the photosurface, photomixing occurs and the difference frequency is detected. Phase coherence is, of course, necessary for this to work successfully, and therefore the laser local oscillator must be very stable.

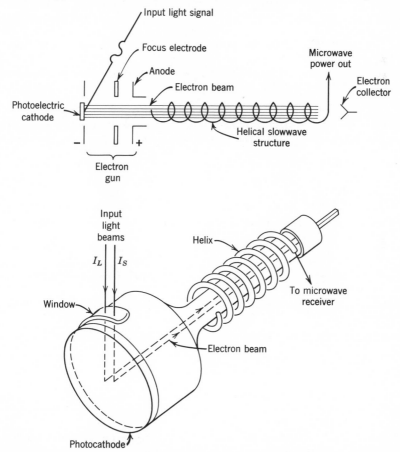

Figure 2-47 Diagram of a traveling wave detector with gain. The photocurrent is amplified as it travels down the slow wave structure to the collector. After Caddes, *Microwave J.* (1965).

Another photoemissive device that has gain is the traveling wave phototube using a traveling wave structure in which the beam current is the photoemissive current. The gain is achieved by the same mechanism as in conventional microwave traveling wave tubes; that is, the electron beam interacts with the electromagnetic field in the helix slow wave structure. The traveling wave phototube is not an electron multiplier, and its

TABLE 2-5   SOME CONVENTIONAL LASER DETECTORS

Laser	Wavelength (A)	Detector	Reference
GaAs p-n junction	8,420	IR converter tube 6911 photomultiplier	*Phys. Rev. Letters*, **9**, 366 (1962) *Appl. Phys. Letters*, **1**, 62 (1962)
$CaWO_4:Nd^{3+}$	10,600	7102 photomultiplier	*Proc. Inst. Radio Eng.*, **49**, 1704 (1961)
$CaWO_4:Tm^{3+}$	19,100	Au-doped Ge photoconductor (cooled to 77°K)	*Proc. Inst. Radio Eng.*, **50**, 86 (1962)
Ruby	6,943	(1) 931A photomultiplier (2) Eppley thermopile (3) 917 photocell, 931A	*Proc. Inst. Radio Eng.*, **49**, 1570 (1961) *Proc. Inst. Radio Eng.*, **50**, 330 (1962) *Proc. Inst. Radio Eng.*, **50**, 1835 (1962)
$CaF_2:Sm^{2+}$	7,082	IP 28 photomultiplier photomultiplier	*Phys. Rev.*, **123**, 766 (1961) *IBM J. Res. Develop.*, **5**, 56 (1961)
$CaF_2:U^{3+}$ $BaF_2:U^{3+}$	25,000	InSb PME cell	*Proc. Inst. Radio Eng.*, **50**, 219 (1962)
$CaF_2:Dy^{2+}$	23,600	PbS photoconductor	*Proc. Inst. Radio Eng.*, **50**, 1699 (1962)
$CaWO_4:Pr^{3+}$	10,468	7102	*J. Appl. Phys.*, **33**, 2519 (1962)
$CaF_2:Nd^{3+}$	10,460	7102	*J. Appl. Phys.*, **33**, 756 (1962)
He-Ne	11,530 6,328	7102 High frequency Photodiode Eppley thermopile	*Phys. Rev.*, **126**, 580 (1962) *Proc. Inst. Radio Eng.*, **50**, 1697 (1962)
$SrF_2:Sm^{2+}$	6,969	Photomultiplier	*Phys. Rev.*, **127**, 503 (1962)
"Organic Molecules"	~ 4,500	EMI 6256 photomultiplier	*J. Chem. Phys.*, **37**, 2041 (1962)
Cs	32,000	PbS(liquid N_2-cooled)	*Phys. Rev. Letters*, **7**, 415 (1961)

postdetection power gain is limited to about 50 db. A schematic drawing of such a structure is shown in Figure 2-47. There are three main portions in this tube: the photoemissive surface, the electron gun, and the interaction region where the beam interacts with the field in the helix.

The functions of the photoelectron gun are to produce and focus an electron beam from the incident light and to accelerate this beam to the proper velocity for interaction with the slow wave circuit.

In a conventional TWT an a-c signal is impressed on a large direct current, and a-c amplification is brought about by increasing the depth of modulation of the combined currents. If there is no direct current, clearly there will be no current amplification; however, there will be an impedance transformation, which can be helpful. This is the case for a photocathode that has no appreciable dark current.

When superheterodyne detection is used, a prime requirement is that the photocathode be illuminated by a strong local oscillator light beam. Heterodyning will then take place at the photocathode. The microwave tube elements will amplify the signal by increasing the depth of modulation into the local oscillator-generated direct current.

A compilation of data on the use of various detectors for specific laser types is shown in Table 2-5. There are included here some specific references to the work reported, which is a starting place for those interested in a specific laser requirement.

REFERENCES

A. General

Ackerman, J. A., "Laser Energy Measuring Device," *Appl. Opt.,* **3**, 644–645 (May 1964).

Fligsten, K. E., and M. L. Wolbarsht, "A Diffusely Transmitting, Integrating Sphere for Measuring Laser Output with a Phototransistor," *Proc. IEEE,* **54**, 1109–1110 (August 1966).

Gessell, R., ed., "Staff Report on Government Laser Support," *Electronic News* (October 19, 1964).

Geusic, J. E., and H. E. D. Scovil, "A Unidirectional Traveling Wave Optical Maser," *Bell System Tech. J.,* **41**, 1386–1396 (July 1962).

Kaplan, R. A., "Design Lasers with Pump Power Charts," *Electronics,* **36**, 23–28 (December 27, 1963).

Marchak, I. S., "Limiting Parameters and Generalized Characteristics of Xenon Lamps," *Appl. Opt.,* **2**, 793–799 (August 1963).

Roess, D., "Exfocal Pumping of Optical Masers in Elliptical Mirrors," *Appl. Opt.,* **3**, 259–265 (February 1964).

Weinberg, J. L., "On the Use of a Pile-of-Plates Polarizer – The Transmitted Component," *Appl. Opt.,* **3**, 1057 (September 1964).

Yariv, A., "Energy and Power Considerations in Lasers," *Proc. IEEE,* **51**, 1723–1731 (December 1963).

B. Isolators

Aplet, L. J., and J. W. Carson, "A Faraday Effect Optical Isolator," *Appl. Opt.*, **3**, 544–545 (April 1964).

George, N., and R. W. Waniek, "Faraday Rotators for High-Power Laser Cavities," *Appl. Opt.*, **5**, 1183–85 (July 1966).

C. Circulators

Fletcher, P. C., and D. L. Weisman, "Circulators for Optical Radar Systems," *Appl. Opt.*, **4**, 867–873 (July 1965).

Ribbens, W. R. "An Optical Circulator," *Appl. Opt.*, **4**, 1037–1038 (August 1965).

D. Modulators

Anderson, L. K., "Microwave Modulation of Light," *Microwaves*, **8**, 42–51 (January 1965).

Blumenthal, R. H., "Design of a Microwave Frequency Light Modulator," *Proc. IRE*, **50**, 452-456 (April 1962).

Buhrer, C. F., L. R. Bloom, and D. W. Baird, "Electro-Optics Light Modulation with Cubic Crystals," *Appl. Opt.*, **2**, 839-846 (August 1963).

Chen, F. S., J. E. Geusic, S. K. Kurtz, J. G. Skinner, and S. H. Wemple, "Light Modulation and Laser Beam Deflection with Potassium-Tantalate-Niobate Crystals," *J. Appl. Phys.*, **37**, 388–398 (January 1966).

Cummins, H. Z., and N. Knable, "Single Sideband Modulation of Coherent Light by Bragg Reflection from Acoustical Waves," *Proc. IEEE*, **51**, 1246 (September 1963).

Enderby, C. E., "Wideband Optical Modulator," *Proc. IEEE*, **52**, 981 (August 1964).

Gordon, E. I., and M. G. Cohen, "Electro-optic Diffraction Grating for Light Beam Modulation and Diffraction," *IEEE J., Quantum Electronics*, **1**, 191–198 (August 1965).

Gordon, E. I., and M. G. Cohen, "Acoustic Scattering of Light in a Fabry-Perot Resonator," *Bell System Tech. J.*, **45**, 945–966 (July–August 1966).

Herriott, D. R., "Spherical-Mirror Oscillating Interferometer," *Appl. Opt.*, **2**, 865–866 (August 1963).

Holsouser, D. F., and F. H. Van Foerster, "Microwave Modulation of Light Using the Kerr Effect," *J. Opt. Soc. Am.*, **51**, 1360–1365 (December 1961).

Johnson, K. M., "Solid State Modulation and Direct Demodulation of Gas Laser Light at a Microwave Frequency," *Proc. IEEE*, **51**, 1368–1369 (October 1963).

Johnson, K. M., "Microwave Light Modulation by the Pockel Effect," *Microwave J.*, **7**, 51–56 (August 1964).

"Retardation-Type Laser Modulators," *Spectra Physics Tech. Memo.* (1966).

Rigrod, W. W., and I. P. Kaminow, "Wideband Microwave Light Modulation," *Proc. IEEE*, **51**, 137–140 (January 1963).

Scanga, W. A., "Traveling-Wave Light Modulator," *Appl. Opt.*, **4**, 1103 (September 1965).

E. FTIR Elements

Appl. Opt., **5**, 1–178 (January 1966): Special Issue on Internal Reflection.

Astheimer, R. W., G. Falbel, and S. Minkowitz, "Infrared Modulation by Means of Frustrated Total Internal Reflection," *Appl. Opt.*, **5**, 87–91 (January 1966).

Court, I. N., and F. D. von Willisen, "Frustrated Total Internal Reflection and Application to Laser Cavity Design," *Appl. Opt.*, **3**, 719 (June 1964).

Steele, E. L., W. C. Davis, and R. L. Treuthart, "A Laser Output Coupler Using FTIR," *Appl. Opt.*, **5**, 5-8 (January 1966).

F. Detectors

Appl. Opt., **4**, 631–766 (June 1965): Issue on Detectors.

Caddes, D. E., "A Ku Band Traveling-Wave Phototube," *Microwave J.*, **8**, 46–50 (March 1965).

Coleman, P. D., and R. C. Eden, "Mixing and Detection of Coherent Light in a Bulk Semiconductor," *IEEE Trans. Electron. Devices,* **ED-11**, 488–497 (November 1964).

DiDomenico, M., and L. K. Anderson, "Microwave Signal-to-Noise Performance of CdSe Bulk Photoconductive Detectors," *Proc. IEEE,* **52**, 815–822 (July 1964).

Kruse, P. W., "Photon Effects in $Hg_{1-x}Cd_xTe$," *Appl. Opt.*, **4**, 687–692 (June 1965).

Lasser, M. E., "Detection of Coherent Optical Radiation," *IEEE Spectrum,* **3**, 73–78 (April 1966).

Levinstein, H., "Extrinsic Detectors," *Appl. Opt.*, **4**, 639–647 (June 1965).

Lucovsky, G., M. E. Lasser, and R. B. Emmons, "Coherent Light Detection in Solid State Photodiodes," *Proc. IEEE,* **51**, 166–172 (January 1963).

McMurty, B. J., and A. E. Siegman, "Photomixing Experiments with Ruby Optical Maser and TW Microwave Phototube," *Appl. Opt.*, **1**, 51–53 (January 1962).

Nudelman, S., "The Detectivity of Infrared Photodetectors," *Appl. Opt.*, **1**, 627–636 (September 1962).

Petritz, R. L., "Fundamentals of Infrared Detectors," *Proc. IRE,* **47**, 1458–1467 (September 1959).

Riesz, R. P., "High-Speed Semiconductor Photodiodes," *Rev. Sci. Instr.*, **33**, 994 (September 1962).

Smith, R. A., "Detectors for Ultraviolet, Visible, and Infrared Radiation," *Appl. Opt.*, **4**, 631–637 (June 1965).

Zitter, R. N. "Fast InSb PEM Detectors for Optical Maser-Studies to 7 Microns," *Rev. Sci. Instr.*, **35**, 594–596 (May 1964).

3

Laser Oscillators

The mechanical, electrical, or optical oscillator is a device in which the output signal is coupled in phase to the input with sufficient gain in the unit to compensate for the losses. Thus the output signal fed back into the input will maintain oscillations. A similar concept is used to construct a laser oscillator. The feedback element in the case of most laser oscillators is the reflecting mirror at the ends of the Fabry-Perot cavity.

We now discuss some of the characteristics of lasers as oscillators and describe some phenomena that have been observed in typical devices.

The laser oscillator is essentially a resonant cavity operating at optical frequencies. The concept arises as follows. The laser material has energy stored in it because of excitation from the pump lamp. This energy now is released to the optical beam by stimulated emission, which, therefore, in turn provides energy or power gain to the optical beam. The optical cavity is bounded on the two ends by mirrors that reflect the optical radiation back and forth in the cavity, thereby implementing optical feedback; the mirrors perform the function of the feedback element. Thus optical radiation bounces back and forth along the axis of the laser cavity, gaining energy as it does so, and thereby maintaining oscillations.

When the mirror or reflector at the output end of the laser is partially transparent, a fraction of the radiation will "leak out" or be emitted from the cavity and can be utilized externally. This comes about by lowering the reflectivity of the output end mirror; it is equivalent to decreasing the feedback factor and increasing the loss due to energy coupled out of the system. The limiting condition on this operation of the laser as an oscillator is that the feedback must be sufficiently large to compensate for the internal and external losses in the system.

The cavity that permits a large amount of energy to be coupled out will appear as a loaded oscillator, with a lower Q or quality factor; conversely, one with low output will have a high Q. This is directly analogous to the case of a loaded electronic oscillator.

It can be seen that the reflectivity of the output reflector of a useful laser oscillator will have a value less than 100%. The lower the value of reflectivity, the greater the amount of energy permitted to leave the optical cavity and, therefore, the greater the useful output. When the reflectivity becomes too low, however, the threshold of the laser will rise to a point at which the gain does not exceed the losses, and the unit will cease to oscillate. Thus a reflectivity should be chosen so that a maximum possible output is achieved while the unit is simultaneously allowed to oscillate with a maximum possible gain factor.

3-1 ELEMENTARY CONSIDERATIONS

A model of the laser oscillator is shown in Figure 3-1. The pump lamp inverts the electron population in the laser material, thereby giving the system a gain factor exceeding unity. The system starts to oscillate, having been triggered by some spontaneous radiation emitted along the axis of the laser. This radiation is amplified and a fraction leaks out of the output mirror. At the same time some radiation is reflected and amplified again as it passes through the material and continues to traverse the laser. To continue oscillating the gain per double pass must exceed the loss; at the oscillation threshold they will be equal. As an example, let us calculate the oscillation threshold condition for this simplified laser oscillator. We assume a gain per unit length of α, an active material of length L, and mirrors having a reflectivity of R_1 and R_2. The fraction

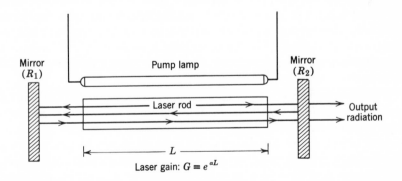

Figure 3-1 Model of a laser oscillator. The radiation emitted from the laser material is reflected back and forth between the mirrors, with some fraction being lost through mirror R_2 on each reflection.

of the energy coupled out of the system through mirror R_2 is given by $(1 - R_2)$. Furthermore, we assume that the laser gain condition is such that the gain is exponential with length. This is shown to be realistic and is derived in detail in Chapter 4. We assume also a photon density of Φ(photons/cm³) just inside mirror R_2 traveling to the left in Figure 3-1.

The threshold condition is established by requiring that the photon density, after passing through the laser material, reflecting off mirror R_1, and returning through the material to R_2 and reflecting, be equal to the initial photon density. The loss will just equal the gain in one round trip. We may then write

$$(\Phi e^{2\alpha L}) R_1 R_2 = \Phi \tag{3-1}$$

or

$$e^{-2\alpha L} = R_1 R_2. \tag{3-2}$$

If we assume that the gain is small at threshold, the exponential can be expanded in series and the expression for the gain per unit length reduces to

$$\alpha = \frac{1}{2L} (1 - R_1 R_2). \tag{3-3}$$

In addition, the output radiation intensity (I_{out}) can be written as in (3-4), where c is the speed of light and $h\nu$ is the energy per photon:

$$I_{out} = \Phi c (1 - R_2) (h\nu). \tag{3-4}$$

For a laser such as we are considering, of course, the photon density (Φ) will depend on the reflectivity of the mirrors as well. This comes about because of the intrinsic nature of the laser action. The greater the photon density, the higher the stimulated emission rate; the photons will thereby be added to the resonant cavity at a greater rate. The higher the reflectivity, the lower the loss rate from the cavity. Thus a determination of the photon density in the cavity requires more extensive analysis. A description in terms of radiation rate coefficients and inverted electron populations is required.

Before proceeding to a discussion of the detailed rate processes and a determination of Φ, however, let us discuss the quality factor of the resonant optical cavity. A photon in the cavity will have some average lifetime in the cavity before being scattered or emitted or lost in other ways to the optical system. This time constant might also be called the ringing time of the cavity. We call this photon lifetime τ_c. Note that it is different from the lifetime of an atom in an excited state. The cavity quality factor (Q) can be expressed in terms of this photon lifetime or cavity ringing time very simply.

Let us recall that the definition of the quality factor (Q) is the energy stored in the cavity divided by the energy loss per radian of oscillation. If the photons in the cavity have a frequency ν, the total energy (E) stored in the cavity is given by

$$E = \Phi h\nu V, \tag{3-5}$$

where h is Planck's constant and V is the cavity volume. The energy loss per radian is given by E_{loss}.

$$E_{\text{loss}} = \frac{\Phi h\nu V}{\tau_c} \times \frac{1}{2\pi\nu}. \tag{3-6}$$

Thus the quality factor is given by

$$Q = \frac{E}{E_{\text{loss}}} = 2\pi\nu\tau_c. \tag{3-7}$$

Conversely, expressing the decay or ringing time in terms of the quality factor, we have

$$\tau_c = \frac{Q}{2\pi\nu}. \tag{3-8}$$

We see that in the description of an optical resonant cavity we may use the same general terms to describe the properties as are used in the electrical analogs.

3-2 PHOTON DENSITY FOR LASER OSCILLATIONS

The essential conditions that must be satisfied to achieve laser oscillations by stimulated emission can be easily derived. In this calculation we consider the case of an optical system that operates between only two energy levels as schematically illustrated in Figure 3-2.

We consider absorption of radiation in the material and emission from the stimulated processes but neglect the spontaneous emission. In monochromatic radiation of frequency ν_0 described by a photon density $\Phi(\nu_0)$, we may write the photon density distribution in frequency by using the impulse symbol or the Dirac δ function $\delta(\nu)$ as follows:

$$\Phi(\nu) = \Phi(\nu_0)\delta(\nu - \nu_0). \tag{3-9}$$

It will be recalled that, by definition,

$$\delta(\nu-\nu_0) = 0 \text{ for } \nu \neq \nu_0; \quad \int_{-\infty}^{+\infty} \delta(\nu-\nu_0) \, d\nu = 1.$$

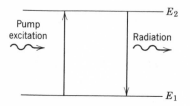

Figure 3-2 Energy level diagram for two-level system. Assume n_2 atoms at energy level E_2 and n_1 atoms at level E_1. The emitted radiation has a frequency of ν_0, related to the system by $h\nu_0 = E_2 - E_1$.

Using it with an arbitrary function $\rho(\nu)$, the integral result is further given by

$$\int_{-\infty}^{+\infty} \rho(\nu) \, \delta(\nu-\nu_0) \, d\nu = \rho(\nu_0). \quad (3\text{-}10)$$

The net rate of induced emission from this two-level system is the difference between the radiation emitted in the transition from level 2 to level 1 and the radiation absorbed between level 1 and level 2. The net rate of induced energy emission in the frequency interval $d\nu$ centered around ν is given by

$$h\nu g(\nu)\Phi(\nu)(B_{21}n_2 - B_{12}n_1)d\nu, \quad (3\text{-}11)$$

where $g(\nu)$ is the probability of emission or absorption per unit frequency interval and B_{21} and B_{12} are the Einstein B coefficients for the induced emission and absorption processes.

It will also be recalled that B_{12} and B_{21} are equal except for a degeneracy factor (g) at the two energy levels. Therefore we may write

$$B_{12} = B_{21}\left(\frac{g_2}{g_1}\right). \quad (3\text{-}12)$$

Using this relationship, the rate equation becomes

$$h\nu g(\nu)\Phi(\nu)B_{21}\left[n_2 - n_1\left(\frac{g_2}{g_1}\right)\right]d\nu. \quad (3\text{-}13)$$

It should be recalled that the probability of emission per unit frequency interval, $g(\nu)$, for a Lorentzian broadened emission line is given by

$$g(\nu) = \frac{a}{\pi}\left[\frac{1}{(\nu-\nu_0)^2 + (a)^2}\right], \quad (3\text{-}14)$$

where $2a$ is the linewidth at half maximum, and it thereby follows that at $\nu = \nu_0$ (3-14) gives

$$g(\nu_0) = \frac{1}{a\pi},$$

which is the effective bandwidth for the monochromatic distribution being considered.

Introducing the monochromatic photon density distribution given by (3-9) and integrating over frequency, we may write the rate equation (3-15) for the induced emission:

$$\frac{d\Phi(\nu_0)}{dt} = h\nu_0 B_{21}g(\nu_0)\Phi(\nu_0)\left[n_2 - n_1\left(\frac{g_2}{g_1}\right)\right]. \tag{3-15}$$

This gives the rate of growth of the photon density at frequency ν_0 when the upper populated state (n_2) is greater than the lower state (n_1).

If losses occur because of photon scattering or absorption by other impurities, or if the photons escape from the system by other means, an additional loss term must be added to account for this. Writing this loss in terms of the cavity ringing time (τ_c), we may then express the rate equation (3-16) as

$$\frac{d\Phi(\nu_0)}{dt} = \frac{h\nu_0 B_{21}}{a\pi}\left[n_2 - n_1\left(\frac{g_2}{g_1}\right)\right]\Phi(\nu_0) - \frac{\Phi(\nu_0)}{\tau_c}, \tag{3-16}$$

where we have also substituted $g(\nu_0) = 1/a\pi$.

On integrating for the photon density, we obtain

$$\Phi(\nu_0) = \Phi_0 \exp\left\{\frac{h\nu_0 B_{21}}{a\pi}\left[n_2 - n_1\left(\frac{g_2}{g_1}\right)\right] - \frac{1}{\tau_c}\right\}t. \tag{3-17}$$

It can be quickly noted that this corresponds to a growing photon density when the exponent is positive, when

$$\frac{h\nu_0 B_{21}}{a\pi}\left[n_2 - n_1\left(\frac{g_2}{g_1}\right)\right] > \frac{1}{\tau_c}, \tag{3-18}$$

or, equivalently, when

$$\left[n_2 - n_1\left(\frac{g_2}{g_1}\right)\right] > \frac{a\pi}{h\nu_0 B_{21}\tau_c}. \tag{3-18}$$

The threshold of oscillation for this laser may also be recognized from this equation by noting that unity gain occurs when the exponent is zero or when

$$\left[n_2 - n_1 \left(\frac{g_2}{g_1} \right) \right] = \frac{a\pi}{h\nu_0 B_{21}\tau_c}. \tag{3-19}$$

Recognizing that the Einstein A coefficient is related to the *spontaneous emission* lifetime (τ_s) and the Einstein B coefficient by the relations

$$A_{21} = \frac{1}{\tau_s} \qquad B_{21} = \frac{c^3 A_{21}}{8\pi h\nu_0{}^3}, \tag{3-20}$$

we may rewrite the threshold relationship in terms of the fundamental laser parameters:

$$\left[n_2 - n_1 \left(\frac{g_2}{g_1} \right) \right] = \left(\frac{\tau_s}{\tau_c} \right) \left(\frac{8\pi^2 \nu_0{}^2 a}{c^3} \right). \tag{3-21}$$

From this equation we can observe those factors favoring high gain and a low threshold for a laser oscillator. These conditions are the following:

1. Select a laser material in which the lower laser level population (n_1) can be kept small. The relaxation time out of the lower level should be fast.

2. The laser linewidth $(2a)$ should be kept narrow; perhaps the laser should be cooled.

3. The spontaneous emission lifetime (τ_s) of the upper laser level should be long.

4 Incidental losses in the laser cavity and crystal should be minimized to decrease the cavity ringing time (τ_c).

5. The output mirror should also have high reflectivity to decrease the cavity ringing time (τ_c).

This analysis has implicitly assumed that the population inversion $(n_2 - n_1)$ is constant in time during which the laser action occurs. This is not necessarily true, although the condition can more easily be reached in a four-level laser system than in a three-level one. If the pump rate is large enough, it is a reasonable approximation and at any rate gives a valid estimate of the laser threshold. As the laser action progresses the population difference will decrease as the photon flux increases, and therefore far above threshold the exponential growth of the photon density will not be accurate.

It can be seen, how a pulsed oscillation can occur in this system by looking closely at the equation (3-17) for photon density. Starting with a low value of photon density (Φ_0), there is an exponential increase in time. As the threshold is exceeded, stimulated emission tends to decrease the electron population inversion $[n_2 - n_1(g_2/g_1)]$, thereby decreasing the exponent. The exponent turns negative and the photon density markedly decreases. The pumping action from the exciting flashlamp then takes over, the population inversion once again increases, and the cycle repeats itself. Thus there occurs in the laser oscillator a phenomenon known as laser pulse spiking. In order to discuss this properly, the dependence of the electron population inversion on the photon density must be factored into the differential rate equation for the photon density. An additional equation must be written for the electron inversion. This is treated in the next section.

3-3   LASER SPIKING OSCILLATIONS

The pulsed light output from an oscillating laser is analyzed by a more detailed formulation of the rate equations. Again, the system is assumed to be a two-level system with a population inversion n and a photon density Φ within the laser cavity. For this solution we simplify the considerations by assuming the degeneracy of the two-laser states to be equal, thereby letting $n = n_2 - n_1$. If this is not valid, the assumption of

$$n = n_2 - n_1\left(\frac{g_2}{g_1}\right)$$

should be carried through. This, however, is an unnecessary elaboration at this point.

The instantaneous state of this laser is determined by the number of excess atoms in the inverted energy state as well as by the photon density in the lowest loss mode of the laser cavity. The rate equation for the inverted population is given by

$$\frac{dn}{dt} = W_p - Bn\Phi - \frac{n_2}{\tau_s}. \tag{3-22}$$

Here W_p is the rate at which the upper level is populated by the pump; the second term ($Bn\Phi$) represents the net loss due to induced transitions or stimulated emission, where (B) is the Einstein coefficient for induced emission per quantum and (Φ) is the density of quanta in the effective mode; the final term represents the loss due to spontaneous emission, where τ_s is the lifetime of the excited state.

It is further assumed that the pump rate is constant during the time the laser action takes place. A detailed treatment of the case for a non-constant pump rate was discussed by Steele[1] and also by Kleinman[2] but is not pursued here. The essence of the process can be understood without this additional complication.

The second rate equation describing the photon density stored in the laser cavity is given by (3-23); this is essentially a restatement, in slightly different terms, of (3-16).

$$\frac{d\Phi}{dt} = Bn\Phi - \frac{\Phi}{\tau_c} - \frac{n_2}{f\tau_s}. \tag{3-23}$$

Here the initial term arises from the addition of photons to the cavity from stimulated emission; the second term represents the loss rate from the cavity with a decay or ringing time of τ_c; the final term represents that fraction of the spontaneous emission of radiation that falls within the appropriate low loss mode of the laser cavity. The fraction $1/f$ represents the inverse of the number of modes available with gain in the laser resonant cavity. Further, note that

$$B = \frac{h\nu_0}{a\pi}B_{21} \tag{3-24}$$

for the Lorentzian linewidth. More generally we note also that the number of modes (f) in a cavity of volume V within the fluorescent linewidth $\Delta\nu$ is given by

$$f = \frac{1}{B\tau_s}, \tag{3-25}$$

where

$$f = \frac{8\pi\nu_0{}^2V}{c^3}\Delta\nu. \tag{3-26}$$

These relations can be confirmed by reference to the discussions on the Einstein A and B coefficients earlier in this volume.

The last terms of both rate equations are negligible except when the oscillation is starting. The term arising from the spontaneous emission

[1]E. L. Steele, "Descriptive Theory of Spiking Pulses in Optically Pumped Lasers," *IEEE. Trans. Quantum Electron.*, **1**, 42–49 (April 1965).

[2]D. A. Kleinman, "The Maser Rate Equations and Spiking," *Bell System Tech. J.* **43**, 1505–1532 (July 1964).

is essential for initiating the oscillation but can be neglected thereafter. Therefore the equations that we use can be rewritten as follows when the spontaneous emission is neglected:

$$\frac{dn}{dt} = W_p - Bn\Phi \tag{3-27}$$

$$\frac{d\Phi}{dt} = Bn\Phi - \frac{\Phi}{\tau_c}. \tag{3-28}$$

For the steady state laser condition, we set the left-hand side of the above equations to zero:

$$W_p - Bn_0\Phi_0 = 0 \tag{3-29}$$

$$Bn_0\Phi_0 - \Phi_0/\tau_c = 0. \tag{3-30}$$

The steady-state value of the inversion (n_0) and the photon density (Φ_0) are then obtained from these relations and are seen to be

$$n_0 = \frac{1}{B\tau_c} \tag{3-31}$$

$$\Phi_0 = W_p\tau_c. \tag{3-32}$$

It should be observed that both steady-state values depend directly on the laser optical cavity Q or loss rate (τ_c). Recalling the relation between the cavity ringing time (τ_c) and the quality factor (Q) from (3-8), we may write alternatively

$$n_0 = \left(\frac{2\pi\nu_0}{B}\right)\frac{1}{Q} \tag{3-33}$$

$$\Phi_0 = \left(\frac{W_p}{2\pi\nu_0}\right)Q. \tag{3-34}$$

These dynamic equations (3-27) and (3-28) which describe the laser action are nonlinear because of the product term $n\Phi$. A computer solution to these rate equations was obtained by Dunsmuir[3] with the result shown

[3]R. Dunsmuir, "Theory of Relaxation Oscillations in Optical Masers," *J. Electron. Control*, **10**, 453–458 (June 1961).

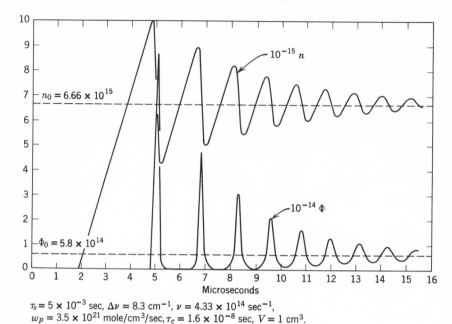

$\tau_s = 5 \times 10^{-3}$ sec, $\Delta\nu = 8.3$ cm^{-1}, $\nu = 4.33 \times 10^{14}$ sec^{-1},
$w_p = 3.5 \times 10^{21}$ mole/cm^3/sec, $\tau_c = 1.6 \times 10^{-8}$ sec, $V = 1$ cm^3.

Figure 3-3 Laser relaxation oscillations in ruby. The computer solutions were obtained using the above values of constants. After Dunsmuir, *J. Electron. Control* (1961).

in Figure 3-3 for ruby. The values of the parameters used are indicated with the figure. The lower curve represents the output spiking pulses as a result of the photon density variation, whereas the upper curve gives the variation with time of the excess population density.

When the pump is first turned on there is a negligible number of photons in the cavity at the appropriate frequency. The pump radiation causes a linear buildup of excited atoms and the population is inverted. The excited population well exceeds the equilibrium or steady-state value before an appreciable increase in photon density occurs and stimulated emission becomes important. The light quanta then suddenly build up rapidly, with a corresponding collapse of the excited atom population. Unless the cavity ringing time is too short, the excess population will again be inverted by pumping and the process will repeat.

Although the equations describing the photon density and excess population are nonlinear, we can obtain approximate solutions in various regions of the laser spiking action.

Between the spiking pulses we can assume that the induced emission is negligible because of the low photon density. During this interval we may neglect the second term ($Bn\Phi$) in (3-27) and write

$$\frac{dn}{dt} = W_p - Bn\Phi \simeq W_p. \qquad (3\text{-}31)$$

Then

$$n = W_p(t - t_0), \qquad (3\text{-}32)$$

where $n = 0$ at $t = t_0$, and t_0 is the time at which the population inversion initially occurs. The population inversion therefore increases *linearly* in time before the development of a large spiking pulse. This solution, when used with the equation (3-28) for photon density, gives the following differential equation:

$$\frac{d\Phi}{dt} = BW_p(t - t_0)\Phi, \qquad (3\text{-}33)$$

where the contribution from the loss term involving the cavity decay time is assumed small because of the low photon density and the short time interval between spikes. The photon density thus builds up rapidly between spikes as an exponential in time squared.

$$\frac{d\Phi}{\Phi} = BW_p(t - t_0)\,dt \qquad (3\text{-}34)$$

$$\Phi \approx \exp\left(+\frac{BW_p}{2}\right)(t - t_0)^2. \qquad (3\text{-}35)$$

Now, as the photon density builds up, the stimulated emission terms become important and for the short duration of one pulse the effect of the pumping can be neglected. Therefore during the actual spiking pulse the rate equations can be written as follows by neglecting both the pumping rate for the excess population and the cavity loss rate in (3-27) and (3-28):

$$\frac{dn}{dt} = -Bn\Phi \qquad (3\text{-}36)$$

$$\frac{d\Phi}{dt} = +Bn\Phi. \qquad (3\text{-}37)$$

As a result, we see immediately that the photon density and inverted population density are related through a constant since

$$\frac{dn}{dt} = -\frac{d\Phi}{dt}, \qquad (3\text{-}38)$$

and by integration we obtain (3-39) where N_{max} is the constant of integration equal to the maximum inverted population.

$$n = N_{max} - \Phi$$

or

$$n + \Phi = N_{max}. \tag{3-39}$$

Note that N_{max} will be different from the steady state population inversion (n_0) previously determined. The condition of $n = N_{max}$ occurs just before the rapid photon buildup with the accompanying rapid decrease of the population inversion. Equations (3-36) and (3-37) can now be integrated by substituting the value for n or Φ from (3-39). With this substitution we see that

$$\frac{dn}{dt} = -Bn(N_{max} - n) \tag{3-40}$$

$$= +B\left(n - \frac{N_{max}}{2}\right)^2 - \frac{BN^2_{max}}{4} \tag{3-41}$$

The solution then becomes

$$n = \frac{N_{max}}{2}\left[1 - \tanh \frac{BN_{max}}{2}(t - t_1)\right], \tag{3-42}$$

where t_1 is the time at which the photon density and the inversion population have equalized. For $t < t_1$ the inverted population (n) exceeds the photon density. Similarly, the photon density can be calculated to the same approximation by solving for Φ in (3-37) with the substitution of $n = N_{max} - \Phi$ from (3-39). Thus we obtain

$$\frac{d\Phi}{dt} = +B\Phi(N_{max} - \Phi), \tag{3-43}$$

and a solution similar to that for the population inversion is obtained.

$$\Phi = \frac{N_{max}}{2}\left[1 + \tanh \frac{BN_{max}}{2}(t - t_1)\right]. \tag{3-44}$$

The photon density thus grows with time and the population inversion decreases with time.

Figure 3-4 shows the buildup in time of the photon density and the corresponding decay of the inverted population during the spiking pulse formation.

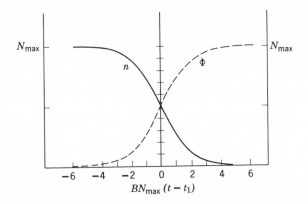

Figure 3-4 Variation of photon density and population inversion with time during the formation of the spiking pulse. The equations plotted are

$$n = \frac{N_{max}}{2}\left[1 - \tanh\frac{BN_{max}}{2}(t-t_1)\right]$$

$$\Phi = \frac{N_{max}}{2}\left[1 + \tanh\frac{BN_{max}}{2}(t-t_1)\right]$$

$$n + \Phi = N_{max}.$$

The discussion so far relates to the formation of a single spiking pulse and the photon density buildup in the interval between two pulses. For a comprehensive look at the repetitive pulse spiking oscillations we return to the steady-state laser solutions and examine small oscillations around the steady state values. These may be treated as perturbations. Returning again to the rate equations (3-27) and (3-28) and recalling that the spontaneous loss term has been neglected, we rewrite the dynamic equations for population inversion and photon density:

$$\frac{dn}{dt} = W_p - Bn\Phi \tag{3-27}$$

$$\frac{d\Phi}{dt} = Bn\Phi - \frac{\Phi}{\tau_c}. \tag{3-28}$$

We now proceed to eliminate the photon density (Φ) from the differential equation for the population inversion. This is done by first taking the derivative of (3-27). Thus

$$\frac{d^2n}{dt^2} = -Bn\frac{d\Phi}{dt} - B\Phi\frac{dn}{dt}. \tag{3-45}$$

Then, using (3-28), we substitute for $d\Phi/dt$, and using (3-27) we eliminate Φ. Thus

$$\frac{d^2n}{dt^2} = -Bn\left(Bn\Phi - \frac{\Phi}{\tau_c}\right) - B\Phi\frac{dn}{dt} \qquad (3\text{-}46)$$

and it follows that

$$\frac{d^2n}{dt^2} = W_p\left(\frac{1}{\tau_c} - Bn\right) + \left(Bn - \frac{1}{\tau_c} - \frac{W_p}{n}\right)\frac{dn}{dt} + \frac{1}{n}\left(\frac{dn}{dt}\right)^2. \qquad (3\text{-}47)$$

This expression indicates clearly the nonlinear nature of the interaction between photon and inverted population densities. Now we introduce a small perturbation (η) on the steady-state value of population inversion (n_0); similarly, a perturbation (q) is introduced into the steady state photon density (Φ_0). Thus we may write

$$n = n_0 - \eta \qquad (3\text{-}48)$$

$$\Phi = \Phi_0 + q. \qquad (3\text{-}49)$$

Neglecting terms of second order in η and q and recognizing that

$$n_0 = \frac{1}{B\tau_c} \qquad (3\text{-}31)$$

$$\Phi_0 = W_p\tau_c$$

the differential equation (3-47) reduces to

$$\frac{d^2\eta}{dt^2} + B\Phi_0\frac{d\eta}{dt} + B^2\Phi_0 n_0\eta = 0. \qquad (3\text{-}50)$$

The time variation of the spiking oscillation then becomes

$$\eta \simeq \exp\left(-\frac{B\Phi_0}{2}t\right)\sin[B(\Phi_0 n_0)^{1/2}t]. \qquad (3\text{-}51)$$

Thus the successive pulses decay in amplitude with a decay constant $(1/t_D)$ of $B\Phi_0/2$, and the spiking angular frequency (ω_s) is $B(\Phi_0 n_0)^{1/2}$.

A corresponding calculation can be made for the photon density. Differentiation of (3-28) yields the following equation:

$$\frac{d^2\Phi}{dt^2} = Bn\frac{d\Phi}{dt} + B\Phi\frac{dn}{dt} - \frac{1}{\tau_c}\frac{d\Phi}{dt}. \qquad (3\text{-}52)$$

This is done by eliminating the population inversion between the rate equations. Thus, by eliminating n and dn/dt by using (3-27) and (3-28), we obtain the following nonlinear equation for photon density:

$$\frac{d^2\Phi}{dt^2} = BW_p\Phi - B\Phi\frac{d\Phi}{dt} + \frac{1}{\Phi}\left(\frac{d\Phi}{dt}\right)^2 - \frac{B\Phi^2}{\tau_c}. \tag{3-53}$$

Now we apply the perturbation $\Phi = \Phi_0 + q$, and recognize that $d\Phi_0/dt = 0$. The above nonlinear equation (3-53) then yields the following differential equation for the perturbed photon density:

$$\frac{d^2q}{dt^2} + B\Phi_0\frac{dq}{dt} + B^2\Phi_0 n_0 q = 0, \tag{3-54}$$

which indicates that the photon density has the same decay constant and frequency dependence as the inverted population density. Therefore

$$q \simeq \exp\left(-\frac{B\Phi_0}{2}t\right)\sin\left[B(\Phi_0 n_0)^{1/2}t.\right] \tag{3-55}$$

The frequency of the oscillation (ω_s) is given by

$$\omega_s = B(\Phi_0 n_0)^{1/2} = (BW_p)^{1/2} \tag{3-56}$$

and the decay time constant (t_D) is given by

$$t_D = \frac{2}{B\Phi_0} = \frac{2}{BW_p\tau_c}. \tag{3-57}$$

Note that the greater the pump rate, the higher the oscillation frequency; for the higher pump rate, however, the decay time of the pulse train will be rapidly increased. In fact, the decay time is more sensitive to changes in pump rate than is the spiking oscillation frequency.

The period (T) or time between optical spiking pulses can readily be seen to be

$$T = \frac{2\pi}{\omega_s} = 2\pi\frac{1}{B(\Phi_0 n_0)^{1/2}} \tag{3-58}$$

or, with suitable substitutions,

$$T = \frac{2\pi}{(BW_p)^{1/2}}. \tag{3-59}$$

If this spiking period (T) is long compared to the decay time of the pulse train (t_D), the pulses will be substantially damped out; no spiking should occur. The decay constant of the spiking pulses is given in (3-57).

$$t_D = \frac{2}{B\Phi_0} = \frac{2}{BW_p\tau_c}. \qquad (3\text{-}57)$$

Thus the condition for no spiking will be established by having a decay time shorter than the pulse repitition period. Therefore we require that

$$t_D < T, \qquad (3\text{-}60)$$

which leads to

$$\frac{2}{BW_p\tau_c} < \frac{2\pi}{(BW_p)^{1/2}}, \qquad (3\text{-}61)$$

or, by rearranging,

$$W_p < \frac{1}{B\pi^2\tau_c^2}. \qquad (3\text{-}62)$$

The governing factor, then, is the pump rate of the laser system relative to the relaxation or ringing time of the optical cavity. If the pump rate is sufficiently fast, no spiking will occur and there will be a smooth rise of the photon and excited electron densities to their steady-state values. In terms of the spiking period and the ringing time the nonspiking criterion can be written as

$$\tau_c > \frac{T}{2\pi^2}. \qquad (3\text{-}63)$$

Thus for a laser with a cavity relaxation time long compared to the period between spiking pulses the spiking bursts will be damped out. The physical reason behind this is that the loss rate from the cavity must be large enough to allow a reasonable amount of radiation to leak out and diminish the photon density so that the inverted population can be restored by the pump.

This theoretical description predicts a regular series of spikes, whereas in practice the spike amplitudes and intervals fluctuate in a manner that appears to be almost random. In many instances, however, the pattern is repeatable from pumping pulse to pumping pulse for a given laser. This

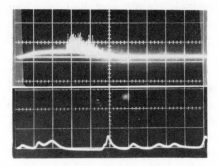

Figure 3-5 *Upper*: spiking pulse oscillations from a ruby laser. Horizontal scale is 200μsec per cm. *Lower*: expanded scale of spiking pulse oscillations in a ruby laser. Horizontal scale is 2μsec per cm.

fluctuation might be due to variations in doping density in the laser host material; it could be associated with pumping radiation distribution in the crystal, which could influence the Q of the various laser modes. Heating of the laser rod could also contribute to this variation as well as cross relaxation between laser modes as a result of a change in gain during heating. A temperature change of the cavity components will also shift the mode structure through many sets of modes, thereby causing a shift of Q of the modes to occur. Figure 3-5 shows a photograph of a series of spiking pulses in a ruby laser using a rod 3in. in length and 1/4in. in diameter. Under carefully controlled conditions where single mode operation is assured, however, regular periodic spiking pulses are observed.

3-4 PULSE REFLECTION AND PULSE TRANSMISSION OPERATION

It seems appropriate here to identify and discuss two general modes of pulsed laser oscillator operation. They have been identified in the laser literature as the pulse reflection mode (PRM) and the pulse transmission mode (PTM). Both modes can be implemented by appropriate Q-switching, but because of the frequency of the use of these terms it seems appropriate to define and describe them at this point. The detailed mathematical analysis, however, is not presented here, but only a summary and discussion of their features.

A laser can be made to emit short duration, high intensity pulses of radiation by suddenly switching the regeneration of the optical resonator. When the regeneration of the laser cavity is kept sufficiently low while the laser is being pumped, a large population excess can be achieved. If the regeneration is then rapidly switched to a high value, the energy stored in the excess population is rapidly converted to photon density or radiation in the cavity. As an example, assume that the mirrors at the ends of the laser have reflectivities of 100 and 0% during the pumping cycle; then, after pumping, assume that the reflectivity of the output mirror is increased from 0 to 99%. The cavity will be highly regenerative because of almost total reflection on both ends and the energy stored in the populated states will suddenly be "dumped" and 1% will then escape through the output mirror as the laser beam pulse. This can be identified as the first pulse reflection mode; there is a minimum amount of coupling between the photon flux in the cavity and the existing laser pulse because of the high reflectivity of the output mirror. There will be a very efficient conversion of stored energy to photon density in the cavity.

The second pulse reflection mode operates very similarly to the first mode except that the output reflectivity is switched to an intermediate value of reflectivity. This value is chosen to optimize the amount of energy appearing in the laser pulse outside the cavity. It is called critical coupling.

The efficiency of energy transfer is increased and higher peak powers are available in this second mode.

An optimum value of reflectivity can be seen to exist from the following argument. If the output mirror has a 100% reflectivity there will be no output laser beam because there is no transmission. Although a high photon density will build up in the laser cavity, it will not escape as a laser beam but will be dissipated. On the other hand, if the reflectivity is 0%, regeneration can never occur because no feedback mechanism is available and again no laser beam will appear. Thus a maximum value of the output peak power will occur at some intermediate value of reflectivity. It can be demonstrated that the optimum value of reflectivity should be selected so that the total cavity loss rate due to dissipative elements equals the loss rate from the cavity through the output mirror.

The pulse transmission mode combines the best features of the pulse reflection modes. It operates as follows. After pumping to a high excess population with the cavity regeneration low the regeneration is rapidly switched to the maximum value attainable. The output reflectivity will approach 100%. There is then a rapid conversion from energy storage in excess population to radiation density in the laser cavity. The rate of energy emission is now relatively low, however, for the external coupling is very low or the output reflectivity is high. Once the peak radiation density is attained in the cavity this low coupling is detrimental to the achievement of high peak power in the output. In this PTM the regeneration is again rapidly switched back to its initial low value when the radiation density in the cavity has reached its peak. When the switching is fast enough, this results in an emission rate determined by the final low value of regeneration. The peak powers to be expected in this case are extremely high, the pulses are of exceedingly short duration, and the ratio of energy emitted to energy initially stored is reasonably large. For optimum results the regeneration must be switched off as nearly as possible when the energy density in the cavity is a maximum. Premature or delayed switching will result in lower peak powers, for either the excess population will not have been fully converted or too great a time will have been allowed for dissipative processes to reduce the energy density from its maximum value.

An evaluation of the results available from the pulse reflection or transmission modes is shown in Table 3-1 for a ruby laser. For evaluation purposes it has been assumed that the volume of the ruby is 1 cm³ and that the doping density permits 2.2 joules to be stored in the rod by pumping.

Thus it can be seen that by selectively switching the regeneration, or Q, of the laser cavity not only the peak output power can be increased but also the efficiency of utilization of the energy stored. It is these features that make the pulse reflection or transmission modes of operation so important. The pulse reflection mode has been utilized extensively; a suitable scheme has yet to be developed for effectively implementing the pulse transmission mode of laser operation.

TABLE 3-1 LASER PULSE OUTPUT FOR PULSE REFLECTION AND PULSE TRANSMISSION MODES

Mode	Peak Power (Mw)	Pulse Width (nsec)	Efficiencies (%)
First PRM (minimum coupling)	17	10	2
Second PRM (critical coupling)	170	8	50
PTM	920	1	52

$$\text{Efficiency} = \frac{\text{energy appearing in laser beam}}{\text{energy stored in excess population}}.$$

Data courtesy of Vuylsteke, *J. Appl. Phys.* (1963).

3-5 LASER CAVITY MODES IN OSCILLATORS

In an optical resonator, such as a laser cavity, not all frequencies are permitted to oscillate. Just as resonances and allowed modes exist in microwave cavities, so discrete resonances exist for a cavity operating in the optical region of the spectrum, the prime difference in these two cases being the wavelength of the radiation relative to the dimensions of the resonator; in the microwave case the wavelength and cavity size are of the same order, whereas in the optical case the cavity dimension is many orders of magnitude larger than the wavelength. Therefore many more modes may exist in the optical case than in the microwave case unless special precautions are adopted to avoid them. It is the purpose of this section to discuss some features of the allowed modes in lasers and the conditions that determine the oscillator resonances.

A mode may be defined as an electric or magnetic field distribution that reproduces itself in spatial distribution and phase as the electromagnetic wave bounces back and forth between two reflectors. The distribution does not have to reproduce itself in amplitude, however, although the *positions* of maximum or minimum amplitude must reproduce themselves.

By reference to Figure 3-6 we can obtain a first-order perspective on the wavelengths permitted in a simple laser resonator. Assume that the resonator has a length L. On either end is a highly reflecting plane parallel

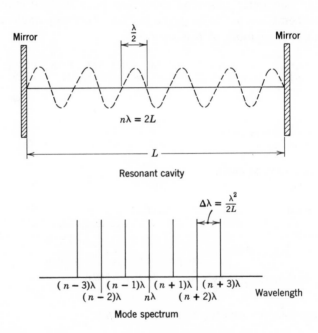

Figure 3-6 Schematic illustration of conditions for a resonant mode in an optical cavity with parallel mirrors.

mirror in which there is an extremely low absorption; the losses in the mirror then are very small and are neglected for purposes of this argument.

Because, for optical waves, $L \gg \lambda$, a large number of half-wavelengths are permitted to exist in the cavity, subject to the following condition:

$$n\frac{\lambda}{2} = L, \tag{3-64}$$

where n is an integer that defines the mode number and will be a large number. As an example, if $L = 5$ cm and $\lambda = 1 \mu$, we see that $n \simeq 10^5$. A further requirement for a useful mode to exist is that the net gain of the cavity at the resonant wavelength exceed unity; the wavelength has to be in a range such that power can be supplied to the cavity at that wavelength to cause oscillations.

A quick examination of this resonant condition will indicate that another mode, near the first but slightly shorter in wavelength, can also exist; for instance, assume the cavity resonant at wavelength λ_1. Then we can write the following condition for resonance, not only for this wavelength (λ_1), but also for one close by (λ_2), as given in (3-65):

$$n\lambda_1 = 2L$$

$$(n+1)\lambda_2 = 2L. \tag{3-65}$$

This can be reduced to the form given in (3-66) by noting that λ_1 and λ_2 are nearly equal. Thus

$$\Delta\lambda = \lambda_1 - \lambda_2$$

$$\lambda_1\lambda_2 \simeq \lambda^2$$

$$\Delta\lambda = \frac{\lambda^2}{2L}. \tag{3-66}$$

The wavelength separation between modes then depends on the wavelength itself as well as on the cavity length. For greater separation a shorter cavity should be used. For $\lambda = 1 \mu$ the mode separation and the above laser cavity ($L = 5$ cm) we see that $\Delta\lambda = 10^{-1}$ A. This relationship for mode separation can also be given in terms of frequency by recognizing that

$$\lambda\nu = c$$

$$\frac{\Delta\lambda}{\lambda} = \frac{\Delta\nu}{\nu}. \tag{3-67}$$

The resulting expression is

$$\Delta\nu = \frac{c}{2L}. \qquad (3\text{-}68)$$

For the case just discussed the frequency separation of the modes would be 3000 mc.

In actual practice, of course, this picture of the mode structure in a cavity is idealized, although it describes the conditions well to a first-order approximation. We have assumed here that there are standing plane waves reflecting back and forth in the cavity. This can be true only for infinite surfaces. Because of the finite size of the mirrors and the fact that they have edges, we find that there will be diffraction losses at the mirrors and a finite cross-sectional size to the resonant wave. Because of losses due to diffraction, reflection, and absorption, the reproduced mode pattern is reduced in intensity on each traversal of the resonator. In an actual laser the medium between the mirrors has a net gain that will compensate for this loss; some modes will have greater gain than others, and thus some will grow and others will die out. The resonator quality factor (Q) for a given cavity geometry can be expressed in terms of the loss per reflection at each mirror. To show this assume that the loss per reflection (β) occurs because of diffraction, transmission, and absorption at or in the mirrors. Then, following the definition of Q, we may write

$$Q = 2\pi\nu\left(\frac{\text{energy stored}}{\text{energy lost per second}}\right).$$

This can be reduced as follows. Define the density of quanta in the cavity as N, the cavity cross-sectional area as A, and the energy per quantum as $h\nu$. Then we can write

$$\text{energy stored in cavity} = Nh\nu AL$$
$$\text{energy loss per second} = Nh\nu Ac\beta$$

and we then see that

$$Q = (2\pi\nu)\frac{(Nh\nu AL)}{(Nh\nu Ac\beta)}$$

$$= \frac{2\pi L}{\beta\lambda}. \qquad (3\text{-}69)$$

If the diffraction losses (α_D) are small compared with reflection losses, the cavity Q can be proportionally increased by a greater spacing of the mirrors. When the increased spacing appreciably changes the diffraction losses, and therefore the value of β, the linear increase of Q with mirror separation no longer holds.

The actual energy distribution over the cross-sectional area of a cavity having plane-parallel mirrors was calculated by using a computer by Fox and Li. They found that the effective mode volume in a laser cavity extended out to about 70% of the radius of the end mirror. Their studies yielded the following conclusions:

1. A Fabry-Perot plane-parallel mirror cavity can be characterized by a discrete set of normal modes, with the dominant mode having a field intensity approaching zero at the mirror edge; thus the losses are lowest.

2. The diffraction losses for the dominant mode are so low that the primary loss mechanism is due to reflection losses.

3. The relative diffraction losses for various modes are independent of the cavity geometry. Thus the dominant mode cannot be shifted to another mode by altering the cavity dimensions.

4. Uniform plane waves do not yield an adequate description of the modes in the flat mirror cavity.

The plane-parallel geometry of the Fabry-Perot resonator is not ideal, however. A resonator formed by two spherical reflectors of equal curvature and separated by their common radius of curvature has some advantages:

1. The diffraction losses are lower even than the Fabry-Perot plane-parallel cavity case.

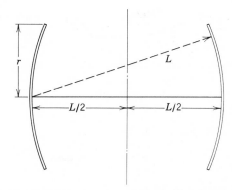

Figure 3-7 Confocal resonator cavity. Two spherical mirrors are used in this configuration, spaced at a separation equal to the radius of curvature (twice the focal length).

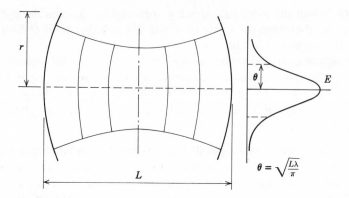

Figure 3-8 Wavefronts of constant phase and the cross-sectional energy distribution of the lowest mode in the confocal resonator are illustrated. Note that the radius of the spot depends only on the cavity length and wavelength. It is independent of the mirror radius or aperture.

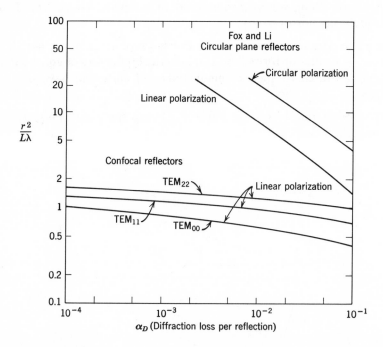

Figure 3-9 Graphical plot comparing losses in a plane mirror case with the confocal resonator. The factor $r^2/L\lambda$ relates the cavity dimensions for different resonators. The plot gives the diffraction loss per reflection (α_D) versus cavity size as defined by the above factor. After Boyd and Gordon, *Bell System Tech. J.* (1961).

2. The optical alignment of the mirrors is not critical.

3. A smaller mode volume exists for this case and therefore less laser material is needed for a given quality factor. This means that less pump power is needed for laser operation than in the parallel mirror case.

This improved resonator configuration is called the confocal arrangement and is shown in Figure 3-7. It has the feature, that many higher order modes are degenerate in frequency with the lowest order mode; this degeneracy can be split by a slightly nonconfocal adjustment.

The traveling waves reflecting back and forth for the lowest order mode in this confocal resonator will have spherical wavefronts of constant phase, as shown in Figure 3-8. For realistic dimensions the curvature will be small and the modes take on the characteristics of TEM modes familiar to microwave designers, for the axial electric and magnetic fields are very small. The mode field distribution is given by a Gaussian variation over the cross section of the cavity. The effective spot size can be defined as the radius (θ) at which the Gaussian falls to $1/e$ of its axial value. It is given by

$$\theta = \left(\frac{L\lambda}{\pi}\right)^{1/2}. \tag{3-70}$$

It can also be demonstrated that for the exact confocal arrangement the diffraction losses and spot size are a minimum for a fixed length of resonator. A comparison of the diffraction losses for the parallel mirror case and the confocal cavity configuration is given in Figure 3-9. The

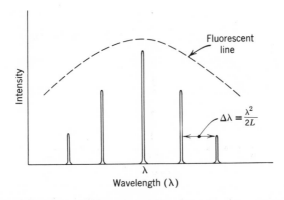

Figure 3-10 Flourescent linewidth of laser transition compared with mode linewidth and mode spacing in a laser material.

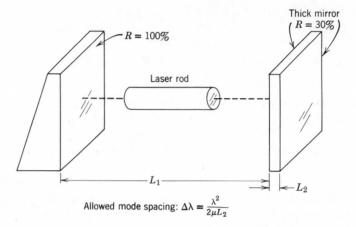

Allowed mode spacing: $\Delta\lambda = \dfrac{\lambda^2}{2\mu L_2}$

Figure 3-11 Mode selector using two coupled cavities in which the mode spacing for one is greater than the fluorescent line width of the laser transition.

TEM notation corresponds to microwave terminology. It will be recalled that the subscripts enter into the mode description and describe distributions for some lower modes across the cross-sectional area of the cavity.

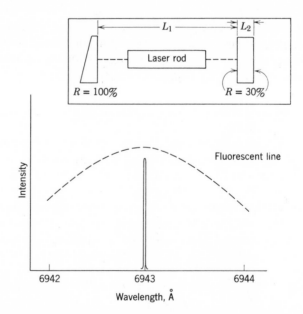

Figure 3-12 Spectrum for the coupled cavity mode selector. The mode separation of the cavity of length L_2 is great enough so that the gain represented by the fluorescent line shape is too low to sustain oscillations of other modes.

It should further be noted that because of the low diffraction losses in the confocal resonator most of the losses will actually arise from the finite reflectivity of the mirrors. Therefore all the modes of the confocal cavity and the plane-parallel resonator will have the same quality factor (Q) in actual practice as given by (3-69).

In a laser the allowed modes that actually oscillate will depend on the gain characteristics of the laser medium versus wavelengths, which will depend on the fluorescent linewidth of the laser transition. If the modes are spaced by $\Delta\lambda$ and the fluorescent line shape is as shown in Figure 3-10, the mode nearest the line center will have the greatest gain. This too, is illustrated schematically. Any mode falling outside of the fluorescent linewidth will not oscillate because of insufficient gain. Because however, the mode spacing is small relative to the linewidth, many modes will in fact oscillate, and if one pure mode is to be selected out some "mode selectors" will be required in the cavity. One suggestion for achieving this is to couple two cavities together as shown in Figure 3-11. Here the reflector at one end is a 100% mirror, whereas at the other we employ two mirrors spaced a short distance apart as a supplementary resonator. The combination will resonate for a mode whose frequency is resonant in both cavities.

The shorter cavity, of length L_2 and index of refraction μ, will have a mode spacing as follows:

$$\Delta\lambda = \frac{\lambda^2}{2\mu L_2}. \qquad (3-70)$$

As an example, assume the mirror material at one end of the laser to have $L_2 = 10^{-1}$ cm and $\mu = 1.5$. Then for ruby radiation ($\lambda = 6,943$ A) we obtain a mode spacing of $\Delta\lambda = 1.5$A. If the fluorescent line-width of the laser rod does not exceed this, only one mode will be permitted to exist, as illustrated in Figure 3-12.

To sustain the single mode oscillation the resonance condition for both cavities must be fulfilled, but it is easier to accomplish for the long cavity than for the short, for the modes are closer together in the longer cavity.

It is apparent that other modifications of laser cavity design, as well as many variations on mode selectors, are possible. The discussion here has described the general approach to the evaluation of modes in lasers and has shown the similarity to microwave terminology.

REFERENCES

A. General

Birnbaum, M., and T. L. Stocker, "Multimode Oscillation of the Ruby Laser Near Threshold," *Appl. Phys. Letters*, 3, 164–166 (November 1963).

Bonch, A. M., E. Kariss, and P. P. Feofilov, "Pulsations in the Spectrum of Stimulated Emission of Neodymium in Glass," *Opt. Spectr.*, **14**, 438–439 (1963).

Dunsmuir, R., "Theory of Relaxation Oscillations in Optical Masers," *J. Electron. Control*, **10**, 453–458 (June 1961).

Galanin, M. D., A. M. Leontovich, Z. A. Sviridenkov, V. N. Smorchkov, and Z. A. Chizhikova, "Pulsations in the Emission from a Ruby Laser," *Opt. Spectr.*, **14**, 86–87 (1963).

Kleinman, D. A., "The Maser Rate Equations and Spiking," *Bell System Tech. J.*, **43**, 1505–1532 (July 1964).

Kumagai, N., and H. Yamamoto, "Generalized Solutions for Optical Maser Amplifiers," *IEEE Trans. Micron. Theory Tech.*, **13**, 445–451 (July 1965).

Makhov, G., "On the Problem of Pulsed Oscillations in Ruby Masers," *J. Appl. Phys.*, **33**, 202–204 (January 1962).

Rigrod, W. W., "Saturation Effects in High-Gain Lasers," *J. Appl. Phys.*, **36**, 2487–2490 (August 1965).

Statz, H., and G. DeMars, "Transients and Oscillation Pulses in Masers," In *Quantum Electronics*, C. Townes, ed,. (1960), 530–537.

Steele, E. L., "Descriptive Theory of Spiking Pulses in Optically Pumped Lasers," *IEEE J. Quantum Electron.*, **1**, 42–49 (April 1965).

Vuylsteke, A. A., "Theory of Laser Regeneration Switching," *J. Appl. Phys.*, **34**, 1615–1622 (June 1963).

Wagner, W. G., and G. Birnbaum, "Theory of Quantum Oscillators in a Multimode Cavity," *J. Appl. Phys.*, **32**, 1185–1194 (July 1961).

B. Laser Cavity Modes

Boyd, G. D., and J. P. Gordon, "Confocal Multimode Resonator for Millimeter Through Optical Wavelength Masers," *Bell System Tech. J.*, **40**, 489–508 (March 1961).

Boyd, G. D., and H. Kogelnik, "Generalized Confocal Resonator," *Bell System Tech. J.*, **41**, 1347–1369 (July 1962).

Fox, A. G., and T. Li, "Resonant Modes in a Maser Interferometer," *Bell System Tech. J.*, **40**, 453–488 (March 1961).

McMurtry, B. J., "Investigation of Ruby Optical Maser Characteristics Using Microwave Phototubes," *Appl. Opt.*, **2**, 767–786 (August 1963).

4

Laser Amplifiers

The fact that energy can be stored in the excited states of an impurity in a laser material and that its release can be triggered by a light wave leads us to contemplate the use of a laser as an amplifier. Under the proper conditions, when a pulse of radiation travels through a material with an inverted population, energy can be extracted from the material and added to the wave and the wave will thereby be amplified.

To a first approximation we would assume the growth of energy in the wave to be exponential, for the amount of stimulated emission is proportional to the exciting photon flux. It will be seen that this is the case only under very restricted circumstances. For a square pulse traversing an amplifier the leading pulse edge sees a larger inverted population than does the trailing edge. This occurs simply because the leading edge will stimulate the release of some of the stored energy and decrease the population inversion, thereby causing the trailing edge to see a different inverted population. Thus less energy will be added to the final portions of a pulse than to the leading regions. In fact, then, a phenomenon of pulse sharpening toward the leading edge can be expected to occur.

Taking another extreme case, we can see that if a high intensity light pulse is incident on a laser rod the stimulated emission could completely

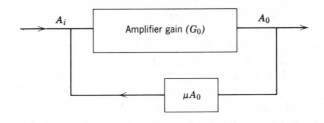

Figure 4-1 Schematic diagram of feedback amplifier.

deplete the stored energy as it progresses along. The gain would be expected to be *linear* with the length of the rod rather than exponential.

The solution to the amplifier problem should then approach these conditions as extreme cases, and it is shown that the growth of the energy in the light wave can be linear or exponential with the length of the laser. A gain factor in between these two cases can also occur, of course, for input pulses of intermediate intensity.

4-1 GENERAL DISCUSSION OF REFLECTIVE AMPLIFIERS

In an amplifier, in general, in which a portion of the output energy is coupled back through the system, enhanced gain, depending on the phase of the feedback signal, may occur.

In a simple picture this may be described as follows. Assume an amplifier with an input A_i, an output A_o, and a single pass gain G_0, as shown in Figure 4-1. Furthermore, the fraction of the output fed back to the input is called μ, the feedback factor. Thus

$$G_0(A_i + \mu A_o) = A_o. \tag{4-1}$$

Defining the gain (G) we see that

$$G = \frac{A_o}{A_i}, \tag{4-2}$$

and combination with (4-1) yields

$$G = \frac{G_0}{1 - \mu G_0}. \tag{4-3}$$

Thus, when the gain is high, that is, when $G_0\mu \simeq 1$, the amplifier is unstable and will break into oscillations that will be limited by nonlinear effects which set in as the output builds up. Furthermore, the noise at the input of the amplifier will be amplified and, even without an input signal, the amplifier may break into oscillations and therefore will not be useful as a stable amplifier when the feedback is positive ($\mu > 0$). It is well known for negative feedback ($\mu < 0$) that the amplifier will be stable but the gain will be less than the single pass gain of this simplified model.

We now look at the laser amplifier. In this case a light wave will enter one end of the laser rod after suffering some reflection loss at the front surface. It will then traverse the length o the amplifier; a certain fraction of the amplified wave will be reflected back and the remainder transmitted as power out of the amplifier. Steps can be taken, of course, to prevent or at least minimize these reflections by placing the optical surfaces at Brewster's angle to the beam, but this will not always be the case. We assume a reflectivity (r) at the optical surfaces, and the gain expression can be calculated by using the model of Figure 4-2. The amplitude of the light wave incident on the laser amplifier is S_i, and a fraction of this, $(1-r)S_i$, passes into the amplifying medium and a fraction, rS_i, is reflected and lost. In passing through the amplifier this wave is amplified by G_0. At the output end a fraction of this amplified wave is transmitted out of the amplifier and a fraction reflected.

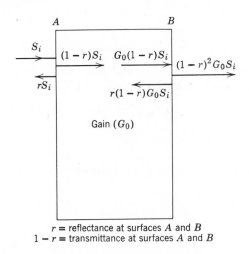

r = reflectance at surfaces A and B
$1-r$ = transmittance at surfaces A and B

Figure 4-2 Reflective amplifier model showing amplitudes of light wave on first pass through the amplifier.

The contribution to the output beam (S_1) from the first pass can then be written as

$$S_1 = (1-r)^2 G_0 S_i. \qquad (4\text{-}4)$$

The second contribution arises from the beam reflecting from B passing through the medium of gain G_0, again being reflected from A, and once more passing through the amplifier and being amplified. If the amplifier is not exactly an even number or wavelengths long, there will be a phase shift between the first pass and subsequent waves incident on surface B. If we assume a total round trip phase shift of θ, the amplitude must be modified by a $\cos\theta$ factor. Thus the contribution to the output beam from this second reflection (S_2) is given by

$$S_2 = r^2(1-r)^2 G_0^3 S_i \cos\theta \qquad (4\text{-}5)$$

and, similarly,

$$S_3 = r^4(1-r)^2 G_0{}^5 S_i \cos 2\theta$$

$$S_4 = r^6(1-r)^2 G_0{}^7 S_i \cos 3\theta$$

$$.$$
$$.$$
$$.$$

$$S_n = r^{2(n-1)}(1-r)^2 G_0{}^{(2n-1)} S_i \cos n\theta. \qquad (4-6)$$

The total output (S_0) can then be written as

$$S_o = S_1 + S_2 + S_3 + \ldots S_n + \ldots \qquad (4-7)$$

$$= G_0 S_i (1-r)^2 \sum_{n=0}^{\infty} (G_0 r)^{2n} \cos n\theta. \qquad (4-8)$$

The last term in (4-8) can be expressed as a double geometric series by expressing the $\cos n\theta$ in terms of exponentials. Then

$$\cos (n\theta) = \tfrac{1}{2}[e^{in\theta} + e^{-in\theta}]$$

and the summation may be written as

$$\sum_{n=0}^{\infty} (G_0 r)^{2n} \cos (n\theta) = \sum_{n=0}^{\infty} \tfrac{1}{2}(G_0 r)^{2n} e^{in\theta} + \sum_{n=0}^{\infty} \tfrac{1}{2}(G_0 r)^{2n} e^{-in\theta} \qquad (4-9)$$

$$= \tfrac{1}{2}[1 - (G_0 r)e^{i\theta}]^{-1} + \tfrac{1}{2}[1 - (G_0 r)e^{-i\theta}]^{-1}$$

$$= \frac{1 - (G_0 r) \cos \theta}{1 + (G_0 r)^2 - 2(G_0 r) \cos \theta}. \qquad (4-10)$$

The output signal may now be written as

$$S_o = G_0 S_i (1-r)^2 \left[\frac{1 - (G_0 r) \cos \theta}{1 + (G_0 r)^2 - 2(G_0 r) \cos \theta} \right]. \qquad (4-11)$$

If we assume that the successive reflections tend to produce a random phase change, then the phase angle will average to zero. Under this condition the output term is given by

$$S_o = \frac{G_0 S_i (1-r)^2}{1 - G_0 r} \qquad (4-12)$$

or the gain (G), including the reflective feedback (r), is

$$G = \frac{S_o}{S_i}$$

$$= \frac{G_0 (1-r)^2}{(1 - G_0 r)}. \qquad (4-13)$$

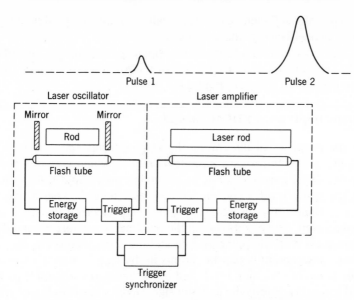

Figure 4-3   Schematic diagram of laser amplifier configuration.

For this type of reflective amplifier, then, the gain is reduced because of reflections off the front and back surfaces that cause a loss to the output beam. This loss, however, is compensated in part by the positive feedback caused by the internal reflection being amplified every time the wave traverses the amplifier medium. The feedback factor here is simply the reflectivity at the face of the laser rod. The averaging effect on the phase angle, in a practical laser case, occurs because of the lack of parallelism between the two faces of a laser rod and also the degree of optical flatness obtainable.

Thus the laser amplifier behaves as a feedback amplifier with positive regeneration and is stable only as long as $G_0 r < 1$. This places a practical limit on the amplifier length. When polarized waves can be used so that Brewster angle faces can be used, the reflectivity r can be greatly dimin-

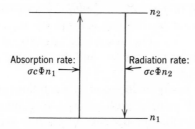

Figure 4-4   Energy level model for laser amplifier.

ished and, with sufficient care, essentially eliminated. In this event the amplifier gain will be the single pass gain G_0.

We now proceed to calculate the single pass gain for an optically pumped laser amplifier. For purposes of this analysis we assume that the laser amplifier is as shown in Figure 4-3.

4-2 SIMPLIFIED ANALYTICAL MODEL

For the purposes of illustrating the amplifier concepts and principles we assume a straightforward three-level model, which is in turn reduced to the two-level approximation by assuming very rapid transitions between the pump level 3 and the excited laser level 2. The symbols are defined in Figure 4-4, in which n_1 and n_2 are electron densities in the levels indicated. The events during the amplifier action are assumed to be fast compared with the pumping rate and the spontaneous emission rate. The basic assumption is that the atoms in the laser material are pumped to some positive inversion level, and the stimulated emission from these excited levels is triggered by an input signal from a laser oscillator preceding the amplifier. Thus the atoms are stimulated to radiate as the light wave passes through the laser rod.

Let us then consider the one-dimensional problem of a beam of monochromatic radiation incident on the surface of a laser material of length L. The point at which the beam enters the laser rod is designated the reference point, $x = 0$. Two equations must then be written: one for the photon density and a second for the population inversion.

The number of photons per unit volume, or the photon density Φ, is described by the differential equation (4-14) in both time and space:

$$\frac{\partial \Phi}{\partial t} = -c\frac{\partial \Phi}{\partial x} + \sigma c \Phi (n_2 - n_1). \tag{4-14}$$

This transport equation simply states that the rate at which the photon density changes in a given volume $(\partial \Phi/\partial t)$ equals the rate at which photons flow out of that volume $[c(\partial \Phi/\partial x)]$ plus the net rate at which photons are generated in that unit volume by the stimulated emission process $[\sigma c \Phi (n_2 - n_1)]$. The resonance absorption cross section per atom active in the laser process (σ) and the speed of light (c) both enter into the generation term.

This can be more easily understood by the following train of reasoning. A photon density Φ moving with velocity c manifests itself as a light beam of intensity $c\Phi$ photons per second per unit area. This photon flux then interacts with an atom of effective cross section σ, which causes the

stimulated emission of a photon. The total number of photons emitted in a unit volume by this process is $\sigma c\Phi$ multiplied by the number of available excited atoms in the unit volume (n_2), or $\sigma c\Phi n_2$. Similarly, the number of photons in the beam that disappear because of absorption can be arrived at by similar reasoning and is given by $\sigma c\Phi n_1$. Therefore the *net rate* of photon generation in the unit volume, assuming $n_2 > n_1$, is given by $\sigma c\Phi(n_2 - n_1)$. Of course, if positive inversion does not exist, that is, if $n_2 < n_1$, the beam will be attenuated because of net absorption and a net loss of photons will occur in the unit volume. In this case we would have a *sink* for photons rather than a *source*.

The electron densities in both the upper and lower state enter because the generation term is the net difference between the emission and absorption between these levels. In the calculation we neglect the finite width of the resonance line by assuming a constant absorption cross section.

The second term that describes the rate at which photons flow out of the unit volume can be understood as follows. Let Φ_1 be the photon density at x_1 and Φ_2 be the photon density at x_2 as seen in Figure 4-5 and assume that the photons move as shown with velocity c.

The flow of photons per unit area across the boundary at x_1 and into the volume is $c\Phi_1$ photons per area per second. The outflow from this volume similarly is $c\Phi_2$ photons per area per second. The *net* flow into the volume is then given by $c(\Phi_1 - \Phi_2)$ photons per unit area per second. Translating this to net inflow per unit volume per second can be obtained by dividing by linear distance between surfaces. Thus

$$\text{net inflow/vol/sec} = c\left(\frac{\Phi_1 - \Phi_2}{x_2 - x_1}\right).$$

For small dimensions define $\Phi_2 - \Phi_1 = \Delta\Phi$ and $x_2 - x_1 = \Delta x$. We then have

$$c\left(\frac{\Phi_1 - \Phi_2}{x_2 - x_1}\right) = c\left(-\frac{\Delta\Phi}{\Delta x}\right)$$

and proceeding to the differential limit, we finally obtain

$$\lim_{\Delta x \to 0} c\left(-\frac{\Delta\Phi}{\Delta x}\right) = -c\frac{\partial\Phi}{\partial x}.$$

We therefore see how the second term in (4-14) is constructed.

There are two additional variables that must be determined to solve the amplifier problem: the electron densities in the excited level (n_2) and the

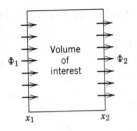

Figure 4-5 Schematic diagram illustrating gradient term in the photon transport equation.

ground or lower level (n_1). The rate equations for these densities can be written as

$$\frac{\partial n_1}{\partial t} = -\sigma c \Phi n_1 + \sigma c \Phi n_2$$

$$= +\sigma c \Phi (n_2 - n_1). \tag{4-15}$$

$$\frac{\partial n_2}{\partial t} = -\sigma c \Phi n_2 - \sigma c \Phi n_1$$

$$= -\sigma c \Phi (n_2 - n_1). \tag{4-16}$$

Their significance can be understood by noting that the decrease of electrons in the ground state $(\sigma c \Phi n_1)$ arises from the absorption of photons. Conversely, the level is populated because of the filling of the lower level from the upper level $(\sigma c \Phi n_2)$ by stimulated emission. In other words, the creation rate of photons, or the source term in (4-14), must be the same as the rate of increase of ground state atoms. This, in turn, is the same as the rate of decrease of excited state atoms.

Furthermore, the total number density (N) of atoms is fixed in the laser system; that is,

$$N = n_1 + n_2. \tag{4-17}$$

This is the total number of impurity atoms involved in the laser action in the host material. It could be the chromium density in the ruby crystal or the neodymium in a conventional glass host material.

We now have four equations for describing the system, only three of which are independent, for (4-16) can be obtained, for example, by combining (4-15) with (4-17). Other derivative combinations are, of course, also possible.

It is convenient to express these equations in terms of different variables. Of primary interest is the population inversion ratio (η), which

is related to the *excess* population in the excited level over the ground level. We define η as follows:

$$\eta = \frac{n_2 - n_1}{N}, \tag{4-18}$$

which then allows the original population densities to be expressed as

$$n_1 = \tfrac{1}{2}N(1 - \eta) \tag{4-19}$$

$$n_2 = \tfrac{1}{2}N(1 + \eta). \tag{4-20}$$

Note that the inversion ratio (η) can never exceed unity. In the limit when total inversion occurs the ground state is entirely empty and the excited state has all the electrons in it. Of course, in practice, this condition is impossible to achieve, and therefore $\eta < 1$ for all real cases.

Furthermore, let us define a new variable as twice the photon density per atom (ϕ) as (4-21):

$$\phi = \frac{2\Phi}{N}. \tag{4-21}$$

We may therefore write the rate equation for the inversion ratio using (4-15) and (4-16):

$$\frac{\partial}{\partial t}(n_2 - n_1) = -2\sigma c\Phi(n_2 - n_1)$$

$$\frac{\partial \eta}{\partial t} = -2\sigma c\Phi\eta$$

$$= -N\sigma c\phi\eta. \tag{4-22}$$

Similarly, the transport equation (4-14) for the photon density can be written in terms of the new variables and yields

$$\frac{\partial \phi}{\partial t} = -c\frac{\partial \phi}{\partial x} + N\sigma c\phi\eta. \tag{4-23}$$

These last two equations form the basis for solving the problem of photon density and population inversion ratio in the active traveling wave laser amplifier.

The boundary conditions for this amplifier problem are now formulated. The point at which the beam enters the medium is $x = 0$; the length of the laser amplifier rod is L, and it is assumed that the beam enters the amplifier at $t = 0$. Let $\eta_0(x)$ be the distribution of the population inversion ratio in the laser rod before the beam to be amplified enters the medium. Then

$$\eta(x,\ t < 0) = \eta_0(x) \qquad 0 < x < L. \qquad (4\text{-}24)$$

The relative photon density is defined at the time it enters the medium at $x = 0$; that is,

$$\phi(0, t > 0) = \phi_0(t) \qquad t > 0. \qquad (4\text{-}25)$$

Thus the pulse shape is defined at the moment the beam enters the amplifier, and the population inversion distribution in the laser rod is also defined at that instant. Subject to these conditions, the equations are solved for particular pulse shapes.

4-3 SOLUTION OF EQUATIONS

The differential equations to be solved here are intrinsically nonlinear. This can be immediately seen by noting that both ϕ and η are unknowns, but they appear in both rate equations as a product term. Fortunately, in spite of this, the separation of variables can be used here and a closed form of solution will actually be obtained.

Solve (4-23) for the inversion ratio (η) and substitute into (4-22):

$$\frac{1}{\phi}\frac{\partial\phi}{\partial t} + \frac{c}{\phi}\frac{\partial\phi}{\partial x} = N\sigma c\eta \qquad (4\text{-}26)$$

$$\eta = \frac{1}{N\sigma c}\left(\frac{1}{\phi}\frac{\partial\phi}{\partial t} + \frac{c}{\phi}\frac{\partial\phi}{\partial x}\right), \qquad (4\text{-}27)$$

which gives the following equation (4-28) for photon density:

$$\frac{\partial}{\partial t}\left(\frac{1}{\phi}\frac{\partial\phi}{\partial t} + \frac{c}{\phi}\frac{\partial\phi}{\partial x}\right) = -N\sigma c\left(\frac{\partial\phi}{\partial t} + c\frac{\partial\phi}{\partial x}\right)$$

$$= -N\sigma c\phi\left(\frac{1}{\phi}\frac{\partial\phi}{\partial t} + \frac{c}{\phi}\frac{\partial\phi}{\partial x}\right). \qquad (4\text{-}28)$$

The factor $[(1/\phi)(\partial\phi/\partial t) + (c/\phi)(\partial\phi/\partial x)]$ suggests a change in variable to simplify it. Therefore define the following transformation:

$$\xi = \frac{x}{c} \qquad \tau = t - \left(\frac{x}{c}\right). \qquad (4\text{-}29)$$

Then, from the transformation

$$\frac{1}{\phi}\frac{\partial\phi}{\partial t} = \frac{1}{\phi}\frac{\partial\phi}{\partial t} \tag{4-30}$$

$$\frac{c}{\phi}\frac{\partial\phi}{\partial x} = \frac{c}{\phi}\left(\frac{\partial\phi}{\partial\tau}\cdot\frac{\partial\tau}{\partial x} + \frac{\partial\phi}{\partial\xi}\cdot\frac{\partial\xi}{\partial x}\right)$$

$$= \frac{1}{\phi}\left(\frac{\partial\phi}{\partial\xi} - \frac{\partial\phi}{\partial\tau}\right) \tag{4-31}$$

and the net result is

$$\frac{1}{\phi}\frac{\partial\phi}{\partial t} + \frac{c}{\phi}\frac{\partial\phi}{\partial x} = \frac{1}{\phi}\frac{\partial\phi}{\partial\xi}. \tag{4-32}$$

We therefore see that

$$\frac{\partial}{\partial\tau}\left(\frac{1}{\phi}\frac{\partial\phi}{\partial\xi}\right) = -N\sigma c\frac{\partial\phi}{\partial\xi} \tag{4-33}$$

or, interchanging the order of differentiation,

$$\frac{\partial}{\partial\xi}\left(\frac{1}{\phi}\frac{\partial\phi}{\partial\tau} + N\sigma c\phi\right) = 0. \tag{4-34}$$

We integrate and note that the constant of integration is a function of τ only: that is, (4-34) may be rewritten as follows after integration:

$$\frac{1}{\phi}\frac{\partial\phi}{\partial\tau} + N\sigma c\phi = f(\tau). \tag{4-35}$$

One further substitution allows this equation to be integrated directly. Let $\rho = 1/\phi$. Then (4-35) is transformed to

$$\frac{\partial\rho}{\partial\tau} + \rho f(\tau) = N\sigma c; \tag{4-36}$$

the solution to this is the well-known integral

$$\rho = \frac{N\sigma c}{(\partial\beta/\partial\tau)}[\beta(\tau) + C(\xi)], \tag{4-37}$$

where

$$\frac{\partial \beta}{\partial \tau} = \exp\left[\int f(\tau)\, dt\right] \tag{4-38}$$

and $C(\xi)$ arises as a constant of integration. The photon density then can be written as

$$\phi(\xi, \tau) = \frac{1}{\rho} = \frac{(\partial \beta/\partial \tau)}{N\sigma c[\beta(\tau) + C(\xi)]} \tag{4-39}$$

or, in terms of the other physical variables $(x,\, t)$, we obtain

$$\phi(x, t) = \frac{(\partial/\partial t)\beta(t - x/c)}{N\sigma c[\beta(t - x/c) + C(x/c)]}. \tag{4-40}$$

Now apply the boundary condition at $x = 0$; this defines the photon density entering the amplifier. Thus, at $x = 0$,

$$\phi_0(t) = \phi(0, t) = \frac{\partial \beta/\partial t}{N\sigma c[\beta(t) + C_0]}. \tag{4-41}$$

Integrating this expression we can determine the factor $\beta(t)$ arising from an earlier integration in terms of $\phi_0(t)$. Thus

$$\frac{\partial}{\partial t}[\ln \beta(t) + C_0] = N\sigma c\phi_0(t)$$

$$\beta(t) = C_1 \exp\left[N\sigma c \int_{-\infty}^{t} \phi_0(t^*)\, dt^*\right] - C_0. \tag{4-42}$$

Here t^* is simply a dummy variable of integration.

Within two arbitrary constants, C_0 and C_1, the factor $\beta(t)$ is now defined in terms of the photon density, $\phi_0(t)$, impinging on the input face of the laser amplifier rod. Note that the factor

$$c \int_{-\infty}^{t} \phi_0(t^*)\, dt^*$$

represents the total number of photons per unit area incident on the input face of the amplifier up to time t. Inserting the expression for $\beta(t)$ given in (4-42) into the equation for the photon density (4-40), we obtain

$$\phi(x,t) = \frac{\phi_0[t-(x/c)]}{1+\left[\dfrac{C(x/c)-C_0}{C_1}\right]\exp\left[-N\sigma c \int\limits_{-\infty}^{t-(x/c)} \phi_0(t^*)\,dt^*\right]} \qquad (4\text{-}43)$$

The factor arising as the constant of integration is

$$K(x) = \left(\frac{C(x/c)-C_0}{C_1}\right). \qquad (4\text{-}44)$$

Thus the equation may be rewritten

$$\phi(x,\ t) = \frac{\phi_0[t-(x/c)]}{1+K(x)\exp\left[-N\sigma c \int\limits_{-\infty}^{t-(x/c)} \phi_0(t^*)\,dt^*\right]} \qquad (4\text{-}45)$$

and must now be evaluated from a second boundary condition. This is determined from the conditions imposed on the initial distribution of the electron inversion at the time the photon beam enters the amplifier.

The equation (4-45) for the photon density can now be inserted in (4-27), which expresses the inversion as a function of photon density.

$$\eta(x,t) = \frac{1}{N\sigma c}\left(\frac{1}{\phi}\frac{\partial\phi}{\partial t} + \frac{c}{\phi}\frac{\partial\phi}{\partial x}\right). \qquad (4\text{-}27)$$

This substitution yields

$$\eta(x,\ t) = \frac{-(1/N\sigma)(\partial K/\partial x)}{K(x)+\exp\left[N\sigma c \int\limits_{-\infty}^{-(x/c)} \phi_0(t^*)\,dt^*\right]}. \qquad (4\text{-}46)$$

The mathematical steps in proceeding from (4-27) and (4-45) to the final expression for inversion in (4-46) are given in Appendix 4-A. The second boundary condition is now applied to determine $K(x)$, for which we specify the inversion density in the rod (η_0) at the time the beam enters the amplifier; thus for time before the beam enters the amplifier or, equivalently, for $t = -\infty$,

$$\eta(x,\ t) = \eta(x,\ -\infty) = \eta_0(x) \qquad (4\text{-}47)$$

The exponent in (4-46) will then be zero and the equation for the constant $K(x)$ can be written

$$\eta_0(x) = -\left(\frac{1}{N\sigma}\right)\left(\frac{1}{1+K}\right)\frac{\partial K}{\partial x} \tag{4-48}$$

$$\frac{d}{dx}[\ln(1+K)] = -N\sigma\eta_0(x). \tag{4-49}$$

The solution then yields

$$K(x) = C_2 \exp\left[-N\sigma \int_0^x \eta_0(x^*)\,dx^*\right] - 1, \tag{4-50}$$

where C_2 is the constant of integration and x^* is a dummy variable. By observing the original definition of K as given in (4-44),

$$K(x) = \frac{C(x/c) - C_0}{C_1}. \tag{4-44}$$

We note that $C_2 = 1$ since $K = 0$ for $x = 0$. Thus this spatial term arising out of the time integration is now defined in terms of the initial inversion density distribution in the laser rod for $0 < x < L$:

$$K(x) = \exp\left[-N\sigma \int_0^x \eta_0(x^*)\,dx^*\right] - 1. \tag{4-51}$$

The physical significance of this term should be noted. The term $N\sigma\eta_0$ is the total number of excited atoms with which the photon flux will interact in a unit distance. Multiplying by the differential distance and integrating yields an exponential factor equal to the total number of excited atoms with which the photons interact in progressing a distance x into the amplifier.

Taking this expression for $K(x)$ and inserting it into (4-46) for the inversion density and (4-45) for the photon density yields the following final expressions:

$$\eta(x, t) = \frac{\eta_0(x) \exp\left[-N\sigma \int_0^x \eta_0(x^*)\,dx^*\right]}{\exp\left[N\sigma c \int_{-\infty}^{t-(x/c)} \phi_0(t^*)\,dt^*\right] + \exp\left[-N\sigma \int_0^x \eta_0(x^*)\,dx^*\right] - 1} \tag{4-52}$$

$$\phi(x, t)$$

$$= \frac{\phi_0[t - (x/c)]}{1 - \left\{1 - \exp\left[-N\sigma \int_0^x \eta_0(x^*)\,dx^*\right]\right\} \exp\left[-N\sigma c \int_{-\infty}^{t-(x/c)} \phi_0(t^*)\,dt^*\right]}. \tag{4-53}$$

These two equations represent the relative inversion ratio and the relative photon density in the amplifier at any position (x) within the laser rod ($0 < x < L$) at a time t after the pulse enters the rod. This is given in terms of the initial photon density incident on the rod face (ϕ_0) and the spatial distribution of the inversion ratio (η_0) at the moment the beam enters the amplifier.

4-4 PULSE AMPLIFIER SOLUTION FOR SQUARE INPUT PULSE

The solution for the laser amplifier of length L is now applied to a square-topped pulse of photons entering the amplifier. As illustrated by Figure 4-6, a photon flux of density Φ_0 is assumed to impinge on the input face of the laser for a time interval τ_0. Define a photon beam intensity (I_0) in terms of photon density Φ_0 and the speed of light (c); the photon beam intensity is the number of photons per unit area per second incident in the pulse.

$$I_0 = \Phi_0 c \text{ photons/area/sec;} \tag{4-54}$$

therefore for the square pulse case

$$\phi_0(t) =: \frac{2\Phi_0}{N} = \left(\frac{2}{Nc}\right) I_0 = \text{constant for } 0 < t < \tau_0$$

$$= 0 \text{ for } t < 0, \ t > \tau_0 \tag{4-55}$$

and

$$\int_{-\infty}^{t-(x/c)} \phi_0(t^*)dt^* = \int_{0}^{t-(x/c)} \frac{2I_0}{Nc}dt = \left(\frac{2I_0}{Nc}\right)\left(t - \frac{x}{c}\right)$$

$$= \frac{2\Phi_0}{N}\left(t - \frac{x}{c}\right). \tag{4-56}$$

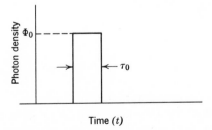

Time (t)

Figure 4-6 Square input pulse to amplifier.

Note that $\Phi_0 c\tau_0 = I_0\tau_0$ is the total number of photons per unit area in the pulse.

An additional assumption for this amplifier is that the impurity ion density is uniform throughout the laser rod and that the pumping to the excited laser state is also uniform. Thus the initial inversion (η_0) throughout the laser rod is constant. We may then write

$$\int_0^x \eta_0(x^*)\, dx^* = \eta_0 x. \tag{4-57}$$

Now light that enters the amplifier at time $t = 0$ leaves it at $t = L/c$. As a consequence, for an input pulse of intensity $I_0(t)$, the corresponding output pulse is $I_L(t) = I[L,\ t - (x/c)]$. The photon density for the square pulse case can be obtained by taking the initial conditions and computing the integral involving the initial inversion given by (4-57) and the initial photon density from (4-56) and inserting them into the general equation for the relative photon density (4-53). The result is

$$\phi(x, t) = \frac{2\Phi(x, t)}{N}$$

$$= \frac{(2\Phi_0/N)}{1 - [1 - \exp(-\sigma\eta_0 Nx)]\exp\{-2\sigma c\Phi_0[t - (x/c)]\}}, \tag{4-58}$$

which is valid for the interval $0 < t - (x/c) < \tau_0$. Expressed in terms of intensity I, it becomes

$$I(x,\ t) = \frac{I_0}{1 - [1 - \exp(-\sigma\eta_0 Nx)]\exp\{-2\sigma I_0[t - (x/c)]\}}. \tag{4-59}$$

The single-pass power gain of the amplifier (G_0) can now be obtained by evaluating the intensity $I(x,\ t)$ at $x = L$ and taking the ratio I/I_0. Therefore

$$G_0 = \frac{I(L,\ t)}{I_0}$$

$$= \frac{1}{1 - [1 - \exp(-\sigma\eta_0 NL)]\exp\{-2\sigma I_0[t - (L/c)]\}}. \tag{4-60}$$

Note that the gain is dependent on time and also on the input intensity I_0. This is to be expected, for the energy gain in the light wave comes about by depleting the upper laser level as the wave passes by, thereby leaving less stored energy available for later portions of the pulse. It actually comes about mathematically because of the nonlinear equations needed to describe the photon flux and the inversion. For the square pulse case considered here, however, we note that for any value of input the gain at the leading edge of the pulse, that is, for the position $x = ct$, is exponential with distance through the amplifier. Thus for $x = ct$ in (4-59):

$$G = I\left(x, \frac{x}{c}\right)/I_0$$
$$= \frac{I}{I_0} = \exp\left(+\sigma\eta_0 Nx\right) \tag{4-61}$$

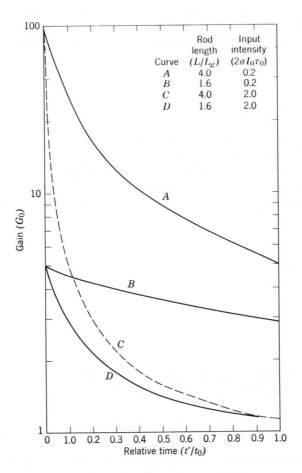

Curve	Rod length (L/L_R)	Input intensity $(2\sigma I_0 \tau_0)$
A	4.0	0.2
B	1.6	0.2
C	4.0	2.0
D	1.6	2.0

Figure 4-7 Power gain of optically pumped laser amplifier for various portions of the square-topped pulse traversing the amplifier.

and the total single pass gain for the leading edge is

$$G_0 = \exp{(\sigma \eta_0 N L)}. \tag{4-62}$$

The power gain is independent of the intensity at the front of the pulse. The gain decreases, however, for later portions of the pulse. The leading edge is amplified more than the remainder, which will give an effect of pulse sharpening of the input photon pulse. A plot of the power gain versus time during the pulse is shown in Figure 4-7. This illustrates the change of gain due to the leading edge of the pulse causing depletion of stored energy in the rod.

The term $\sigma \eta_0 N$ has the dimensions of reciprocal length and can be related to the gain per unit length for a laser system pumped to an inversion level of η_0. If we define a photon gain per unit length $1/L_g$ for this inversion we may write

$$L_g = \frac{1}{\sigma \eta_0 N}$$

and the power gain equation may be written by using this factor. Also, for evaluating the single-pass power gain of the pulse as it emerges from the amplifier we may also define a time t' as a time during the square-topped pulse after it leaves the amplifier. A parameter of interest then would be the ratio t'/τ_0, which will indicate what portion of the pulse is being examined. Thus define

$$t' = t - \frac{L}{c}$$

with the result that

$$2\sigma I_0 \left(t - \frac{L}{c} \right) = (2\sigma I_0 \tau_0) \left(\frac{t'}{\tau_0} \right)$$

and we see that the gain equation (4-60) may also be rewritten by using these new variables; it takes the following form:

$$G_0 = \frac{1}{1 - [1 - \exp{(-L/L_g)}] \exp{[2\sigma I_0 \tau_0 (t'/\tau_0)]}}. \tag{4-60a}$$

The curves illustrating the dependence of gain on length and initial intensity are expressed in terms of this parametric notation, as applied to Figures 4-8 and 4-9.

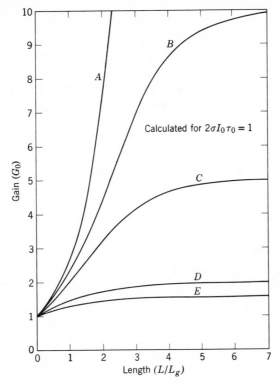

Figure 4-8 The plot of power gain versus amplifier length for different portions of the square input pulse. The individual curves are identified as follows: A — leading edge of pulse ($t'/\tau_0 = 0$); B — 10% through the pulse ($t'/\tau_0 = 0.10$); C — 22% through the pulse ($t'/\tau_0 = 0.22$); D — 70% through the pulse ($t'/\tau_0 = 0.70$); E — trailing edge of pulse ($t'/\tau_0 = 1.0$). Observe that the leading edge has exponential gain with length while the gain toward the trailing edge saturates.

For a moment let us examine the gain at the end of the pulse, which can be evaluated from (4-59) at $t = \tau_0 + (L/c)$ and $x = L$. Thus with this substitution the gain becomes

$$G_0 = \frac{1}{1 - [1 - \exp(-\sigma\eta_0 NL)]\exp(-2\sigma I_0 \tau_0)}. \qquad (4\text{-}63)$$

We can now determine the necessary input signal conditions that will allow the power gain to be essentially exponential with length over the full pulse width. For this to occur it is necessary that $2\sigma I_0 \tau_0 < 1$. The exact measure can be ascertained by a series expansion of this exponential in (4-63), which gives the following result:

$$\exp(-2\sigma I_0 \tau_0) \simeq 1 - 2\sigma I_0 \tau_0.$$

Then, to first order in small terms, we obtain the approximate power gain:

$$G_0 = \frac{1}{\exp{(-\sigma\eta_0 NL)} + (2\sigma I_0 \tau_0)} \approx \exp{(\sigma\eta_0 NL)}, \qquad (4\text{-}64)$$

from which it can be seen that the condition $2\sigma I_0 \tau_0 \ll \exp{(-\sigma\eta_0 NL)}$ is necessary to obtain an exponential gain, independent of the input photon intensity over the full pulse length. The gain then depends only on the initial inversion ratio (η_0) and the length of the amplifier rod.

A parametric plot of power gain versus amplifier length as defined by (4-60a) is shown in Figure 4-8, and the significance of these curves, can be described as follows. Let us recall that the results are for a square-topped input pulse. For a pulse of any input intensity the power gain curve for the leading edge $(t = L/c)$ is given by curve A, the exponential gain curve. The parameter that distinguishes the curves from one another involves the exponential term $2\sigma I_0 t'$ which includes the initial intensity I_0 and the time during which the pulse emerges from the amplifier t'. The curves proceeding from A to E indicate the power gain in a given length amplifier decreases for later portions of the pulse. Also for a given

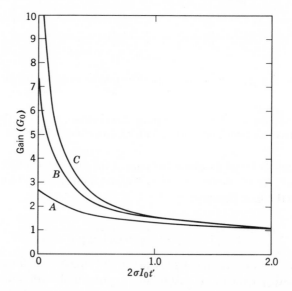

Figure 4-9 Plot of gain versus position in the square-topped pulse for a given length amplifier. The front portion of the pulse reduces the inverted population, thereby reducing the gain for latter portions of the pulse. Curve $A - L/L_g = 1$; $B - L/L_g = 2$; $C - L/L_g = 3$. The gain is dependent upon input intensity. Thus, this curve also shows that at a given position in time during the pulse, the gain is lower for higher input intensity pulses.

length of amplifier the gain is lower for high intensity pulses then for low ones. The reason for this decrease of gain is that the additional energy available and added to the pulse from that stored in excited states will make a larger percentage incremental addition at low-power levels than at high-power levels. Thus the gain drops with intensity.

Alternatively, if the input intensity is assumed fixed for these curves and the gain is examined at various times during the square pulse, the loss of gain is immediately discernible. The gain given by curve A is for the leading edge of pulse $t = (L/c)$, and the lower gain occurs for later portions as seen by proceeding from curves B through E in Figure 4-8.

Table 4-1 illustrates the drop of gain during the pulse for a fixed amplifier length and input intensity.

Figure 4-9 illustrates the variation in gain (G_0) as a function of the total number of photons through the amplifier as given by $(I_0 t')$. For a few photons, the gain is high. When many photons have traversed the amplifier, the total inverted population is greatly reduced and the gain approaches unity independent of amplifier length.

TABLE 4-1   DROP OF GAIN
DURING THE PULSE FOR A
FIXED AMPLIFIER LENGTH AND
INPUT INTENSITY

$\dfrac{t'}{\tau_0}$	$\dfrac{G_0}{(L/L_g = 2)}$	$\dfrac{G_0}{(L/L_g = 5)}$
0	7.4	148
0.1	4.5	9.4
0.22	3.24	4.85
0.7	1.75	1.99
1.0	1.46	1.59

For evaluation above assume $2\sigma I_0 \tau_0 = 1$, where $\tau_0 = $ pulse length and $t' = $ time after pulse reaches end of amplifier.

Another parameter of interest, in addition to the power gain, is the total energy gain in the pulse as it traverses the amplifier medium. This can be obtained by integrating the intensity over time and taking the ratio of the output to the input of the amplifier. Thus the energy gain (G_E) is defined as

$$G_L = \frac{\displaystyle\int_{-\infty}^{+\infty} I(L, \ t) \, dt}{\displaystyle\int_{-\infty}^{+\infty} I(0, \ t) \, dt}. \tag{4-65}$$

Now for the square-topped input pulse under consideration we note that

$$I(0, t) = 0 \quad \text{for} \quad t < 0 \quad \text{and} \quad t > \tau_0$$

and, similarly,

$$I(L, t) = 0 \quad \text{for} \quad t < \frac{L}{c} \quad \text{and} \quad t > \tau_0 + \frac{L}{c}.$$

Then the gain equation (4-65) may be written as

$$G_E = \frac{\displaystyle\int_{L/c}^{\tau_0+(L/c)} I(L, t) \, dt}{\displaystyle\int_0^{\tau_0} I_0 \, dt}. \tag{4-66}$$

The denominator can be simply evaluated since I_0 is constant over the pulse length, τ_0.

$$\int_0^{\tau_0} I_0 \, dt = I_0 \tau_0. \tag{4-67}$$

The numerator of this ratio can be evaluated by the substitution of $I(L, t)$ from (4-59) into the integral (4-66), and the gain expression becomes

$$G_E = \frac{1}{\tau_0} \int_{L/c}^{\tau_0+(L/c)} \frac{dt}{1 - [1 - \exp(-\sigma\eta_0 NL)] \exp\{-2\sigma I_0[t - (L/c)]\}}. \tag{4-68}$$

Let us now make a substitution of variable, where

$$u = \exp\{-2\sigma I_0[t - (L/c]\}$$

$$du = -2\sigma I_0 \exp\{-2\sigma I_0[t - (L/c)]\} \, dt \tag{4-69}$$

$$dt = -\frac{1}{2\sigma I_0} \frac{du}{u}$$

and, because it is a constant, independent of time, let

$$\Gamma = 1 - \exp(-\sigma\eta_0 NL). \tag{4-70}$$

With these substitutions the integral becomes

$$G_E = \frac{1}{2\sigma I_0 \tau_0} \int\limits_1^{\exp(-2\sigma I_0 \tau_0)} \frac{-dx}{x(1-\Gamma x)} \tag{4-71}$$

$$= \frac{1}{2\sigma I_0 \tau_0}\left[\ln\left(\frac{1-\Gamma x}{x}\right)\right]_1^{\exp(-2\sigma I_0 \tau_0)}. \tag{4-72}$$

Substituting the limits into this expression results in the following form:

$$G_E = \frac{1}{2\sigma I_0 \tau_0} \ln\left[\frac{1-\Gamma\ \exp(-2\sigma I_0 \tau_0)}{(1-\Gamma)\ \exp(-2\sigma I_0 \tau_0)}\right]. \tag{4-73}$$

Replace the constant term (Γ) by its value given in (4-70) and, on rearranging, the equation for the energy gain of the amplifier becomes

$$G_E = \frac{1}{2\sigma I_0 \tau_0} \ln\left\{1 + [\exp(2\sigma I_0 \tau_0) - 1]\exp(+\sigma\eta_0 NL)\right\}. \tag{4-74}$$

The physical significance of this result can most easily be seen by evaluating three extreme conditions:

Case I: Extremely Short Input Pulse

The first condition is for extremely short input pulses, and in this case we assume that $2\sigma I_0 \tau_0 \ll 1$ and $\exp(2\sigma I_0 \tau_0) - 1 \simeq 2\sigma I_0 \tau_0$. Furthermore,

$$\ln[1 + (2\sigma I_0 \tau_0)\exp(\sigma\eta_0 NL)] \simeq 2\sigma I_0 \tau_0 \exp(\sigma\eta_0 NL)$$

and it follows that

$$G_E = \exp(\sigma\eta_0 NL) = \exp\left(\frac{L}{L_g}\right) \qquad \sigma I_0 \tau_0 \ll 1. \tag{4-75}$$

Thus for the infinitesimally short pulse, approaching that characterized by a δ-function, the energy gain of the amplifier is exponential with the length of the amplifier. This, of course, also assumes a finite length subject to the condition that

$$(2\sigma I_0 \tau_0)\exp(\sigma\eta_0 NL) \ll 1, \tag{4-76}$$

the same condition imposed for exponential power gain illustrated in

(4-64), and requires a small total input photon density entering the amplifier.

Case II: Large Number of Input Photons

In a large input pulse of photons the condition required is that

$$\exp{(2\sigma I_0 \tau_0)} \gg 1 \tag{4-77}$$

and also

$$[\exp{(2\sigma I_0 \tau_0)}][\exp{(\sigma \eta_0 NL)}] \gg 1.$$

In this event we note that

$$\ln{[\exp{(2\sigma I_0 \tau_0 + \sigma \eta_0 NL)}]} \simeq 2\sigma I_0 \tau_0 + \sigma \eta_0 NL \tag{4-78}$$

and

$$G_E = 1 + \frac{\eta_0 NL}{2I_0 \tau_0} \qquad \sigma I_0 \tau_0 \gg 1. \tag{4-79}$$

The energy gain is linear in length for the large input signal and reflects the fact that the input pulse is large enough to induce the stimulated decay of every excited atom in the laser amplifier. The pulse thus increases in energy linearly as it progresses down the laser amplifier rod. This case represents the example in which the maximum total energy can be extracated from the laser medium.

Case III: Moderate Input Pulse but Long Amplifier

In a very long amplifier even a small input pulse may grow to the point at which the same phenomenon occurs. In this event the gain in the initial region of the laser rod would be approximately exponential, and after attaining a certain energy density the linear gain region would be reached. Thus in the latter regions the amplifier rod would be denuded of its stored energy but in the initial regions only partly so, as evidenced by the exponential gain. Thus, assuming that the exponential gain region is short compared with the linear gain region, the energy gain for moderate input pulses but long amplifiers is given by

$$G_E \simeq \frac{\eta_0 NL}{2I_0 \tau_0} \qquad \eta_0 NL \gg 1. \tag{4-80}$$

A parametric plot of energy gain versus input photon intensity is shown in Figure 4-10. Figure 4-11 illustrates the energy gain versus amplifier

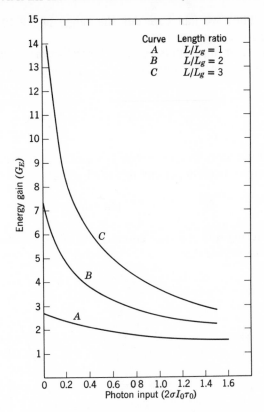

Figure 4-10   Energy gain versus total number of photons into amplifier.

length, with the exponential gain and linear gain regions clearly discernible for the moderate pulse input.

It is time now to evaluate the physical size of the factors entering into the gain equations. For ruby doped with 0.05% chromium the atomic doping density calculates to be $N = 1.6 \times 10^{19}$ chromium atoms per cm^3 and the absorption constant has been measured to be $\alpha = 0.4$ per cm. Thus the atomic cross section per atom can be ascertained:

$$\sigma N = \alpha$$

$$\sigma = \frac{0.4}{1.6 \times 10^{-19}} = 2.5 \times 10^{-20} cm^2. \tag{4-81}$$

A fast giant pulse that might be available at the input of the amplifier would typically be 5 nsec long; a slower one could stretch out to as much as 100 nsec. Thus we can consider the range of 5×10^{-9} sec $< \tau_0 <$ 100×10^{-9} sec for evaluation purposes.

If we estimate an input pulse of $P = 1$ MW from a rod of $A = 1$ cm² cross-sectional area at the ruby emission wavelength (λ) of 6943 Å, we see that

$$I_0 = \frac{P\lambda}{hcA} = 3.5 \times 10^{24} \text{ photons/cm}^2/\text{sec.} \qquad (4\text{-}82)$$

Then for a moderately fast Q-switch pulse of $\tau_0 = 10$ nsec duration the number of photons incident per cm² is given by

$$I_0\tau_0 = 3.5 \times 10^{16} \text{ photons/cm}^2.$$

The factor entering into the gain equation includes the absorption cross section, and thus we see that

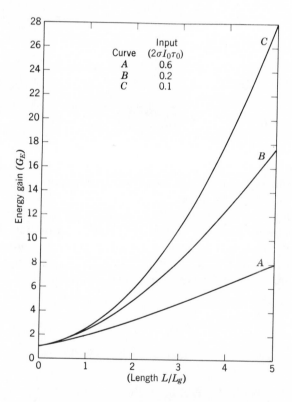

Figure 4-11   Energy gain of amplifier versus length.

$$2\sigma I_0 \tau_0 = 2(2.5 \times 10^{-20})(3.5 \times 10^{16})$$

$$= 17.5 \times 10^{-4}. \tag{4-83}$$

It can be seen that for this ruby system with an input power level of 1 MW the criterion for low-power input asserted by (4-75) and exponential gain is adequately satisfied. At higher power levels or an equivalent power level and a smaller beam area, the higher power range can be approached. In this instance an input pulse of 100 MW over an area half the previously assumed diameter would place the input near the high-input power range. This is extremely difficult to achieve, however, and may, in fact, be virtually impossible to utilize in a real case.

For the term involving the length we must take into account the fact that the excited laser level in ruby is a split level but that only one level contributes to laser action. Thus we must use a value of $N = \frac{1}{2} \times 1.6 \times 10^{+19}$ cm³. Then for a 10-cm-long laser rod with 80% inversion we see that

$$\sigma\eta_0 NL = (2.5 \times 10^{-20})(0.8)(0.8 \times 10^{19})(10) = 1.6. \tag{4-84}$$

The values of L required for a realistic laser amplifier are such that the exponential factor involving the length will always exceed unity. More typical values in ruby now run to several centimeters and in neodymium-doped glass, in excess of 1 m.

4-5 PULSE AMPLIFIER SOLUTION FOR IMPULSE-FUNCTION INPUT

The energy gain for an impulse-function input can now be calculated by reference to (4-74):

$$G_E = \frac{1}{2\sigma I_0 \tau_0} \ln \{1 + [\exp(2\sigma I_0 \tau_0) - 1] \exp(\sigma\eta_0 NL)\}. \tag{4-74}$$

For the impulse input we let the pulse length approach zero, $\tau_0 \to 0$, but require that the product $I_0\tau_0$ still be finite and subject to the further condition that $2\sigma I_0 \tau_0 \ll 1$. Then

$$\exp(2\sigma I_0 \tau_0) \simeq 1 + 2\sigma I_0 \tau_0 \tag{4-84}$$

and for a finite length amplifier we see that

$$G_E = \frac{1}{2\sigma I_0 \tau_0} \ln [1 + (2\sigma I_0 \tau_0)\exp(\sigma\eta_0 NL)]. \tag{4-85}$$

Now, noting that this can be expanded by the series approximation,

$$\ln(1+x) \simeq x \qquad x \ll 1,$$

we obtain

$$G_E = \exp(\sigma\eta_0 NL) = \exp(L/L_g). \qquad (4\text{-}86)$$

The exponential energy gain thus occurs for very narrow, or impulse-function pulses incident on the amplifier input. The gain curve is plotted in Figure 4-12.

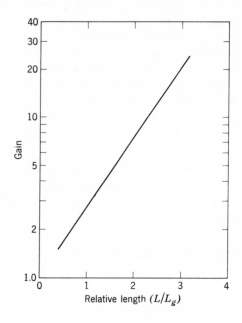

Figure 4-12   Energy gain of a laser amplifier for an impulse-function input.

4-6 PULSE AMPLIFIER SOLUTION FOR LORENTZIAN-SHAPED PULSE INPUT

The photon density $\Phi_0(t)$ in an input pulse of half-width T is given by (4-87), which is normalized so that D represents the total number of photons per unit area in the beam:

$$\Phi_0(t) = \left(\frac{DT}{c}\right)\left(\frac{1}{\pi}\right)\left(\frac{1}{t^2+T^2}\right). \qquad (4\text{-}87)$$

The shape of this pulse as a function of time is shown in the inset of Figure 4-13 and curve C of Figure 4-15.

The normalization can be verified by noting that

$$c \int_{-\infty}^{+\infty} \Phi_0(t)\, dt = \int_{-\infty}^{+\infty} \left(\frac{DT}{\pi}\right) \frac{dt}{t^2 + T^2}$$

$$= \frac{D}{\pi} \left[\tan^{-1}\left(\frac{t}{T}\right) \right]_{-\infty}^{+\infty}$$

$$= D. \qquad (4\text{-}88)$$

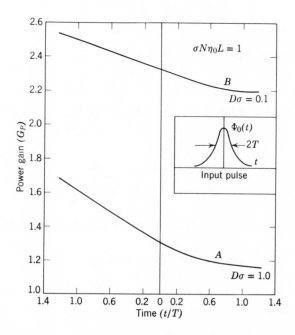

Figure 4-13 Plot of power gain for Lorentzian pulse input for $N\sigma\eta_0 L = 1$.

Recalling from the normalization of variables in (4-21) or (4-55) that

$$\phi_0(t) = \frac{2\Phi_0}{N} = \frac{2DT}{N\pi c}\left(\frac{1}{t^2 + T^2}\right), \qquad (4\text{-}89)$$

we assume that the impurity ion density is uniform in the laser rod and that the inversion is also uniform as assumed for the preceding examples. We may now make the appropriate substitution in the general expression for photon density (4-53).

An evaluation of the following integral is needed:

$$\int_{-\infty}^{t-(x/c)} \phi_0(t^*) \, dt^* = \int_{-\infty}^{t-(x/c)} \left(\frac{2DT}{N\pi c}\right) \frac{dt}{t^2 + T^2} = \frac{2D}{N\pi c} \left. \tan^{-1}\frac{t}{T} \right]_{-\infty}^{t-(x/c)} \quad (4\text{-}90)$$

$$= \frac{2D}{N\pi c} \tan^{-1}\left[\frac{t-(x/c)}{T}\right] + \frac{D}{Nc}$$

$$= \frac{D}{Nc}\left\{\frac{2}{\pi} \tan^{-1}\left[\frac{t-(x/c)}{T}\right] + 1\right\}.$$

Thus the photon density becomes

$$\phi(x,t) = \frac{(2DT/N\pi c)\{[t-(x/c)]^2 + T^2\}^{-1}}{1 - \left[1 - \exp\left(-\sigma\eta_0 Nx\right)\right]\exp\left\{-D\sigma\left[1 + \frac{2}{\pi}\tan^{-1}\left(\frac{t-(x/c)}{T}\right)\right]\right\}}. \quad (4\text{-}91)$$

The input photon density is given by

$$\phi(x, t) = \phi_{in}(0, t) = \phi_{in} \quad (4\text{-}92)$$

and the output photon density corresponding to this input is evaluated by

$$\phi(x, t) = \phi_{out}[L, t+(L/c)] = \phi_{out}. \quad (4\text{-}93)$$

The power gain for this case (G_p) is defined by the ratio of input to output photon density:

$$G_p = \frac{\phi_{in}(0, t)}{\phi_{out}[L, t+(L/c)]}. \quad (4\text{-}94)$$

Thus, by making the appropriate substitutions in (4-91) to obtain input and output photon densities we arrive at the following:

$$\phi_{in}(t) = \frac{2DT}{N\pi c}\left[\frac{1}{t^2 + T^2}\right] \quad (4\text{-}95)$$

$$\phi_{out}(t) = \frac{(2DT/N\pi c)[1/(t^2 + T^2)]}{1 - \{1 - \exp\left(-\sigma\eta_0 NL\right)\}\exp\left\{-D\sigma[1 + (2/\pi) \tan^{-1}(t/T)]\right\}} \quad (4\text{-}96)$$

Thus the power gain for the Lorenzian pulse becomes

$$G_p = \left\{ 1 - \left[1 - \exp\left(-\sigma\eta_0 NL\right) \right] \exp\left[-D\sigma\left(1 + \frac{2}{\pi}\tan^{-1}\frac{t}{T} \right) \right] \right\}^{-1}. \qquad (4\text{-}97)$$

To get an idea of the order of magnitude of the above quantities, we assume the following parameters for a ruby system.

$$\sigma = 2.5 \times 10^{-20} \text{ cm}^2$$

$$\eta_0 N = 8 \times 10^{18} \text{ atoms/cm}^3$$

$$L = 10 \text{ cm}$$

$$D = 4 \times 10^{19} \text{ photons/cm}^2 \text{ (a high-energy pulse)}.$$

Then we see that

$$\sigma\eta_0 NL = 2; \qquad D\sigma = 1.$$

The power gain as a function of relative time is plotted in Figures 4-13 and 4-14 for various sets of parameters. These variations might be introduced by varying the length of the laser, the inversion, the doping density in the rod, or the input photon intensity. Similarly, the input photon density pulse shape is compared with the output density pulse shape for

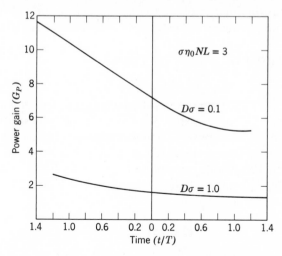

Figure 4-14   Plot of power gain for Lorentzian pulse input for $N\sigma\eta_0 L = 3$.

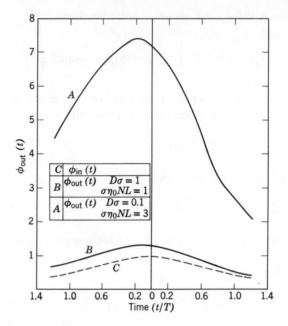

Figure 4-15 Photon pulse shape at output of amplifier normalized to input for a Lorentzian-shaped pulse.

two conditions in Figure 4-15. The higher gain at earlier portions of the pulse is illustrated here. One immediate effect to notice is the shift of the peak of the pulse at the output relative to the input. The second is the distortion showing higher photon densities before the pulse peak when compared with a symmetrical point in time past the pulse peak.

4-7 BANDWIDTH OF LASER AMPLIFIER

The bandwidth of a laser amplifier is determined by the interaction or absorption cross section between the incoming radiation and the excited atoms in the laser host material. We calculate the bandwidth only for the case in which the input pulse is of lower intensity. In this event the power gain is expressed by the approximate form given in (4-64). It should be noted that the bandwidth calculation is also valid for the energy gain for an impulse-function input of photons as shown by (4-86). Thus, reiterating the expression for power gain,

$$G = \exp(\sigma\eta_0 NL). \tag{4-98}$$

The absorption cross section for a line with a Lorentzian distribution

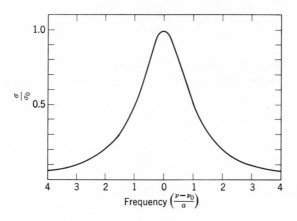

Figure 4-16 Variation of absorption cross section with frequency for a Lorentzian line shape.

in frequency can be described by the following equation:

$$\sigma = \frac{\sigma_0 a^2}{(\nu - \nu_0)^2 + a^2},$$ (4-99)

where σ_0 is a constant and the maximum value of cross section at center frequency ν_0, a is the half-width of the line, and ν is the frequency. This is illustrated in Figure 4-16. The power gain G will then have a frequency dependence:

$$G = \exp\left\{\sigma_0 \eta_0 NL\left[\frac{a^2}{(\nu - \nu_0)^2 + a^2}\right]\right\}$$ (4-100)

Now define the maximum single-pass power gain as G_0, or, in other terms,

$$G_0 = G(\nu_0) = \exp\left(\sigma_0 \eta_0 NL\right)$$ (4-101)

$$\ln G_0 = \sigma_0 \eta_0 NL.$$ (4-102)

This equation for gain (4-100) can be solved for frequency. Thus

$$\frac{a^2}{(\nu - \nu_0)^2 + a^2} = \frac{1}{\sigma_0 \eta_0 NL}\ln G = \frac{\ln G}{\ln G_0}$$ (4-103)

$$\nu - \nu_0 = a\left(\frac{\ln G_0}{\ln G} - 1\right)^{1/2}. \tag{4-104}$$

The bandwidth of the amplifier (B) is now defined as that frequency range over which the power gain drops to half its maximum value. Thus when

$$\nu - \nu_0 = \frac{B}{2}$$

$$G = \frac{G_0}{2}.$$

Therefore the expression for bandwidth becomes

$$2B = a\left[\frac{\ln G_0}{\ln (G_0/2)} - 1\right]^{1/2} \tag{4-105}$$

$$B = \frac{a}{2}\left[\frac{\ln 2}{\ln (G_0/2)}\right]^{1/2}. \tag{4-106}$$

This last expression can be written completely in terms of fundamental laser parameters by observing that

$$G_0 = \exp (\sigma_0 \eta_0 NL),$$

and the bandwidth equation (4-106) is alternatively expressed as

$$B = \frac{a}{2}\left[\frac{\ln 2}{\sigma_0 \eta_0 NL - \ln 2}\right]^{1/2}. \tag{4-107}$$

The familiar relationship between gain and bandwidth is seen to hold for laser amplifiers. For a high gain factor the bandwidth is reduced, whereas for a lower gain a larger bandwidth is possible. The bandwidth is also seen to depend directly on the atomic line half-width as well.

4-8 NOISE FIGURE OF LASER AMPLIFIER

A parameter of an amplifier that is always of concern to the user, especially when low-power signals are to be investigated, is the noise generated in the amplifier. The noise already in a signal is amplified right along with the signal and is always present. Of great concern however, is noise added to the signal by the amplifier or amplifier elements. Its measure is defined as the noise factor. The noise factor of an amplifier, sometimes called the noise figure, is defined as "the ratio of the total noise power available at the output which is of thermal origin."

For example, let us consider an amplifier of gain G, which has a bandwidth of $\Delta\nu$ and both input and output at temperature T_0. The thermal noise at the input of the amplifier is

$$P_{in} = k \cdot T_0 \cdot \Delta\nu \qquad (4\text{-}108)$$

and at the output the available noise power from this source is

$$P_{out} = G \cdot k \cdot T_0 \cdot \Delta\nu. \qquad (4\text{-}109)$$

If the only noise at the output of the system came from that at the input, that is, if we had an ideal amplifier, the noise factor (F) would be unity. For an ideal amplifier

$$F = \frac{P_{out}}{GP_{in}} = 1. \qquad (4\text{-}110)$$

With other noise sources available however, such as temperature differences in the system, losses in the laser that could also be sources of noise, and other contributing effects, the output noise is greater than indicated by (4-109) and the noise factor exceeds unity. In fact, an "equivalent temperature" can be defined to cover the output noise power (P_{all}) due to the input as well as the other noise sources:

$$P_{all} = G \cdot k \cdot T_{eff} \cdot \Delta\nu. \qquad (4\text{-}111)$$

Then the noise factor can be written as

$$F = \frac{P_{all}}{GP_{in}} = \frac{T_{eff}}{T_0}. \qquad (4\text{-}112)$$

This new term, "noise equivalent temperature," can also be used to describe the noise properties of the amplifier as well as the noise figure.

Some of the factors contributing to noise in a laser amplifier are thermal radiation from the cavity walls, high-temperature radiation from the flash lamps, and incoherent spontaneous emission from the excited laser levels in the laser material.

The noise figure for the laser amplifier can be calculated by the following procedure. Let the noise power (P) be the noise incident on a unit volume of material in a laser cavity. We may write the increase in noise power (dP) over the length (dx) of the laser active material in (4-113) as

$$dP = \alpha_g P \, dx + \frac{n_2 h\nu A}{\tau_s} \, dx - \alpha_s P \, dx + \alpha_s P_w(T_w) \, dx. \qquad (4\text{-}113)$$

The terms may be identified as follows:

1. The first term on the right-hand side of the equation is simply the incremental power increase due to the stimulated emission in the laser of gain factor α_g. It is assumed here that the amplifier gain (G) is exponential with laser length and $G = \exp(\alpha_g - \alpha_s)L$, where α_s is the loss coefficient.

2. The next term gives the power increase in the volume $(A \, dx)$ due to spontaneous transitions. This is proportional to the total number of excited atoms in this volume $(n_2 A \, dx)$ and depends on the spontaneous emission lifetime (τ_s) of the excited state. We are interested here only in the noise contributed to the particular frequency under consideration.

3. The third term $(-\alpha_s P \, dx)$ is the power loss due to scattering or other attenuation in the laser rod or optical cavity with a loss factor α_s per unit length.

4. The final term $(+\alpha_s P_w \, dx)$ gives the contribution to the noise power from thermal radiation sources surrounding the laser rod. In an optically pumped laser it comes primarily from the pump lamp, which has an effective temperature (T_w) considerably higher than the other surroundings. Thus this term arises mainly from the heated pump. The loss coefficient α_s is used appropriately here, as can be demonstrated by considerations of thermal equilibrium and detailed balancing.

From Planck's radiation law the thermal noise power from the surrounding heated sources at temperature T_w in the frequency interval $\Delta\nu$ can be written as

$$P_w(T_w) = \left(\frac{8\pi\nu^2 A}{c^2}\right)\left[\frac{h\nu}{\exp(h\nu/kT_w) - 1}\right]\Delta\nu. \qquad (4\text{-}114)$$

We now wish to express the second term in the noise differential equation in terms of the gain coefficient and noise power from the spontaneous emission. We proceed to do this by first recognizing that an "equivalent atomic temperature" (T_a) can be defined and written in terms of the inverted population by

$$\frac{n_2}{n_1} = \exp\left(-\frac{h\nu}{kT_a}\right). \qquad (4\text{-}115)$$

A positive population inversion ($n_2 > n_1$) results in a "negative temperature" (T_a), but when we recognize that this is a useful tool and not a temperature describing an equilibrium distribution the negative temperature concept is not difficult to appreciate.

Let us now note that the power flow can be given in terms of photon density [$\Phi(\nu)$], the cross-sectional area of the stream (A), the speed of light (c), and the photon energy ($h\nu$). Thus

$$P_a = \Phi(\nu)h\nu Ac. \tag{4-116}$$

Using the Planck radiation law for the photon density, we see that the spontaneous emission noise power in a frequency interval $\Delta\nu$ can be written in a form similar to that for the thermal noise power.

$$\Phi(\nu) = \left(\frac{8\pi\nu^2}{c^3}\right)\frac{\Delta\nu}{\exp{(h\nu/kT_a)} - 1}. \tag{4-117}$$

Substituting for this photon density, it follows that

$$P_a = \frac{8\pi h\nu^3}{c^3}\frac{Ac\Delta\nu}{\exp{(h\nu/kT_a)} - 1} \tag{4-118}$$

or, using (4-115),

$$P_a = \left(\frac{8\pi\nu^2 A}{c^2}\right)\left[\frac{h\nu}{(n_1/n_2) - 1}\right]\Delta\nu. \tag{4-119}$$

Similarly, the gradient of the power flow can be written in terms of the stimulated emission Einstein B coefficient:

$$\frac{dP_a}{dx} = (n_2 - n_1)h\nu AB_{21}\left(\frac{\Phi(\nu)h\nu}{\Delta\nu}\right). \tag{4-120}$$

Furthermore, the laser gain factor (α_g) per unit length can be recognized when written in terms of the population inversion and the Einstein B coefficient. If we use (4-116) and (4-120) it follows that

$$\alpha_g = \frac{1}{P}\frac{dP}{dx} = \left(\frac{(n_2 - n_1)B_{21}}{c}\right)\left(\frac{h\nu}{\Delta\nu}\right); \tag{4-121}$$

recalling the relationship between the spontaneous emission lifetime and the Einstein B coefficient,

$$\frac{1}{\tau_s} = B_{21}\left(\frac{8\pi h\nu^3}{c^3}\right),$$

we see that

$$\alpha_g = \left(\frac{n_2 - n_1}{\tau_s}\right)\left(\frac{c^2}{\nu^2}\right)\left(\frac{1}{8\pi\Delta\nu}\right) \qquad (4\text{-}122)$$

or, rearranging terms,

$$\frac{1}{\tau_s} = \left(\frac{\alpha_g}{n_2 - n_1}\right)\left(\frac{8\pi\nu^2\Delta\nu}{c^2}\right). \qquad (4\text{-}123)$$

Then, substituting for the spontaneous lifetime by using (4-123), we find that the second term in the differential equation (4-113) for noise power can be written as

$$\frac{n_2 h\nu A\, dx}{\tau_s} = n_2 h\nu A\left(\frac{\alpha_g}{n_2 - n_1}\right)\left(\frac{8\pi\nu^2\Delta\nu}{c^2}\right)dx \qquad (4\text{-}124)$$

$$= \alpha_g\left(\frac{8\pi\nu^2 A}{c^2}\right)\left[\frac{h\nu}{1 - (n_1/n_2)}\right]\Delta\nu\, dx \qquad (4\text{-}125)$$

and by comparing with (4-119)

$$\frac{n_2 h\nu A\, dx}{\tau_s} = -\alpha_g P_a\, dx. \qquad (4\text{-}126)$$

Thus the second term in the noise equation can now be written in terms of the gain coefficient (α_g) and the spontaneous emission noise power (P_a) as shown in (4-126).

The differential equation (4-113) for the incremental noise power can now be written with the new quantities as follows:

$$\frac{dP}{dx} = \alpha_g P - \alpha_g P_a(T_a) - \alpha_s P + \alpha_s P_w(T_w)$$

$$= (\alpha_g - \alpha_s)P + \alpha_s P_w(T_w) - \alpha_g P_a(T_a). \qquad (4\text{-}127)$$

We recognize that $P_a(T_a)$ is fixed by the population inversion and $P_w(T_w)$ is determined by the surroundings of the laser rod, the primary contributor being the laser flash lamp.

The differential equation can now be integrated subject to the boundary condition that at $x = 0$, $P = P_{in}$. The result is

$$P = P_{in}\exp\left[(\alpha_g - \alpha_s)x\right] + \left(\frac{\alpha_s P_w - \alpha_g P_a}{\alpha_g - \alpha_s}\right)\{\exp\left[(\alpha_g - \alpha_s)x\right] - 1\}. \qquad (4\text{-}128)$$

Furthermore, let us assert that at $x = L$, $P = P_{out}$. Recognizing that the gain of the amplifier (G) is given by

$$G = \exp\left[(\alpha_g - \alpha_s)L\right], \tag{4-129}$$

we can write

$$P_{out} = GP_{in} + \left(\frac{\alpha_s P_w - \alpha_g P_a}{\alpha_g - \alpha_s}\right)(G-1). \tag{4-130}$$

The definition of noise factor F will be recalled from (4-110):

$$F = \frac{P_{out}}{GP_{in}}, \tag{4-110}$$

using this substitution, we can rewrite (4-130) as the noise factor for the laser amplifier:

$$F = 1 + \left(\frac{G-1}{G}\right)\left[\frac{\alpha_s P_w - \alpha_g P_a}{(\alpha_g - \alpha_s)P_{in}}\right] \tag{4-131}$$

$$= 1 + \left(\frac{G-1}{G}\right)\left[\left(\frac{\alpha_s}{\alpha_g - \alpha_s}\right)\left(\frac{P_w - P_a}{P_{in}}\right) - \left(\frac{P_a}{P_{in}}\right)\right].$$

Let us now evaluate this noise factor for a laser in which the surroundings are at room temperature, that is, a nonoptically pumped laser. Further, let us also assume that the input to the amplifier (P_{in}) is at room temperature (T_0). Then, recognizing that $P_{in} = P_w$ for this example and further assuming a high gain system $(G \gg 1)$, the noise factor expression reduces to the following:

$$F \simeq \left(1 + \frac{\alpha_s}{\alpha_g - \alpha_s}\right) - \left(\frac{\alpha_g}{\alpha_g - \alpha_s}\right)\left(\frac{P_a}{P_{in}}\right) \tag{4-132}$$

$$\simeq \left(1 - \frac{P_a}{P_{in}}\right)\left(1 + \frac{\alpha_s}{\alpha_g - \alpha_s}\right). \tag{4-133}$$

Relating P_a to the population inversion from (4-119) and realizing that for the high-gain system we also have $\alpha_s/(\alpha_g - \alpha_s) \ll 1$, we see that the noise factor expression becomes

$$F \simeq 1 + \left(\frac{n_2}{n_2 - n_1}\right)\frac{h\nu}{kT_0} \tag{4-134}$$

and for high population inversion

$$F \simeq 1 + \frac{h\nu}{kT_0},\tag{4-135}$$

where $P_{in} \sim kT_0$ with the input at room temperature.

As a result of this relationship, it is recognized that an optical laser has a considerably higher noise factor than one operating at microwave frequencies because of the enormous difference in the frequency (ν). At the microwave frequency of 10 kmc $(\nu = 10^{10}$ c), the noise factor becomes

$$F = 1 + \frac{h\nu}{kT_0} \simeq 1.0016 \qquad \nu = 10^{10} \text{ c,}$$

whereas for an optical laser with emission in the red region $(\lambda = 6000$ A or $\nu = 5 \times 10^{14}$ c) the noise factor would be very high:

$$F \simeq 1 + \frac{h\nu}{kT_0} \simeq 81 \qquad \nu = 5 \times 10^{14} \text{ c.}$$

If we return now to the case of the optically pumped laser in which the surroundings *are not* at room temperature that is, $T_w \neq T_0$, the expression for noise figure takes the slightly modified form seen in (4-136):

$$F = 1 - \frac{P_a}{P_{in}} + \left(\frac{\alpha_g}{\alpha_g - \alpha_s}\right)\left(\frac{P_w - P_a}{P_{in}}\right)\tag{4-136}$$

$$= 1 - \frac{P_a}{P_{in}}\left(1 + \frac{\alpha_s}{\alpha_g - \alpha_s}\right) + \frac{P_w}{P_{in}}\left(\frac{\alpha_s}{\alpha_g - \alpha_s}\right).\tag{4-137}$$

We have also assumed here that the laser amplifier has high gain $(G \gg 1)$.

Using the Boltzmann relation, we can write the ratio for P_w/P_{in} in terms of the temperature of the surroundings (T_w) and room temperature of the input (T_o):

$$\frac{P_w}{P_{in}} = \frac{\exp\,(h\nu/kT_o) - 1}{\exp\,(h\nu/kT_w) - 1} \simeq \frac{T_w}{T_o},\tag{4-138}$$

at these temperatures the exponential can be expanded by series approximation and only the first terms retained.

$$\exp\,(h\nu/kT_0) - 1 \simeq 1 + \frac{h\nu}{kT_0} - 1 \simeq \frac{h\nu}{kT_0}.$$

Again, with suitable substitutions, the noise factor can be written as

$$F = \left(1 - \frac{P_a}{P_{in}}\right)\left(1 + \frac{\alpha_s}{\alpha_g - \alpha_s}\right) + \left(\frac{T_w}{T_0} - 1\right)\left(\frac{\alpha_s}{\alpha_g - \alpha_s}\right), \qquad (4\text{-}139)$$

or, in terms of population inversion for the room temperature input, we obtain

$$F = \left(1 + \frac{n_2}{n_2 - n_1} \cdot \frac{h\nu}{kT_0}\right)\left(1 + \frac{\alpha_s}{\alpha_g - \alpha_s}\right) + \left(\frac{T_w}{T_0} - 1\right)\left(\frac{\alpha_s}{\alpha_g - \alpha_s}\right).$$

The particular factors that influence the noise factor of a laser amplifier can now be identified. To minimize the noise factor the following operating features should be emphasized.

1. The laser amplifier should have a high-gain factor.
2. The population inversion should be as large as possible.
3. The loss factor (α_s) from the system should be minimized and the gain (α_g) per unit length maximized.
4. The surroundings should be kept at a temperature as low as possible.

It is recognized that some of the requirements are self-competing. Generally, a high inversion ratio will accompany the high pump-lamp energy or temperature; here a trade-off has to be made. The loss factors

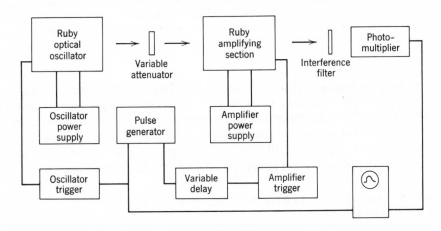

Figure 4-17 Schematic diagram for optical gain measurements. After Geusic and Scovil, *Bell System Tech. J.* (1962).

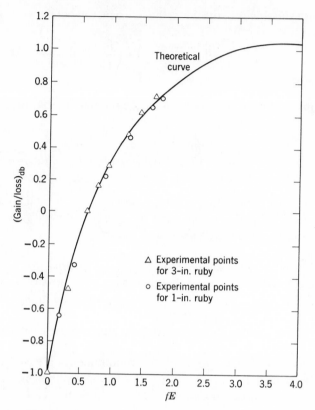

Figure 4-18 Amplifier gain versus input pump energy for a pulsed ruby laser amplifier. The measured loss was determined by shining a ruby light through the unpumped amplifier rod. The gain was determined by using an auxiliary ruby laser beam through the pumped amplifier. The threshold occurs when $(\text{gain/loss})_{db} = 0$. After Geusic and Scovil, *Bell System Tech. J.* (1962).

can be minimized independently of the gain factor. The actual laser system will, of course, determine the ease of control on the individual factors; for instance, filtering the actual radiation from the flash lamp to the laser rod to only that required in the absorption band of the material will have the effect of reducing the effective flash lamp temperature and therefore T_w will be reduced without adversely affecting the laser performance.

4-9 EXPERIMENTAL PERFORMANCE OF A TYPICAL LASER AMPLIFIER

This section describes the performance and actual measurements of some typical optically pumped solid-state amplifiers. It highlights the types of measurement to be observed and indicates the degree of agreement with the theoretical treatment. The lasers described here are single-pass, pulsed units of the traveling wave configuration.

The first amplifier measurements described here are from the work of Geusic and Scovil.[1] This laser consisted of an amplifying section of ruby 3 in. long. The measurement configuration for the experiment is shown in Figure 4-17, which shows the pulse trigger circuits for the flash lamps and the detector for measuring the output beam from the laser. The actual results, corrected for regeneration reflections and averaged over the phases between various reflections, are given in Figure 4-18. Here the ratio of gain to loss is plotted versus the input pumping parameter which is related to the energy supplied to the flash lamps; f is a pumping efficiency factor and E is the energy absorbed by the material at the pumping transition.

The correlation between the values of fE of the abscissa was made by measuring the light intensity photoelectrically at the green and blue absorption bands of ruby. Then an absolute calibration for the particular cavity was made by noting the intensity value at which the net amplifier gain is zero or where the gain equals the loss in the unit. Thus a correlation can be made of input energy versus net gain as shown in Figure 4-18.

In another set of measurements, reported by Steele and Davis,[2] a similar result was obtained but the method of correlating the input energy from the flash lamps with gain employed an adjustable parameter dependent on the laser threshold.

The experimental equipment used in this work consisted of two ruby lasers. One performs as an oscillator whose controlled and measured output is used as the incident light beam on the second laser, which functions as an amplifier. The output pulse from the second laser is compared with the input beam, subject to some regenerative corrections, and the power or energy gain from the amplifier stage is ascertained.

In the current experiments the power in both the input and output light pulses was measured using phototubes and a cathode ray tube display. A schematic diagram of the equipment is shown in Figure 4-19, and a photograph of the arrangement is shown in Figure 4-20. The oscillator is on the left and the amplifier stage is on the right.

The laser oscillator is an extremely important element in this work inasmuch as repeatable pulses of a known energy and power are required.

[1]J. E. Geusic and H. E. D. Scovil, "A Unidirectional Traveling Wave Optical Maser," *Bell System Tech. J.*, **41**, 1371–1396 (July 1962).

[2]E. L. Steele and W. C. Davis, "Laser Amplifiers," *J. Appl. Phys.*, **36**, 348–351 (February 1965).

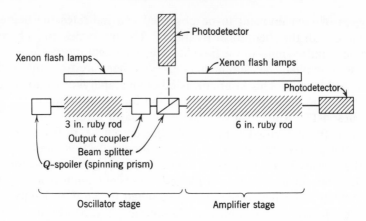

Figure 4-19 Experimental laser amplifier and driver oscillator.

The pulses were generated by Q-spoiling a ruby rod (3 in. long and 0.25 in. in diameter) with a spinning rooftop prism. This prism becomes totally reflecting once every rotation and thereby creates the high Q optical cavity for the pulse. The flash lamps used in this laser were xenon-filled PEK type XE-1-3. An output pulse of 9 MW and 20-nsec duration was generated using a capacitor bank charged to 2300 V.

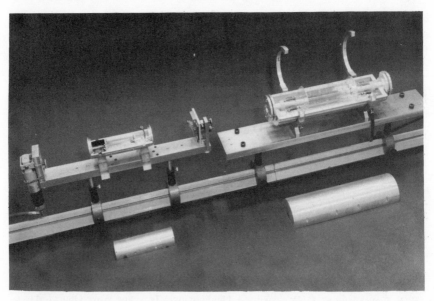

Figure 4-20 Laser amplifier experimental arrangement showing the oscillator unit on the left and the amplifier on the right. A motor-driven spinning prism is shown at the extreme left for Q-spoiling the oscillator laser.

The laser amplifier section of the experimental configuration consists of a ruby rod (6 in. long and 0.5 in. in diameter) doped with 0.05% by weight of CrO_3 in Al_2O_3. This gives a chromium ion density of 1.0×10^{19} per/cm³. The ends of the rod are polished. The pump radiation is furnished by two FX-47 xenon-filled flash lamps. The oscillator and amplifier pump lamps are triggered together with a built-in known advance relative to the reflecting position of the Q-spoiling prism. In this way the two ruby systems are fully pumped and the electron population is inverted before the formation of the high Q optical cavity and the subsequent emission of the pulse into the amplifier.

The pulses out of the oscillator and the amplifier are observed by using a fast phototube (type 925 with S-1 surface) and are recorded by a Tektronix model 517 oscilloscope.

The relation between the pump light from the flash lamp in the amplifier and the population inversion is now calculated. Assume that the differential relationship between electron density n_1 in the lower state and the energy (E) emitted by the pump lamp has the form

$$dn_1 = \beta n_1 \, dE. \tag{4-141}$$

This can be solved to yield

$$n_1 = N_0 e^{-\beta E} \tag{4-142}$$

where N is the total electron population, which is assumed to be in the lowest level when there is no pump illumination. The upper excited level is assumed to be totally empty. Because of the split energy level structure at the ruby laser level, only one half of the electrons pumped into it are available for the laser transition (n_2). We can then write for the population inversion

$$n_0 = n_2 - n_1 = n_2 - N_0 e^{-\beta E}.$$

Under conditions for total inversion ($E = \infty$) we see that

$$n_0 = \frac{N_0}{2}$$

because of the split level mentioned above; at that pump illumination intensity the lower energy level would be completely empty ($n_1 = 0$).

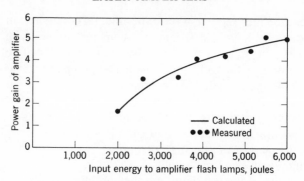

Figure 4-21 Gain versus energy input to flash lamps.

Assuming that the net filling of level N_2 occurs by means of relaxation from the pump band, we may write

$$n_2 = \frac{N_0 - n_1}{2} = \frac{N_0}{2} - \frac{1}{2} N_0 e^{-\beta E}.$$

Therefore

$$n_0 = \frac{N_0}{2}(1 - 3e^{-\beta E})$$

$$\frac{n_0}{N_0} = \frac{1}{2}(1 - 3e^{-\beta E}). \tag{4-143}$$

The value of the coefficient β is now determined from threshold data from the amplifier gain curve. The threshold ($n_0 = 0$) from data taken in obtaining Figure 4-21 is found to be 1500 joules, and the coefficient has the value

$$\beta = 7.3 \times 10^{-4} \text{ joule.} \tag{4-144}$$

The value of the pumping coefficient was combined with the expression for population inversion as a function of flash lamp energy (4-143). These data were used to compute the gain curves shown in Figure 4-21 for the 6-in. laser amplifier. The population inversion dependence on pump energy is shown in Figure 4-22.

APPENDIX 4-A

This appendix lists the detailed steps in the evaluation of the electron inversion ratio in terms of $k(x)$ based on the solution of the photon density equation.

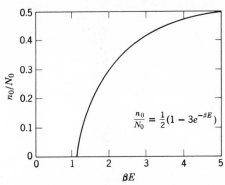

Figure 4-22 Fractional population inversion versus relative pumping energy.

The photon density is given by the following equation [see (4-45]:

$$\phi(x, t) = \frac{\phi_0[t - (x/c)]}{1 + k(x) \exp\left[-N\sigma c \int_{-\infty}^{t-(x/c)} \phi_0(t^*)\, dt^*\right]}. \qquad (4\text{-}A\text{-}1)$$

The inversion ratio can be given in terms of the photon density by (4-A-2) [see also (4-27)].

$$\eta(x, t) = \frac{1}{\phi}\left[\frac{\partial \phi}{\partial t} + c\frac{\partial \phi}{\partial x}\right]\frac{1}{N\sigma c}. \qquad (4\text{-}A\text{-}2)$$

The question now is what steps are necessary to express $\eta(x, t)$ in terms available from the right-hand side of (4-A-1).

Begin by defining the factor α to simplify the algebra of the calculation:

$$\alpha = \alpha[t - (x/c)] = N\sigma c \int_{-\infty}^{t-(x/c)} \phi_0(t^*)\, dt^*. \qquad (4\text{-}A\text{-}3)$$

Then (4-A-1) may be rewritten

$$\phi(x, t) = \frac{\phi_0[t - (x/c)]}{1 + k(x)e^{-\alpha}} = \frac{\phi_0}{1 + ke^{-\alpha}}. \qquad (4\text{-}A\text{-}4)$$

Now note that the following equations can be derived by differentiating (4-A-3):

$$\frac{\partial \alpha}{\partial t} = N\sigma c\phi_0 \qquad (4\text{-}A\text{-}5)$$

$$\frac{\partial \alpha}{\partial x} = - N\sigma\phi_0. \tag{4-A-6}$$

Thus it follows that

$$\frac{\partial \alpha}{\partial t} = -c\frac{\partial \alpha}{\partial x}$$

and therefore

$$\frac{\partial \alpha}{\partial t} + c\frac{\partial \alpha}{\partial x} = 0. \tag{4-A-7}$$

These equations are used in the derivatives obtained by differentiating (4-A-4). To obtain the partial derivatives, then we see that

$$\frac{\partial \phi}{\partial t} = \frac{(1+ke^{-\alpha})\,(\partial\phi_0/\partial t) + \phi_0 ke^{-\alpha}(\partial\alpha/\partial t)}{(1+ke^{-\alpha})^2}$$

and

$$\frac{1}{\phi}\frac{\partial \phi}{\partial t} = \frac{1}{\phi_0}\left(\frac{\partial\phi_0}{\partial t}\right) + \frac{ke^{-\alpha}}{1+ke^{-\alpha}}\left(\frac{\partial\alpha}{\partial t}\right). \tag{4-A-8}$$

Similarly

$$\frac{\partial \phi}{\partial x} = \frac{(1+ke^{-\alpha})\,(\partial\phi_0/\partial x) - \phi_0[-ke^{-\alpha}(\partial\alpha/\partial x) + e^{-\alpha}(\partial k/\partial x)]}{(1+ke^{-\alpha})^2}$$

$$\frac{c}{\phi}\left(\frac{\partial\phi}{\partial x}\right) = \frac{c}{\phi_0}\left(\frac{\partial\phi_0}{\partial x}\right) + \frac{ce^{-\alpha}}{1+ke^{-\alpha}}\left(k\frac{\partial\alpha}{\partial x} - \frac{\partial k}{\partial x}\right). \tag{4-A-9}$$

Adding (4-A-8) and (4-A-9),

$$\frac{1}{\phi}\left(\frac{\partial\phi}{\partial t} + c\frac{\partial\phi}{\partial x}\right) = \frac{1}{\phi_0}\left(\frac{\partial\phi_0}{\partial t} + c\frac{\partial\phi_0}{\partial x}\right) + \frac{ke^{-\alpha}}{1+ke^{-\alpha}}\left(\frac{\partial\alpha}{\partial t} + c\frac{\partial\alpha}{\partial x} - \frac{c}{k}\frac{\partial k}{\partial x}\right). \tag{4-A-10}$$

Noting (4-A-7), the expression for the population inversion can now be written as

$$\eta(x,\ t) = \frac{1}{N\sigma c}\left[\frac{1}{\phi_0}\left(\frac{\partial\phi_0}{\partial t} + c\frac{\partial\phi_0}{\partial x}\right) - \frac{ce^{-\alpha}}{1+ke^{-\alpha}}\left(\frac{\partial k}{\partial x}\right)\right]. \tag{4-A-11}$$

Now just outside the front face of the laser amplifier rod there is no population inversion and no source or sink for photons. The first term in

(4-A-11) is therefore evaluated just outside this surface and is seen to be zero from the continuity equation. Thus, because

$$\frac{1}{\phi_0}\left(\frac{\partial \phi_0}{\partial t} + c\,\frac{\partial \phi_0}{\partial x}\right) = 0, \qquad (4\text{-}A\text{-}12)$$

we write the population inversion as

$$\eta(x,\ t) = -\frac{e^{-\alpha}\!\left(\dfrac{\partial k}{\partial x}\right)}{N\sigma(1+ke^{-\alpha})} = -\frac{(\partial k/\partial x)}{N\sigma(k+e^{+\alpha})} \qquad (4\text{-}A\text{-}13)$$

and, substituting back into the original variables for α, we see that

$$\eta(x,\ t) = -\frac{1}{N\sigma}\,\frac{(\partial k/\partial x)}{k(x) + \exp\!\Big[N\sigma c \displaystyle\int_{-\infty}^{t-(x/c)} \phi_0(t^*)\,dt^*\Big]} \qquad (4\text{-}A\text{-}13)$$

This establishes the transformation that yields the inversion ratio described in (4-46) in terms of an integration term $k(x)$ and the initial boundary condition on the photon density.

REFERENCES

A. General

Arecchi, F. T., and R. Bonifacio, "Theory of Optical Maser Amplifiers," *IEEEJ. Quantum Electron.*, **1**, 169–178 (July 1965).

Avizoniz, P. V., and R. L. Grotbeck, "Experimental and Theoretical Ruby Laser Amplifier Analysis," *J. Appl. Phys.*, **37**, 687–693 (February 1966).

Bellman, R., G. Birnbaum, and W. G. Wagner, "Transmission of Monochromatic Radiation in a Two-Level Material," *J. Appl. Phys.*, **34**, 780–782 (April 1963).

Davis, J. I. and W. R. Sooy, "The Effects of Saturation and Regeneration in Ruby Laser Amplifiers," *Appl. Opt.*, **3**, 715–718 (June 1964).

Frantz L. M., and J. S. Nodvik, "Theory of Pulse Propagation in a Laser Amplifier," *J. Appl. Phys.*, **34**, 2346–2349 (August 1963).

Geusic, J. E., and H. E. D. Scovil, "A Unidirectional Traveling Wave Optical Maser," *Bell System Tech. J.*, **41**, 1371–1396 (July 1962).

Kogelnik, H., and A. Yariv, "Considerations of Noise and Schemes for Its Reduction in Laser Amplifiers," *Proc. IEEE*, **52**, 165–172 (February 1964).

Kumagai, N., and H. Yamamoto, "Generalized Solutions for Optical Maser Amplifiers," *IEEE Trans. Microwave Theory Tech.*, **13**, 445–451 (July 1965).

McWhorter, A. S., J. W. Meyer, and P. D. Strum, "Noise Temperature Measurement on a Solid State Maser," *Phys. Rev.*, **108**, 1642–1644 (December 15, 1957).

Miyamoto, K., "Propagation of Laser Light," *J. Opt. Soc. Am.*, **54**, 989–991 (August 1964).

Siegman, A. E., "Design Considerations for Laser Pulse Amplifiers," *J. Appl. Phys.*, **35**, 460 (February 1964).

Steele, E. L., and W. C. Davis, "Laser Amplifiers," *J. Appl. Phys.*, **36**, 348–351 (February 1965).

Strandberg, M. W. P., "Inherent Noise of Quantum Mechanical Amplifiers," *Phys. Rev.*, **106**, 617–620 (May 15, 1957).

Weber, J., "Maser Noise Considerations," *Phys. Rev.*, **108**, 537–541 (November 1957).

Wittke, J. P., "Molecular Amplification and Generation of Microwaves," *Proc. IRE*, **45**, 291–316 (March 1957).

5

Laser Q-Switching

A mode of laser operation extensively employed for the generation of high pulse power is known as Q-spoiling or Q-switching. It has been so designated because the optical Q of the resonant cavity is altered when this operation is used.

It will be recalled from electrical terminology, that a resonant circuit or a microwave cavity can be characterized by a Q or quality factor. This is defined as the ratio of the energy stored in the element or cavity to the energy loss per cycle. The higher the quality factor, the lower the losses; it will take many cycles for a high Q cavity to dissipate the energy stored in it.

This analogy is carried over to the optical cavity constituting the laser. Descriptively, the Q-switched mode of operation occurs as follows. While the laser rod is being pumped the optical cavity is made lossy so that a photon flux cannot be built up and stimulated emission cannot occur. In this interval the Q is kept low, for, although the energy stored in the laser rod is high, the cavity losses are also high. After there is considerable energy stored in the rod the cavity Q is increased, generally by changing the reflectivity of one of the end mirrors. This results in a sudden increase of photon flux and accompanying stimulated emission resulting in laser action. The energy stored in the excited atoms in the laser rod is suddenly converted to optical radiation because of stimulated emission at the laser wavelength, and a "giant pulse" is emitted by the laser. Generally a considerable fraction of the total stored energy is emitted in a short time span to yield this single large pulse.

The term Q-spoiling has been used to indicate that the cavity Q is low during the initial pumping phase. The more adequate description is Q-switching, for it indicates a change in cavity quality. This term is also in extensive use in the laser field today.

Several important elements are involved in the Q-switching process.

177

One requires the laser rod to be pumped fast enough to prevent the spontaneous emission of the excited atoms from appreciably depopulating the upper state. Thus a long-lived excited state is preferred for maximizing the possible effectiveness of pumping. A second important element is to use a Q-switch that switches fast compared with the buildup time of the photon density in the cavity. It will be seen later that the switching time should probably be less than 10 nsec for highest performance.

5-1 METHODS OF Q-SWITCHING

Several methods for Q-switching have been satisfactorily used for high-pulse power generation with lasers. These methods may be classified, generally, into three categories and are illustrated schematically in Figure 5-1: (a) mechanical Q-switches, (b) electrooptical Q-switches, and (c) photochemical or thin film switches. Examples of mechanical Q-switches include spinning prisms, rotating mirrors, and a rapidly revolving chopper wheel. The electro-optical switches employ the photo-optical effect in a Kerr cell, Pockels cell, or Faraday rotator in which the plane of polarization of the light beam is shifted and the transmission thereby varied. Finally, a very successful Q-switch, which uses a photochemical process, employs a saturable dye whose absorption changes with intensity; it

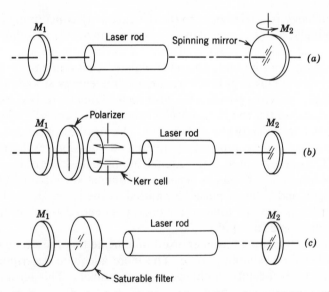

Figure 5-1 Various methods of Q-switching: (a) rotating mirror; (b) Kerr cell shutter; (c) saturable filter.

bleaches out during the buildup of a laser pulse, thereby rapidly altering the properties of the laser cavity. Evaporation of thin films by the laser light has also been effectively employed.

A light chopper acting as a mechanical *Q*-switch is schematically illustrated in Figure 5-2. Most of the time the chopper wheel shields one end mirror in the laser, thereby keeping the laser cavity *Q* below threshold. At an appropriate advanced time interval the pump lamps are flashed; the laser cavity *Q* is then increased as the opening in the chopper wheel comes around, just as the flash illumination is at an optimum level. The wheel has the effect of allowing the laser radiation to impinge on the end mirror in the cavity during a short interval, thereby giving rise to a laser burst of energy.

A similar mechanical process operates with the spinning prism of Figure 5-3. Here the Porro prism, operating as the end reflector, itself rotates; the firing of the flash lamps must be carefully timed with the prism

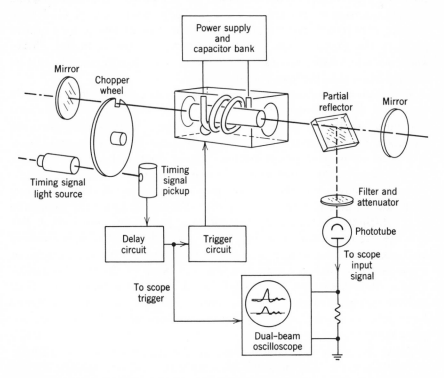

Figure 5-2 Schematic diagram of an experimental arrangement using a mechanical light chopper for a *Q*-switch. After Underwood, *EDN* (1966).

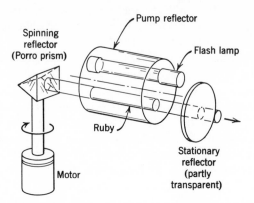

Figure 5-3 Diagram of a ruby laser using a spinning reflector prism as a Q-switch. After Underwood, *EDN* (1966).

position. This system has the advantage that the Porro prism can be aligned without pricision instrumentation and final adjustments can be made with relative ease to achieve minimum threshold. Losses due to long optical paths in the Porro prisms can be minimized by use of higher quality materials and smaller prisms; the minimum prism size, however, must be slightly larger than the laser rod diameter.

With high rotational prism speeds pulses considerably shorter than 50 nsec have been obtained. Peak power will increase with switching speed and pulse width will decrease until the point is approached when the switching time becomes equal to pulse rise time. Beyond this point there is a decrease in peak power output. Higher rotational speeds also raise the double pulse threshold because of over pumping.

Analysis shows that the dividing point between fast or slow switching is the development time for the pulse; that is, the time after switching over which the excited state population is essentially undisturbed. For average size resonators, pumping levels, and reflectivities this is typically 10^{-7} sec; that is, a switch is "fast" if the transition between resonator states is accomplished within this time and "slow" if the switching takes longer. It follows that a straightforward spinning reflector, which at 30,000 rpm will switch in approximately 1000 nsec, is a slow switch and Kerr cells, which are easily capable of switching within 10 nsec, are fast switches.

There are many desirable features of the spinning reflector—namely, its usefulness in the infrared, its simplicity, and its stability. It can approach the status of a fast switch by the use of a total internal reflection technique known as the Daly-Sims Q-switch. To understand its operation

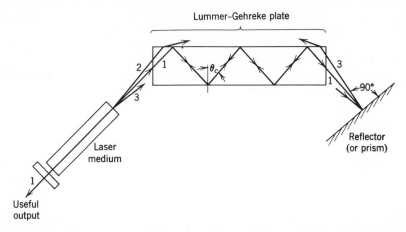

Figure 5-4 Schematic ray diagram showing the mode selection properties of the Lummer-Gehreke plate when used in conjunction with a laser Q-switch.

consider the effect of interposing between the spinning reflector and the laser rod a flat, polished, transparent plate similar to that used in the Lummer-Gehreke interferometer shown in Figure 5-4. Now consider the special case in which the reflector is precisely normal to the axial ray (labeled ray 1) and the plate arranged so that ray 1 makes an internal angle of incidence with the plate surfaces at the critical angle. For this discussion the refraction of the rays on entering the plate is neglected for the present. This in no way affects the explanation. Ray 1, the axial ray, is thus transmitted through the plate unattenuated. It strikes the mirror and returns on itself. Ray 2, on the other hand, strikes the plate surfaces at less than the critical angle and suffers an attenuation through the plate, the magnitude of which depends on the angular deviation from critical and the number of internal reflections. It turns out that for approximately 10 reflections and small angular deviations from the critical angle (10^{-3} rad) the one-way ray attentuation is of the order of 10. Note that ray 3, being beyond the critical angle on the first pass, returns after reflections at an angle less then critical and suffers the same net attentuation as ray 2; that is, the plate is symmetrical with respect to rays that deviate from the axis.

Consider now the development of the Lummer-Gehreke plate reflectivity when the opaque reflector is spinning (Figure 5-5). Note that for a reflector position before lineup ray 1 is returned through the Lummer-Gehreke plate at less than critical angle of reflection and suffers attenuation. Ray 3, of course, is incident at an even smaller angle, and ray 2 is attenuated on its first pass as previously shown. Thus the reflectivity for

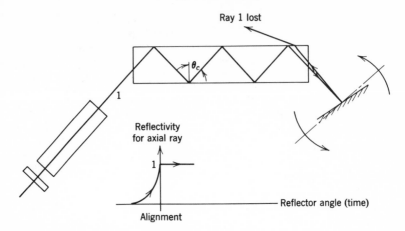

Figure 5-5   Diagram illustrating the development of reflectivity for an axial ray when the Lummer-Gehreke plate is combined with a rotating reflector.

any ray is low. The earliest time at which a ray may be returned from the plate-reflector combination is when the reflector comes to the aligned position and the *axial* ray "slides" up the multiple TIR curve. For a fixed rotational speed the time rate of change of axial ray reflectivity is limited only by practical plate sizes.

The *"switching"* interval — that is, the time interval between, say, 10% and 100% reflectivity — is determined by the number of internal reflections or the length of the plate and the reflector spin speed; the *"on"* interval is set by the angle between the axial ray and critical angle as well as the reflector speed. For 12 internal reflections on one pass analysis shows a 10–100% switching interval for a 0.2-mrad rotation of the spinning reflector. At a 30,000-rpm spinning speed this corresponds to a switch interval of 70 nsec and thus approaches a fast Q-switch.

The spinning reflector techniques have been used universally because of compactness, simplicity, reliability, and low cost. The use of the Porro prism reflector in this application has shown a significant advantage over plane or spherical mirrors because of the ease of alignment in a Fabry-Perot cavity.

Electro-optical shutters have been operated satisfactorily in the laboratory as fast Q-switches. The liquid Kerr cell, which uses nitrobenzene and associated polarizers, will give switching speeds in the 10-nsec range. A typical Q-switch using a Kerr cell with a laser is shown in Figure 5-6. In this operation the Kerr cell shifts the plane of polarization of the laser radiation when a voltage is applied and thereby reduces the losses in the laser system, increasing the Q of the laser and generating the

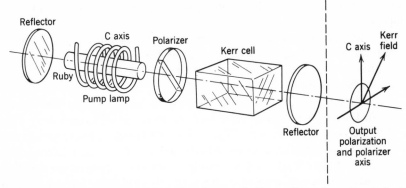

Figure 5-6 Schematic diagram illustrating the use of aKerr cell as a laser Q-switch. After Underwood, *EDN* (1966).

giant pulse. Similarly, the Faraday rotation can be employed to Q-switch, as illustrated in Figure 5-7. Here the polarization is controlled with a magnetic field, whereas in the Kerr cell the electric field is the governing factor.

The use of a saturable dye in the laser cavity has also led to effective Q-switching. In this switch, as shown in Figure 5-1, a thin film of dye or an optical absorption cell filled with appropriate liquid is placed in the laser cavity between the rod and one of the end mirrors. As the laser radiation builds up, the dye absorbs so heavily that the absorption centers are saturated and the material becomes transparent; the laser threshold then falls, and a Q-pulse of laser radiation is emitted. Materials such as cryptocyamine, using the liquid in an absorption cell, permit repeated shots to be made without having to replace a thin film. Uranium-doped glass also exhibits this saturable dye action with the ruby laser; consideration has

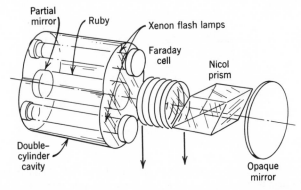

Figure 5-7 Laser using the Faraday effect for Q-switching. After Underwood, *EDN* (1966).

been given to the Q-switch action in the laser rod itself by doping with uranyl ions.

An excellent scheme for sharpening Q-switched pulses is to combine the saturable dye element with the rotating Porro prism for Q-switching. This proves to be a simple yet extremely effective combination for obtaining fast Q-pulses.

As mentioned, exploding film has been used for Q-spoiling, and narrow pulses in the order of 20–40 nsec have been obtained from a ruby laser by the method illustrated in Figure 5-8. Although the exploding film method of Q-modulation does not lend itself to applications requiring high pulse rates, it does lend itself to simple single-shot applications (such as range finders) in which no moving parts or external fields are used and no unusual alignment problems are presented.

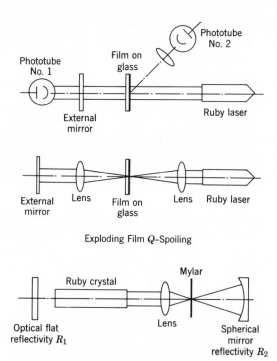

Exploding Film Q-Spoiling

Mylar Film Q-Switching

Figure 5-8 Q-Switching using exploding or vaporized thin films. The film keeps the laser cavity Q lower than threshold until a small hole is burned in the thin film, at which time the second external mirror causes regeneration and laser action to occur. After Underwood, *EDN* (1966).

The film Q-spoiler consists of a thin film of transparent material on a flat plate such as glass. The film has an absorption coefficient in the vicinity of the laser transition frequency. The oscillations begin at low Q with some radiation passing through the film. This technique depends on the film vaporizing in a time that is short with respect to the stimulated radiation lifetime of the laser. The presence of the film in this system raises the threshold more than 20% and thus holds off laser action. The absorbing film shows a clear hole after each shot; a small residue remains. The peak power gains with this system are reported to compare favorably with other systems, but variations in performance are caused by the thin film structure.

Other Q-switching experiments which use an aluminized coating on Mylar film with a spherical surface for focusing action, have also performed satisfactorily.

The shape of the giant pulse from the laser is determined partly by the time variation of the Q-switch. This allows for some pulse shaping of power output by tailoring the switching action.

5-2   FORMULATION OF EQUATIONS

The analysis of the development of the giant pulse by Q-switching proceeds from the basic description of laser action. The two-level approximation to the actual three-level system forms the model for the analytical treatment. The three-level laser system is shown in Figure 5-9.

The approximation is made that the nonradiative transition rate (S_{32}) is much greater than any other rates in the system. Therefore the transfer of electrons to level 2 is not governed by the filling of level 3 but by the pump rate, w_{13}. Furthermore, the transition to level 2 is fast so that a negligible loss of electron population in level 3 occurs because of spontaneous

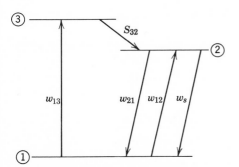

Figure 5-9 Three-level laser system.

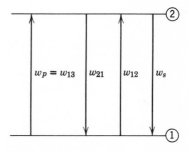

Figure 5-10 Two-level approximation of atomic system.

radiation. Thus the two-level system of Figure 5-10 can be used; we define the pump rate to level 2 by way of level 3 as w_p:

$$w_p = w_{13}.$$

The atomic system is assumed to be homogeneously broadened. This then allows the assumption to be made that the induced direct absorption transition rate from level 1 to level 2 (w_{12}) is equal to the induced emission transition rate (w_{21}) for a given atom:

$$w_{12} = w_{21}$$

The probability for induced transitions per photon per particle between level 2 and level 1 is $w_i/N = w_{12} = w_{21}$. The spontaneous decay rate of radiation from level 2 is w_s. The number of photons per unit volume at the laser frequency traveling along the x-axis is given by Φ. Only those photons traveling along the x axis of the laser are of interest here.

If n_1 and n_2 are defined as the electron population density in level 1 and level 2 and N is the total density of active atoms in the laser, the rate equation (5-1) can be written

$$\frac{dn_1}{dt} = -n_1(w_p + w_i\frac{\Phi}{N}) + n_2(w_s + w_i\frac{\Phi}{N}). \qquad (5\text{-}1)$$

Note also that

$$n_1 + n_2 = N. \qquad (5\text{-}2)$$

Furthermore, define the electron population excess (n) as given in (5-3):

$$n_2 - n_1 = n. \qquad (5\text{-}3)$$

This electron population excess is an important quantity, for only when it is positive will laser action be possible. This results from the fact that an excess of radiating transitions over absorbing transitions occurs between level 2 and level 1 only when the excess electron population is positive.

Using (5-2) for the elimination of n_2 in (5-1), we obtain

$$\frac{dn_1}{dt} = -n_1(w_s + w_p + 2w_i\frac{\Phi}{N}) + N(w_s + w_i\frac{\Phi}{N}). \qquad (5\text{-}4)$$

A quantity that is more meaningful to work with is the inversion ratio (η), which is defined as

$$\eta = \frac{n_2 - n_1}{n_2 + n_1} = \frac{N - 2n_1}{N}. \tag{5-5}$$

Thus

$$n_1 = \frac{N}{2}(1 - \eta). \tag{5-6}$$

Noting from (5-2) that

$$\frac{dn_1}{dt} = -\frac{dn_2}{dt} \tag{5-7}$$

and using (5-3), we observed that the time rate of change of the electron inversion ratio is

$$\frac{dn}{dt} = -2\frac{dn_1}{dt}.$$

This leads to the time rate of change of the inversion ratio ($d\eta/dt$):

$$\frac{d\eta}{dt} = -\frac{1}{N}\frac{dn}{dt} = -\frac{2}{N}\frac{dn_1}{dt}. \tag{5-8}$$

The rate equation for the inversion ratio can now be written by using (5-6) and (5-4):

$$\frac{d\eta}{dt} = (1 - \eta)\left(w_s + w_p + 2w_i\frac{\Phi}{N}\right) - 2\left(w_s + w_i\frac{\Phi}{N}\right). \tag{5-9}$$

This can also be written in the form

$$\frac{d\eta}{dt} = w_p(1 - \eta) - w_s(1 + \eta) - 2\eta w_i\frac{\Phi}{N}. \tag{5-10}$$

We now introduce a normalized variable (ϕ) for the photon density by defining it thus:

$$\phi = \frac{2\Phi}{N}. \tag{5-11}$$

This rate equation can finally be expressed as

$$\frac{d\eta}{dt} = w_p(1-\eta) - w_s(1+\eta) - \eta\phi w_i. \qquad (5\text{-}12)$$

It should be observed that the inversion ratio is a dimensionless measure of the excess population in the laser structure and is restricted to values between -1 and $+1$. When the electron population is totally in the ground state, before pumping, $\eta = -1$; when the system is totally inverted, which is virtually impossible to achieve in a practical sense, $\eta = +1$.

The total energy available (E_{max}) for extraction in a laser beam is given in terms of Planck's constant and laser radiation frequency (ν_{21}) by

$$E_{max} = \eta N h \nu_{21}. \qquad (5\text{-}13)$$

This is only one half the total energy stored, for one half the energy is required to raise the population of the upper state from $\eta = -1$ to $\eta = 0$; that is, to make $n_1 = n_2$. In practice, it is impossible to extract all of this energy, but we should like to extract the maximum for most effective laser performance.

The rate equation that describes the population inversion ratio contains, in addition to the atomic transition rates, another variable, the normalized photon density ϕ. A rate equation must now be formulated for this in order to describe the system completely. Thus we may write

$$\frac{d\Phi}{dt} = -n_1 w_i \frac{\Phi}{N} + n_2 \left(w_i \frac{\Phi}{N} + w_s' \right) - [\gamma_s + \gamma_0(t)]\Phi, \qquad (5\text{-}14)$$

where γ_s is the photon loss rate from incidental losses such as diffraction, scattering, and absorption in the end mirrors. The loss rate term $\gamma_0(t)$ arises from the radiation loss resulting from energy being transmitted through the output reflector of the laser. This will vary with time during Q-switching. The term given by $w_s'n_2$ represents that amount of radiation added to the laser beam because of spontaneous emission into a small cone or solid angle along the laser axis. It should be noted that this radiation will be only a small fraction of the total radiation emitted by the spontaneous process; that is, $w_s' \ll w_s$. In any case, the spontaneous emission loss must be kept low in order to achieve laser action at all.

The first term on the right of (5-14) $(n_1 w_i \Phi/N)$ represents a loss to the beam, namely, the radiation absorbed by the electrons in the ground state 1 and excited to the upper state 2 by a direct induced transition. Similarly, the second term $(n_2 w_i \Phi/N)$ represents the contribution to the photon beam from the induced emission arising from the transition between the excited state 2 and the ground state 1. Again, introducing the normalized variables,

$$\eta = \frac{n_2 - n_1}{N}; \quad \phi = \frac{2\Phi}{N},$$ (5-15)

the rate equation for the photon density (5-14) may be rewritten

$$\frac{d\phi}{dt} = -\phi[\gamma_s + \gamma_o(t)] + w_s'(1+\eta) + w_i\phi\eta.$$ (5-16)

The two equations that describe the factors entering into the laser process are now available as (5-12) and (5-16). The problem at hand is to solve them for the Q-switch case. Unfortunately, these two equations are nonlinear, for the last term in each contains a product ($w_i\phi\eta$) of both the photon density and the electron inversion ratio. Also unknown is the exact form of the variable output term $\gamma_o(t)$, which, depending on the particular method used for Q-switching, will vary.

A simplified laser structure is now assumed for the purpose of illustrating the Q-switch action and evaluating the constants involved. The model is represented in Figure 5-11, where the reflector A forms both the Q-switch element and the output port. It is also assumed that the fixed mirror has a high unchanging reflectivity and that the change of optical cavity Q occurs by the change of optical transmission of the output mirror. By close observation of (5-16) we can ascertain the train of events that results in the giant pulse. Initially the photon density is low while the laser is being pumped, and the output loss rate is $\gamma_o(t) = W_1$; this raises the inversion ratio, and the photon density slowly starts

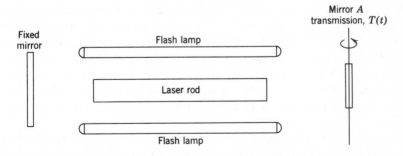

Figure 5-11   Model of laser for Q-switch calculation.

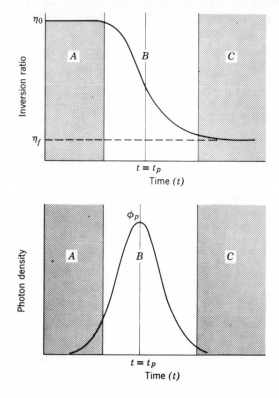

Figure 5-12   Schematic representation of inversion ratio and photon density during Q-switching.

to increase primarily because of the middle term on the right of (5-16), $w'_s(1+\eta)$. Q-Switching now occurs, and the output loss rate is suddenly reduced to $\gamma_0(t) = W_2$; as the inversion ratio η decreases, the photon density increases. This brings the other terms in the equation into play, and the photon density builds up tremendously as the inversion ratio continues to decrease. As the inversion decreases, or even becomes negative, the rate of change of photon density ($d\phi/dt$) becomes negative and is governed by the output loss term $\gamma_0(t) = W_2$, for the inversion ratio is now low. The negative rate of photon density change signifies a depletion of photons in the laser cavity, which manifests itself as the giant pulse.

Generally speaking, we can sketch out the approximate behavior with time of the inversion ratio and the photon density. Figure 5-12 illustrates what we might expect on the basis of the preceding discussion.

5-3 ESTIMATION OF PARAMETERS

In order to establish meaningful solutions to the photon and electron population rate equations, we must first evaluate the values and relative sizes of the explicit parameters. This has a strong bearing on the approximations permitted in the solutions to the equations, which are recapitulated in Table 5-1 along with the values established in the subsequent

TABLE 5-1 PARAMETERS FOR TYPICAL RUBY LASER

Parameter	Description	Value
N	Doping density in laser rod (chromium ions)	1.6×10^{19} atoms/cm^3
w_i	Probability rate for induced or stimulated emission	3.5×10^9 /sec
w_s	Probability rate for spontaneous emission from excited laser level	230/sec
w_s'	Probability rate for spontaneous emission into a small solid angle along the laser axis	20×10^{-6}/sec
γ_0	Output loss rate from laser	Assumed related to reflectivity (see Table 5-2)
γ_s	Incidental loss rate from absorption loss in mirrors, scattering by inhomogeneities or impurities, and diffraction losses	6×10^8/sec
w_p	Pump rate to excited level via pump band	Assumed related to η_0 (see Table 5-3)
η_0	Initial inversion ratio at beginning of Q-switch	Assumed value, $0 < \eta_0 < +1$
ϕ	Initial normalized photon density at time of Q-switch	$\sim 10^{-15}$, generally assume $\simeq 0$
τ_c	Cavity ringing time in low loss mode ($\sim 1/\gamma_s$)	1.7×10^{-9} sec
τ_s	Lifetime of excited laser level ($\sim 1/w_s$)	4.3×10^{-3} sec

discussion. Of course, it must be recognized that the particular values listed here are dependent on the doping density in the laser rod and, to a certain extent, the quality and optical properties of the host medium. The quantities calculated here are based on a ruby (Al$_2$O$_3$) doped with 0.05% by weight of Cr$_2$O$_3$. The unknowns in the rate equations are the normalized photon density (ϕ) and the inversion ratio (η), which are to be determined as a function of time when the optical Q of the laser cavity is changed in a manner defined by the loss term $\gamma_0(t)$.

Measurements have been made on the absorption coefficients of laser materials. The *absorption coefficient* (α) is defined in terms of the change in intensity of a beam of radiation by the following expression:

$$\frac{dI}{I} = -\alpha \, dx, \tag{5-17}$$

where the intensity (I) decreases by an amount dI in penetrating a distance dx in the material. This same decrease in intensity can be expressed in terms of a *loss rate coefficient* (γ) by the relation

$$\frac{dI}{I} = -\gamma \, dt \tag{5-18}$$

By relating (5-17) and (5-18), the loss rate coefficient can be expressed in terms of the readily measured absorption constant.

$$\frac{dI}{I} = -\gamma dt = -\alpha \, dx, \tag{5-19}$$

leading to the following relationship, where c is the speed of light and μ is the index of refraction in the material:

$$\gamma = \frac{\alpha c}{\mu}. \tag{5-20}$$

The ratio c/μ is simply the speed of light in the material under examination.

For a Lorentzian line shape it has been shown[1] that the stimulated emission probability rate (w_i) is related to the absorption constant at the center of the line (α_p) by the preceding expression, modified by a factor of 2. Thus, noting that the measured value[2] of $\alpha_p = 0.4 \, cm^{-1}$ and $\mu = 1.76$, we obtain

$$w_i = \frac{c\alpha_p}{2\mu}$$

$$= 3.5 \times 10^9/sec. \tag{5-21}$$

[1] A. A. Vuylsteke, "Theory of Laser Regeneration Switching," *J. Appl. Phys.* **34**, 1615 (June 1963).

[2] T. Maiman et al., "Stimulated Optical Emission in Fluorescent Solids. **11**. Spectroscopy and Stimulated Emission in Ruby." *Phys. Rev.*, **123**, 1151 (August 1961).

The spontaneous emission rate (w_s) is related inversely to the life-time (τ_s) of the excited laser level. This has been measured[3] as approximately $\tau_s = 4.3 \times 10^{-3}$ sec. Thus

$$w_s = 1/\tau_s$$
$$= 230/\text{sec.} \qquad (5\text{-}22)$$

The probability of spontaneous emission into the small solid angle near the laser axis (w'_s) can be estimated from the value for w_s and the observed angular beam divergence of the ruby laser. Now, define this small effective solid angle $(\Delta\Omega)$ in which the propagation vector must lie in order to permit an appreciable number of reflections to occur before the radiation is lost to the system. Then w'_s is that portion of the total rate included in $\Delta\Omega$ out of a total solid angle of 4π steradians. Thus, for an angular beam divergence of 10^{-6} steradian, we obtain

$$w'_s = w_s \frac{\Delta\Omega}{4\pi}$$
$$= 20 \times 10^{-6}/\text{sec.} \qquad (5\text{-}23)$$

The size of the incidental loss rate factor (γ_s) can be evaluated in terms of an equivalent linear loss coefficient (α_s) defined in a manner similar to that of an absorption coefficient. Thus the linear loss coefficient (α_s) may be expressed as

$$\alpha_s = \frac{I}{\Delta x} \ln\left(\frac{I}{I_0}\right) \qquad (5\text{-}24)$$

where I_0 is the incident radiation intensity and I is the radiation intensity after traversing a thickness of material Δx. Furthermore, if we express the ratio I/I_0 in terms of the fractional loss $f = (I - I_0)/I_0$, then, noting that the laser rod length is L_a and, therefore, for a double pass, $\Delta x = 2L_a$, we may rewrite the equation as

$$\alpha_s = \frac{1}{2L_a} \ln(1-f). \qquad (5\text{-}25)$$

One measure of this incidental loss fraction has been reported[4] for a

[3]F. Varsanyi, E. L. Wood, and A. L. Schawlow, "Self-Absorption and Trapping of Sharp Line Resonance Radiation in Ruby," *Phys. Rev. Letters*, **3**, 544 (December 15, 1949).

[4]D. F. Nelson and J. P. Remeika, "Laser Action in a Flux Grown Ruby," *J. Appl. Phys.* **35**, 522 (March 1964).

ruby rod 5 cm long. This correlates with another evaluation[5] related to this factor and indicates that approximately 35% loss occurs in a double pass. This value seems high. This result, however, was for ruby rods prepared in an early state of the art and should be improved at this date. For the present purposes we take the figure of 35% reported in the literature for this evaluation. Along with the above dimensions, we see that

$$\alpha_s = \frac{1}{2L_a} \ln (1-f)$$

$$= 0.031/\text{cm}. \tag{5-26}$$

It then follows, when this is converted to the loss rate coefficient by the relation formerly derived in (5-20), that we obtain

$$\gamma_s = \frac{\alpha_s c}{\mu}$$

$$= 6 \times 10^8/\text{sec}. \tag{5-27}$$

Similarly, the output loss term can be related to the reflectivity of the end mirrors of the laser cavity. Let T represent the fractional transmission of the end mirrors and R the reflectivity. Then for low internal absorption loss mirrors $T = 1 - R$. For one mirror $T_1 = 1 - R_1$, and for the second mirror let $T_2 = 1 - R_2$. The fractional loss per double pass from the laser cavity due to transmission through the end mirrors is

$$f = T_1 + T_2(1 - T_1) = 1 - R_1 R_2$$

$$1 - f = R_1 R_2. \tag{5-28}$$

Therefore the loss rate factor is given for the case in which the mirrors are near the ends of the laser rod so that the cavity length is approximately equal to the rod length:

$$\gamma_0 = -\frac{c}{2\mu L_a} \ln (R_1 R_2). \tag{5-29}$$

Some values are shown in Table 5-2 for a ruby rod 5 cm long.

For a low Q-mode of operation the reflectivity of the output end for a glass/air interface at normal incidence is of the order of 8%. The high

[5]J. I. Masters, "Estimation of Ruby Laser Oscillation Loss," *Nature*, **199**, 442 (August 3, 1963).

TABLE 5-2 OUTPUT LOSS RATE
VERSUS REFLECTIVITY

Reflectivity (R_1)*	Loss Rate (γ_0)† (sec^{-1})
0.10	3.9×10^9
0.25	2.4×10^9
0.40	1.8×10^9
0.50	1.2×10^9
0.60	8.9×10^8
0.70	6.3×10^8
0.80	4.1×10^8
0.90	2.0×10^8
0.95	1.05×10^8
0.99	3.4×10^7

*Assumes $R_2 = 99\%$.
†Calculated from $\gamma_0 = -(c/2L\mu) \ln (R_1 R_2)$ for
$L = 5$ cm, $\mu = 1.76$.

reflectivity mirror, which is probably of a dielectric composition, can be of the order of 98%. Assume that Q-switching occurs at $t = 0$. Thus for the low Q state

$$\gamma_0(t < 0) = 4.3 \times 10^9/\text{sec} \qquad \text{(low } Q \text{ state).} \qquad (5\text{-}30)$$

For the high Q state the reflectivity would normally be of the order of 98% maximum and would result in maximum internal pulse buildup:

$$\gamma_0(t > 0) = 3.4 \times 10^7/\text{sec} \qquad \text{(high } Q \text{ state).} \qquad (5\text{-}31)$$

TABLE 5-3 PUMP RATE REQUIRED TO ACHIEVE PREDETERMINED INITIAL INVERSION RATIO

Inversion Ratio (η_0)	Pump Rate (w_p)* (sec^{-1})
1.0	∞
0.8	2070
0.6	920
0.4	540
0.2	345
0.1	282

*Calculated from $w_p = w_s[(1+\eta_0)/(1-\eta_0)]$, $w_s = 230/\text{sec}$.

For other laser configurations, however, a lower reflectivity may be required. For instance, in a laser configuration in which the output mirror is kept at $R_2 = 50\%$ while the Q-switching reflector, such as a spinning prism, varies in reflectivity from $R_1 = 8\%$ to $R_1 = 98\%$, the loss rate factors will be constant as fixed by the output reflectivity, whereas the optical Q of the cavity will vary between the high and low values determined by the above reflectivities.

The pumping rate necessary to achieve a given population inversion in a low Q cavity prior to switching can be calculated from (5–12). Let $d\eta/dt = 0$ and note that $\phi \cong 0$; the results are given in Table 5-3.

5-4 SOLUTION FOR STEP FUNCTION Q-SWITCH

In this case the output loss factor is assumed to have a sharp change with time, essentially a step function, as illustrated in Figure 5-13. Table 5-4 describes the significance of these changes and relates them to the Q-switch parameter pertinent to the laser action.

TABLE 5-4   STEP FUNCTION Q-SWITCH
DESCRIPTION

Period	Loss Rate	Description
$t < 0$	$W_1 = \gamma_0(t < 0)$	High loss Low cavity Q Laser is pumped Upper state is populated
$t > 0$	$W_2 = \gamma_0(t > 0)$	Low loss High cavity Q Giant pulse develops Upper state is depleted

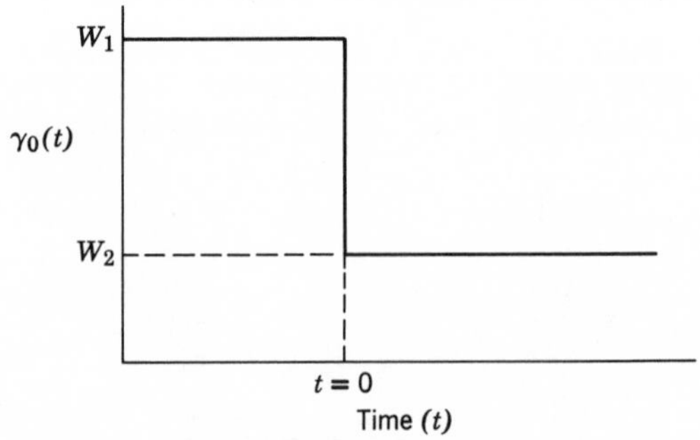

Figure 5-13   Time variation of output loss factor for step function Q-switch.

The rate equations to be solved are restated here:

$$\frac{d\eta}{dt} = w_p(1-\eta) - w_s(1+\eta) - w_i\phi\eta \tag{5-12}$$

$$\frac{d\phi}{dt} = -\phi[\gamma_s + \gamma_0(t)] + w_s'(1+\eta) + w_i\phi\eta. \tag{5-16}$$

Subject to the Q-switch condition that the output loss rate factor changes abruptly with time,

$$\gamma_0(t < 0) = W_1 \quad \text{(low } Q \text{ condition)}$$

$$\gamma_0(t > 0) = W_2 \quad \text{(high } Q \text{ condition)} \tag{5-32}$$

In this discussion we are interested only in the course of events for $t > 0$, for the conditions before that time will produce the initial condition $\eta = \eta_0$; that is, the pumping history will fix the inversion ratio at the moment of Q-switching $(t = 0)$. Furthermore, it is assumed that events happen fast enough that the terms involving the pumping rate w_p and the spontaneous loss rate, w_s will not contribute significantly to the rate equation for the inversion ratio during the development phase of the giant pulse formation.

In the equation for the photon density the term involving w_s' will be significant at the beginning but will rapidly be rendered insignificant by the other terms. It will contribute to a "delay time" in the pulse after the pulse starts building up.

Therefore the equations are expressed in the following approximate form for $t > 0$:

$$\frac{d\eta}{dt} = -w_i\phi\eta \tag{5-33}$$

$$\frac{d\phi}{dt} = -\phi(\gamma_s + W_2) + w_i\phi\eta. \tag{5-34}$$

By examination of (5-34) we can determine the laser threshold value of the inversion ratio (η_t) from $d\phi/dt = 0$. It is at just this point in the photon density buildup at which the leakage or absorption loss of photons equals the gain of photons from stimulated emission. Thus

$$\frac{d\phi}{dt} = 0 = -\phi(\gamma_s + W_2) + w_i\phi\eta_t \tag{5-35}$$

$$\eta_t = \frac{\gamma_s + W_2}{w_i} = \frac{1}{w_i \tau_c}. \tag{5-36}$$

This threshold value of the inversion ratio is simply the fraction composed of the total loss rate of photons divided by the stimulated emission rate term. Note further that because η can never exceed unity the loss rate must always be less than the stimulated rate in order for a threshold to exist. Furthermore, it should be noted that a lifetime (τ_c) of a photon in the laser cavity, or the ringing time of the optical cavity, can be defined as

$$\frac{1}{\tau_c} = \gamma_s + W_2 \tag{5-37}$$

and follows directly from (5-36).

We may then write the rate equation for the photon density in a slightly altered form as

$$\frac{d\phi}{dt} = \left(\frac{\eta}{\eta_t} - 1\right)\frac{\phi}{\tau_c}. \tag{5-36a}$$

Similarly, a simplified expression in terms of optical cavity variables can be written for the inversion ratio rate equation:

$$\frac{d\eta}{dt} = -\left(\frac{1}{\eta_t \tau_c}\right)\phi\eta. \tag{5-36b}$$

These simpler forms are used later for solving the time variation of the giant pulse.

Eliminating time (t) from these equations, we may express them as follows:

$$\begin{aligned}
\frac{d\phi}{d\eta} &= -\left[\frac{w_i\eta - (\gamma_s + W_2)}{w_i\eta}\right] \\
&= -\left[1 - \left(\frac{\gamma_s + W_2}{w_i}\right)\frac{1}{\eta}\right] \\
&= -\left[1 - \frac{\eta_t}{\eta}\right].
\end{aligned} \tag{5-38}$$

A side observation at this point notes that the maximum photon density occurs when the inversion rate has fallen to the threshold value ($\eta = \eta_t$), for at this point $d\phi/d\eta = 0$.

Solving (5-38) and noting the definition of the initial photon density (ϕ_i) as well as initial inversion ratio (η_0), we obtain

$$\phi - \phi_i = \eta_t \ln \left(\frac{\eta}{\eta_0}\right) - (\eta - \eta_0). \tag{5-39}$$

If we now note that the photon density at both the beginning (ϕ_i) and end (ϕ_f) of the giant pulse is very small, we can obtain the final value of the inversion ratio (η_f) from (5-39) with the appropriate substitution:

$$\phi_i \simeq 0$$

$$\phi_f \simeq 0$$

$$\eta_t \ln \left(\frac{\eta_f}{\eta_0}\right) = (\eta_f - \eta_0).$$

Restating this in terms of η_f/η_0, we obtain

$$\left(\frac{\eta_f}{\eta_0} - 1\right) = \left(\frac{\eta_t}{\eta_0}\right) \ln \left(\frac{\eta_f}{\eta_0}\right). \tag{5-40}$$

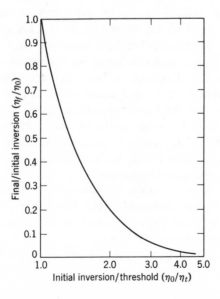

Figure 5-14 Relationship showing fraction of inversion remaining after laser giant pulse [plot of (5-40)].

Figure 5-14 shows the relationship between the final value of the inversion in terms of the initial inversion value and threshold. This ratio (η_f/η_0) is important, for it will determine the amount of energy stored but unutilized in the giant pulse.

The total energy per unit volume stored in the laser material that might be extracted as useful optical energy in the laser beam is defined as E_0.

$$E_0 = \tfrac{1}{2}h\nu\eta_0 N.$$

The final available energy per unit volume remaining in the material after emission of the giant pulse is E_f, where

$$E_f = \tfrac{1}{2}h\nu\eta_f N.$$

The energy utilization factor then may be defined as

$$\epsilon_u = \frac{E_0 - E_f}{E_0} = \frac{\eta_0 - \eta_f}{\eta_0} = 1 - \frac{\eta_f}{\eta_0}. \tag{5-41}$$

Note that this is not the same as the efficiency of the process. The total energy stored in the laser material is that required to change the inversion ratio from $\eta = -1$ to $\eta = \eta_0$. That amount of energy required to raise the inversion from $\eta = -1$ to $\eta = 0$, however, is not available to the laser pulse, for only that in excess of $\eta = 0$ can be extracted. The remainder manifests itself as an absorption loss. This is why the factor $\tfrac{1}{2}$ appears in these equations. Thus we speak of the energy utilization factor in the laser, rather than efficiency, on comparing the performance of various laser modes of operation. Note that the efficiency can never exceed 50% and that such a case could occur only with 100% initial inversion, $\eta_0 = +1$, if a final inversion were zero, $\eta_f = 0$. The energy utilization factor could be made unity by reducing the final inversion ratio to zero, $\eta_f = 0$, for any value of the initial inversion η_0. For a finite value of the final inversion factor η_f the utilization factor can be maximized by both reducing η_f and increasing η_0.

Figure 5-15 shows the relationship between this factor and the inversion ratio related to the threshold value. Note that for $\eta_0/\eta_t > 2.5$, ϵ_u exceeds 90%, that is, more than 90% of the energy available is extracted when this level of inversion is reached.

The term $\eta_f - \eta_0$ can be evaluated by combining (5-33) and (5-34) and integrating. Thus

$$\frac{d\phi}{dt} = -\phi(\gamma_s + W_2) - \frac{d\eta}{dt}$$

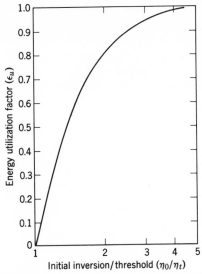

Figure 5-15 Energy utilization factor as it relates to population inversion.

$$\frac{d}{dt}(\eta + \phi) = -(\gamma_s + W_2)\,\phi = -\frac{\phi}{\tau_c}, \qquad (5\text{-}42)$$

where (τ_c) is the photon lifetime in the cavity (5-37).

$$(\eta_f - \eta_0) + (\phi_f - \phi_i) = -\frac{1}{\tau_c}\int_0^\infty \phi\, dt.$$

Now, because $\phi_f \simeq 0$ and $\phi_i \simeq 0$, it can be seen that the change of inversion just equals the time integral of the photon loss rate.

$$(\eta_0 - \eta_f) = \int_0^\infty \left(\frac{\phi}{\tau_c}\right) dt. \qquad (5\text{-}43)$$

In simpler terms the energy added to the photon gas in the cavity comes as a result of stimulated transitions accompanied by the decrease in electron inversion. Thus the actual energy emitted in the pulse is given by the following equation (5-44), in which the substitution is made for the actual photon density rather than the normalized photon variable, from

(5-11), $\phi = 2\Phi/N$, and we factor in the energy per photon ($h\nu$) and the total cavity volume (V):

$$E_{\text{out}} = h\nu \int_0^\infty \left(\frac{\Phi}{\tau_c}\right) dt. \tag{5-44}$$

Note that

$$\int_0^\infty \left(\frac{\Phi}{\tau_c}\right) dt = \left(\frac{N}{2}\right) \int_0^\infty \left(\frac{\phi}{\tau_c}\right) dt,$$

which then leads to

$$E_{\text{out}} = \tfrac{1}{2} N h\nu (\eta_0 - \eta_f) V$$

$$= \tfrac{1}{2} N \eta_0 h\nu \epsilon_u V. \tag{5-45}$$

Consider now the two cases of high and low inversion.

Case I: High Inversion

For high inversion we evaluate the case of $\eta_0/\eta_f \gg 1$ and it is seen that the utilization factor approaches unity:

$$\epsilon_u = \frac{\eta_0 - \eta_f}{\eta_0} = 1 - \frac{\eta_f}{\eta_0} \simeq 1.$$

Therefore

$$E_{\text{out}} = \tfrac{1}{2} N \eta_0 h\nu V. \tag{5-46}$$

It can be seen that for values in which the laser is pumped hard enough to yield $\eta_0/\eta_t > 2.5$, $\eta_f/\eta_0 < 10\%$ and η_f can be neglected. The threshold (η_t) should then be kept low for high utilization.

Case II: Low Inversion

In this instance the inversion ratio does not appreciable exceed unity; that is, $\eta_0 \simeq \eta_f$. The energy utilization factor (ϵ_u) is small and can be evaluated in this instance by expanding (5-40) for $\eta_0/\eta_f \simeq 1$. Thus

$$\ln\left(\frac{\eta_f}{\eta_0}\right) \simeq \left(\frac{\eta_f}{\eta_0} - 1\right) - \frac{1}{2}\left(\frac{\eta_f}{\eta_0} - 1\right)^2. \tag{5-47}$$

To express the energy utilization factor in terms of the threshold inversion value we combine (5-47) with (5-40), which relates the threshold to the final value of inversion. Therefore

$$\frac{\eta_f}{\eta_0} = \left(3 - 2\frac{\eta_0}{\eta_t}\right)$$

or

$$\epsilon_u \simeq 1 - \frac{\eta_f}{\eta_0} = 2\left(\frac{\eta_0}{\eta_t} - 1\right). \tag{5-48}$$

The energy output in this case is then

$$E_{\text{out}} = N\eta_0 h\nu\left(\frac{\eta_0}{\eta_t} - 1\right)V$$

$$= Nh\nu\left(\frac{\eta_0}{\eta_t}\right)(\eta_0 - \eta_t)V. \tag{5-49}$$

This expression indicates that the energy in the output pulse will be considerably smaller than in the former case and will depend heavily on the threshold. The pumping is not strong enough to raise the population inversion ratio appreciably over the threshold; that is, a corollary to this case is also that $\eta_0/\eta_t \simeq 1$.

Recalling, now, that the peak photon density (ϕ_p) occurs when $\eta = \eta_t$ and also noting that $\phi_i \simeq 0$, we can calculate the peak power in the giant pulse. Thus, from (5-39) for the normalized photon density, we write

$$\phi_p = (\eta_0 - \eta_t) - \eta_t \ln\left(\frac{\eta_0}{\eta_t}\right). \tag{5-50}$$

The peak photon density is shown as a function of initial inversion in Figure 5-16.

This result, when the approximation is applied to the low inversion case $\eta_0/\eta_t \simeq 1$, yields the simplified expression

$$\phi_p = \frac{(\eta_0 - \eta_t)^2}{2\eta_t}. \tag{5-51}$$

This is not valid in many cases of high pumping power, in which the

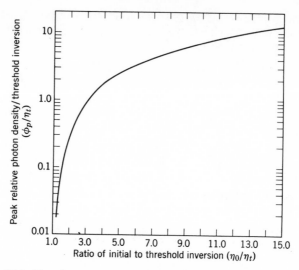

Figure 5-16   Plot of peak photon density versus initial electron inversion ratio.

objective is to obtain large power outputs by using high population inversion. The output power is proportional to $W_2\phi$ or, more exactly,

$$P = h\nu\left(\frac{NV}{2}\right)\phi W_2;$$

the peak power output can be written

$$P_p = h\nu\left(\frac{NV}{2}\right)\phi_p W_2$$

$$= h\nu\left(\frac{\eta_0 NV}{2}\right)\left[\left(1 - \frac{\eta_t}{\eta_0}\right) - \frac{\eta_t}{\eta_0}\ln\left(\frac{\eta_0}{\eta_t}\right)\right]W_2. \qquad (5\text{-}52)$$

Now this output power can be expressed in terms of the cavity ringing time by noting that $W_2 = (1/\tau_c) - \gamma_s = (1 - \gamma_s\tau_c)/\tau_c$. Thus we can see that in the high Q mode, in which W_2 is low and the cavity ringing time (τ_c) is high and determined primarily by γ_s, the output power will be low. This occurs because $\gamma_s\tau_c \simeq 1$. Its physical significance is that although the photon density is large in the optical cavity, because of relatively lower threshold η_t, the energy is dissipated by incidental losses such as scattering and does not appear as useful output as measured by $W_2\Phi$. The total power emitted from the cavity is

$$P_{\text{total}} = h\nu\left(\frac{NV}{2}\right)\left(\frac{\Phi}{\tau_c}\right)$$

but the useful portion of this is only the fraction $[W_2/(W_2 + \gamma_s)]$ emerging from the output port. Thus

$$P_{\text{out}} = P_{\text{total}}\frac{W_2}{\gamma_s + W_2}$$

$$= P_{\text{total}}(W_2 \tau_c). \tag{5-53}$$

A plot showing the variation of useful output peak power as a function of the transmission of the output reflector is shown in Figure 5-17. The fixed reflector is assumed as 100% reflectance for purposes of this calculation. Note that the peak power depends on both the photon density (Φ_p) and the output rate factor (γ_0). The threshold inversion (η_t) is also influenced by the output loss rate factor.

The variation of the normalized photon density and the inversion ratio with time is now discussed for the step function Q-switch case. In principle, the solution can be written in integral form by reference to (5-33) or (5-36b) for the photon density has been expressed in terms of population inversion. Thus

$$\frac{d\eta}{dt} = -w_i \phi \eta = -\frac{\phi}{\tau_c}\left(\frac{\eta}{\eta_t}\right) \tag{5-33}$$

$$\left(\frac{\eta_t}{\eta}\right)\frac{d\eta}{\phi} = -\frac{dt}{\tau_c}$$

$$\frac{t}{\tau_c} = \eta_t \int_{\eta_0}^{\eta} \frac{d\eta'}{\eta'\phi(\eta')}$$

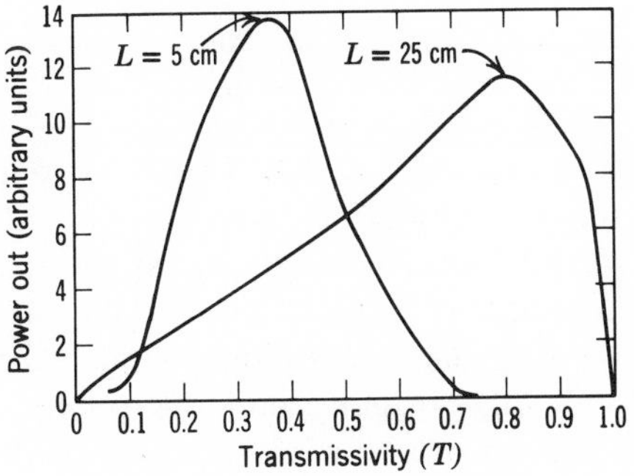

Figure 5-17   Output peak power versus transmission of output reflector.

and therefore, using the solution for ϕ in terms of η as stated in (5-39),

$$\frac{t}{\tau_c} = -\int_{\eta_0}^{\eta} \frac{\eta_t \, d\eta'}{\eta' \left[\phi_i + \eta_t \ln \left(\eta'/\eta_0 \right) + \left(\eta_0 - \eta' \right) \right]}. \tag{5-54}$$

This equation can be put in a more convenient analytical form by a change of variable.
Let

$$\xi = -\ln \left(\frac{\eta}{\eta_t} \right) \tag{5-55}$$

Then

$$d\xi = \frac{-d\eta}{\eta}$$

$$\eta_0 = \eta_t e^{-\xi_0}$$

$$\eta = \eta_t e^{-\xi}$$

and the equation can be rewritten

$$\frac{t}{\tau_c} = \int_{\xi_0}^{\xi} \frac{d\xi}{F(\xi)}, \tag{5-56}$$

where

$$F(\xi) = \left(\frac{\phi_i}{\eta_t} \right) + \left(\xi_0 - \xi \right) + \left(e^{-\xi_0} - e^{-\xi} \right). \tag{5-57}$$

Note, too, that this also gives the photon density:

$$F(\xi) = \frac{\phi}{\eta_t}.$$

Referring to Figure 5-12, we see that the photon density can be characterized by three regions: a buildup region (A), where the photon density is low and the inversion ratio relatively constant, a final decay region (C), where the photon density is again low and the inversion ratio is low because of depletion after laser action, and a central region (B), where the inversion ratio changes rapidly and the photon density is large. Analytical approximations allow a closed expression to be obtained in the two side regions (A) and (C), but the central region (B) can be satisfactorily attacked only by a computer solution. The solution for

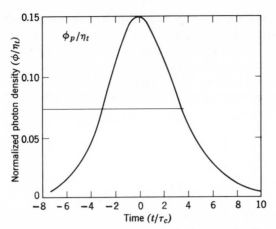

Figure 5-18 Normalized photon density versus time in the central region of the giant pulse for $\ln \eta_0/\eta_t = 0.5$; $\eta_0/\eta_t = 1.649$. After Wagner and Lengyel, *J. Appl. Phys.* (1963).

the central region (B) of the pulse is obtained by a computer routine in which ϕ_i/η_t is ignored with valid reason in this interval. The results from this computation for some typical values are given in Figures 5-18 through 5-21. The side regions A and C of Figure 5-12 are calculated by an analytical approximation to (5-57), which permits a determination of the early buildup and decay characteristics of the giant pulse.

After Q-switching starts and the cavity is in the high Q condition, the buildup of photon density is characterized by a delay time. This is an interval in which the photon density increases to such a level that the stimulated emission can exert an appreciable effect on the inversion

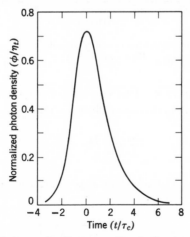

Figure 5-19 Normalized photon density versus time in the giant pulse for $\ln \eta_0/\eta_t = 1.0$; $\eta_0/\eta_t = 2.718$. After Wagner and Lengyel, *J. Appl. Phys.* (1963).

ratio. A considerable time is required, for the photon density starts at such an extremely low value. This phase is represented as region *A* in Figure 5-12. This delay time can be calculated as follows.

For typical ruby laser systems, such as we have already characterized, the delay time in building up the giant pulse is of the order of 20 nsec. This can be approximated by reference to (5-36*a*), where η is assumed to

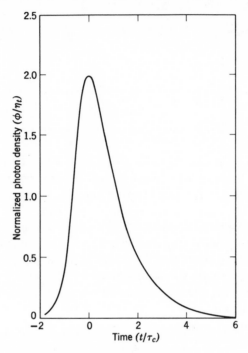

Figure 5-20   Photon density versus time in the giant pulse for $\ln \eta_0/\eta_t = 1.5$; $\eta_0/\eta_t = 4.482$. After Wagner and Lengyel, *J. Appl. Phys.* (1963).

be constant and equal to η_0. This can be assumed, for the inversion will not change appreciably in this early phase. Then

$$\frac{d\phi}{dt} = \left(\frac{\eta_0}{\eta_t} - 1\right)\frac{\phi}{\tau_c}. \tag{5-58}$$

The rise time (τ_{rise}) calculated from this approximation then is given by assuming $\tau_c \simeq 1.7 \times 10^{-9}$ sec.

$$\tau_{\text{rise}} = \frac{\tau_c}{(\eta_0/\eta_t) - 1} \tag{5-59}$$
$$= 1.1 \text{ nsec.}$$

Because the photon density starts at such a very low level, it will require a time period encompassing many rise times and a change in photon density of the order of 10^{10} to become significant and herald the end of

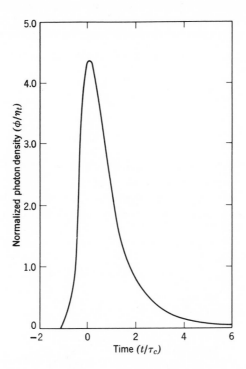

Figure 5-21 Normalized photon density versus time in the giant pulse for ln $\eta_0/\eta_t = 2.0$; $\eta_0/\eta_t = 7.389$. After Wagner and Lengyel, *J. Appl. Phys.* (1963).

the delay period. Thus the delay time (τ_D) for this laser system can be calculated from (5-58) to be.

$$\tau_D = \frac{\tau_c}{(\eta_0/\eta_c) - 1} \ln\left(\frac{\phi_D}{\phi_i}\right)$$

$$= \tau_c \ln(10^{10}) \cong 23 \text{ nsec}, \tag{5-60}$$

where ϕ_D is the relative photon density at the end of the delay time and ϕ_i is the density when Q-switching starts.

This is admittedly a rough estimate, for it can be changed by the pumping level, threshold, and initial photon density. Others[6] indicate a value of 130 nsec and various values[7] from 20 to 200 nsec against an indicated experimental value[8,9] of several nanoseconds. Furthermore, an estimate of the initial photon density (ϕ_i) can be obtained by referring to (5-16) and noting that in the early phase $d\phi/dt$ is slow in rising while $\eta = \eta_0$. Thus, with the approximation that $d\phi/dt = 0$ and $\eta = \eta_0$,

$$\phi_i[w_i\eta_0 - \gamma_s - W_2] + w_s'(1 + \eta_0) = 0$$

$$\phi_i = \frac{w_s'(1 + \eta_0)}{w_i\eta_0 - (\gamma_s + W_2)}$$

$$= \frac{(1 + \eta_0)(w_s'/w_i)}{\eta_0 - \eta_t} \tag{5-61}$$

Again, assuming $\eta_0/\eta_t = 2.5$, noting that $w_s'/w_i \simeq 10^{-15}$, and assuming η_0 of the order of unity, we obtain $\phi_i \simeq 10^{-15}$.

The value of photon density that will determine the end of the delay time can be estimated from the more complete rate equation for the inversion ratio (5-12):

$$\frac{d\eta}{dt} = w_p(1 + \eta) - w_s(1 + \eta) - w_i\phi\eta. \tag{5-12}$$

Putting this in another form, we may write

$$\frac{d\eta}{\eta} = \left[w_p\left(\frac{1-\eta}{\eta}\right) - w_s\left(\frac{1+\eta}{\eta}\right) - w_i\phi\right]dt. \tag{5-61a}$$

For a reasonable system the ratio $(1 \pm \eta)/\eta$ will be of the order of unity; for $d\eta/\eta$ to be in the range of a large negative value necessary to herald the end of the delay time, we can state that

$$w_i\phi_D \gg w_p\left(\frac{1-\eta_0}{\eta_0}\right) - w_s\left(\frac{1+\eta_0}{\eta_0}\right), \tag{5-61b}$$

[6]W. G. Wagner, and B. A. Lengyel, "Evolution of the Giant Pulse in a Laser," *J. Appl. Phys.*, **34**, 2040–2046 (July 1963).

[7]R. B. Kay and G. S. Waldman, "Complete Solutions to the Rate Equations Describing Q Spoiled and PTM Laser Operation," *J. Appl. Phys.*, **36**, 1319 (April 1965).

[8]F. J. McClung and R. W. Hellwarth, "Characteristics of Giant Optical Pulsations from Ruby," *Proc. IRE*, **51**, 46 (January 1963).

[9]R. W. Hellwarth, "Control of Fluorescent Radiation," *Advances in Quantum Electronics*, Columbia University Press (1961), p. 334.

or the inversion ratio does not vary appreciably from η_0 during this interval. The photon density term ϕ_D, is the value at the end of the delay time. Then, asserting that

$$\phi_D \gg w_i \left[w_p \left(\frac{1 - \eta_0}{\eta_0} \right) - w_s \left(\frac{1 + \eta_0}{\eta_0} \right) \right] \qquad (5\text{-}61c)$$

and using the values from Tables 5-1 and 5-3 for $\eta_0 = 0.5$, we obtain

$$\phi_D \gg 4.2 \times 10^{-6},$$

and a value of $\phi_D = 10^{-5}$ is assumed for the photon density at the end of the delay period. Thus we can assert that $\phi_D/\phi_i \simeq 10^{-5}/10^{-15} \simeq 10^{10}$, which verifies the calculation.

5-5 SOLUTION FOR Q-SWITCH VARIATION LINEAR IN TIME

The solution is now examined for the case of a variable reflectivity that changes linearly in time rather than as a step function. This means that the loss rate varies linearly in time, also, and is illustrated graphically in Figure 5-22. The time for which the loss through the output reflector is high, or the Q of the optical cavity is low, occurs for $t < 0$; the loss rate in this instance is given by $W_1 + W_2$. The time interval during which the loss is low, or the Q is high, is $t > t_1$ and has a value of W_2. This will also be the time in which the giant pulse grows. The Q increase time is $0 < t < t_1$. The steepness of the Q increase time interval determines whether the Q-switch is fast or slow, and this in turn is determined by its relationship to other terms in the rate equation describing the photon density (5-16).

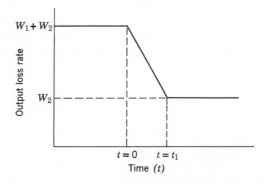

Figure 5-22 Variable output loss term for the case of linear Q-switch.

TABLE 5-5   LINEAR Q-SWITCH DESCRIPTION

Period	Description	Loss Rate
$t < 0$	High loss, low Q, excited state filled by pump	$W_1 + W_2$
$0 < t < t_1$	Q increases, loss decreases	Decreases linearly in time
$t > t_1$	Low loss, high Q, giant pulse grows, excited state is depleted	W_2

It should be noted that the switching interval $\Delta t = t_1$ must not stretch out too long or the loss of inversion from spontaneous emission will reduce the system below threshold and laser action will not occur; in essence, the photon density will not rise fast enough because the high loss condition continues too long and, therefore, insufficient stimulated emission will result.

We assert that the switch starting time is set at $t = 0$. Let us further assume that a loss rate relationship is defined by (5-62):

$$\gamma_0(t) = W_2 + W_1\left(1 - \frac{t}{t_1}\right). \tag{5-62}$$

We then proceed to calculate the photon density buildup during the linear switching time. Table 5-5 associates the loss rate with cavity Q for the various time periods.

Then for the switching time intervals the loss rate equation (5-16) can be written in the form

$$\frac{d\phi}{dt} = -\phi\left[\gamma_s + W_2 + W_1\left(1 - \frac{t}{t_1}\right)\right] + w_s'(1 + \eta) + w_i\phi\eta. \tag{5-63}$$

Again, in the early stages of the pulse formation the inversion ratio is not greatly changed from $\eta = \eta_0$. The rate equation can then be expressed as

$$\frac{d\phi}{dt} = \left[w_i\eta_0 - \gamma_s - W_2 - W_1\left(1 - \frac{t}{t_1}\right)\right]\phi + w_s'(1 + \eta_0) \tag{5-64}$$

or, collecting terms,

$$P(t) = \gamma_s + W_2 + W_1\left(1 - \frac{t}{t_1}\right) - w_i\eta_0$$

$$= A - 2Bt,$$

where $A = \gamma_s + W_2 + W_1 - w_i \eta_0$

$$2B = \frac{W_1}{t_1}$$

$$Q = w_s'(1 + \eta_0).$$

The equation can be written more simply as

$$\frac{d\phi}{dt} + P(t)\phi = Q. \tag{5-65}$$

This is in the form similar to the well known Bernoulli equation. The solution takes the form

$$\phi(t) = \left[\phi_0 + QI(t)\right]e^{-(At - Bt^2)}, \tag{5-66}$$

where

$$I(t) = \int_0^t e^{Ax - Bx^2}\, dx,$$

and can be expressed as an error function by completing the square in the exponent. The other constants are defined above. This has been evaluated in the technical literature[7], and the results are given in Table 5-6.

TABLE 5-6 PHOTON DENSITY
GROWTH IN LINEAR SWITCHING
PERIOD

t_1(nsec)	η_0	ϕ_0	$\phi(t_1)$
5	0.8	10^{-14}	5.4×10^{-14}
	0.4	10^{-15}	3×10^{-15}
10	0.8	10^{-14}	9.1×10^{-13}
	0.4	10^{-15}	9.3×10^{-15}

Notice the small total change in the photon density in this time. The buildup of photon density is still slow, even after $t = t_1$. Kay and Waldman assumed that the delay time would continue until the normalized photon density achieved a level of 5×10^{-4}, a value chosen because it was a convenient crossover point for their analog computer. After this delay time they proceeded to calculate the photon density and inversion ratio by using equations similar to (5-36a) and (5-36b); this amounts to neglecting the spontaneous emission losses and having a fixed low rate loss output element. For a ramp or Q increase time of 5 nsec and the

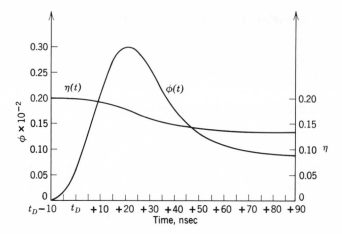

Figure 5-23 Plot of relative photon density (ϕ) and population inversion ratio (η) for Q-spoiled operation with $\eta_0 = 0.2$. After Kay and Waldman, *J. Appl. Phys.* (1965).

laser parameter values tabulated in Table 5-1 the results yield the inversion ratio and photon density as shown in Figures 5-23 through 5-25 for several values of initial population inversion. The delay time, τ_D, in this case is given by the sum of t_1 and the additional delay term as given in (5-59). Thus

$$\tau_D = t_1 + \frac{\tau_c}{(\eta_0/\eta_t) - 1} \ln\left(\frac{\phi_D}{\phi_i}\right). \qquad (5\text{-}67)$$

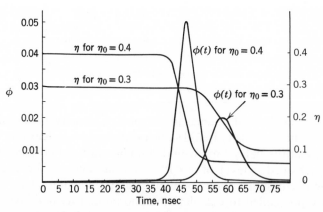

Figure 5-24 Plot of relative photon density (ϕ) and population inversion ratio (η) for Q-spoiled operation with $\eta_0 = 0.3$ and $\eta_0 = 0.4$. After Kay and Waldman, *J. Appl. Phys.* (1965).

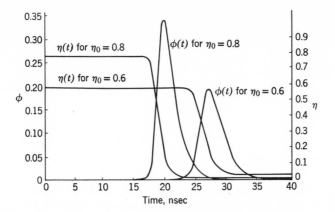

Figure 5-25 Plot of relative photon density (ϕ) and population inversion ratio (η) for Q-spoiled operation with $\eta_0 = 0.6$ and $\eta_0 = 0.8$. After Kay and Waldman, *J. Appl. Phys.* (1965).

The primary effect on the formation of the giant pulse by the linear Q-switch is to extend the delay time by the amount of time equal to the length of the ramp. For some timing applications this may be a significant factor. In any event, it cannot be extended to a point near the lifetime of the excited state. Spontaneous losses would then be excessive, as previously discussed.

5-6 SOLUTION FOR Q-SWITCH WITH COSINE VARIATION IN TIME

A form of Q-switch commonly used in practice is the rotating mirror or prism, driven by a high speed air motor. A typical spinning rate would be 24,000 rpm. Some small prisms approach 50,000 rpm. At the slower rate of rotation it would take approximately 40 nsec to sweep out an angle of 10^{-4} radian. This would be considered a slow switch as far as Q-switches go. The exact angle that is significant in a given case depends on the rod length and diameter and the gain per unit length, but the above figure provides an estimate from which to commence calculations. The loss rate variation for this case is assumed to be of the form

$$\gamma_0(t) = A + B \cos\left(\frac{2\pi t}{t_s}\right) \tag{5-68}$$

and is illustrated by Fig. 5-26. The loss factor varies from a high value of $A + B$, which would allow for pumping, to the low loss value of $A - B$ in the high Q region.

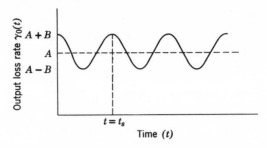

Figure 5-26   Loss rate variation for Q-switch as a cosine function in time.

A typical case of this cosine variation of the Q-switch was computed by Midwinter.[10] The treatment of this variable loss factor is feasible only through the use of a computer. For this evaluation he chose a loss factor with a maximum value of $A + B = 5 \times 10^{-9}$ sec and a minimum value of $A - B = 1 \times 10^{-9}$ sec. Thus

$$\gamma_0(t) = \left[3 + 2 \cos\left(\frac{2\pi t}{t_s}\right)\right]/\text{nsec.} \qquad (5\text{-}69)$$

The basic rate equations to be solved can be immediately stated by referring to (5-12) and (5-16).

$$\frac{d\eta}{dt} = w_p(1 - \eta) - w_s(1 + \eta) - w_i\phi\eta \qquad (5\text{-}12)$$

$$\frac{d\phi}{dt} = -\phi[\gamma_s + \gamma_0(t)] + w_s'(1 + \eta) + w_i\phi\eta; \qquad (5\text{-}16)$$

(5-16) reduces to the following when the loss rate term is inserted:

$$\frac{d\phi}{dt} = -\phi\left[\gamma_s + A + B \cos\left(\frac{2\pi t}{t_s}\right)\right] + w_s'(1 + \eta) + w_i\phi\eta. \qquad (5\text{-}70)$$

Assuming the parameters for the laser given in Table 5-1, and an initial population inversion ratio of $\eta_0 = 0.8$, we solve the equations for several values of t_s. The results are presented in Figures 5-27 and 5-28 for the faster spinning reflectors. In these two instances $t_s = 50$ nsec, $t_s = 100$ nsec, and the inversion ratio and power output are about as expected. The variable plotted in this instance is the product of loss

[10]J. E. Midwinter, "The Theory of Q-Switching Applied to Slow Switching and Pulse Shaping for Solid State Lasers," *Brit. J. Appl. Phys.*, **16**, 1125 (August 1965).

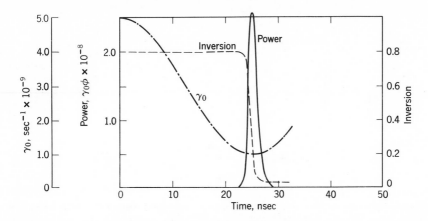

Figure 5-27   Plot of inversion ratio and power output for cosine *Q*-switch when $t_s = 50$ nsec and $\eta_0 = 0.8$. After Midwinter, *Brit. J. Appl. Phys.* (1965).

factor and the photon density, $\phi\gamma_0$, for the loss rate factor is not a constant. In this case the coordinate of the curve gives a factor proportional to the power as a function of time rather than a factor proportional to the energy. Note that the delay time here, too, is in the range between 20 and 40 nsec. Also shown here is the variation of loss factor with time.

For slower switches a double pulsing effect occurs. This develops for $t_s = 300$ nsec and also for $t_s = 500$ nsec and arises when the delay time becomes very short compared with t_s. The results for the slower switches are shown in Figures 5-29 and 5-30.

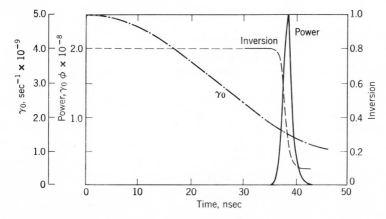

Figure 5-28   Plot of inversion ratio and power output for cosine *Q*-switch when $t_s = 100$ nsec and $\eta_0 = 0.8$. After Midwinter, *Brit. J. Appl. Phys.* (1965).

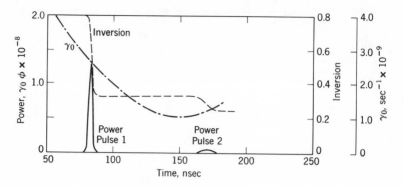

Figure 5-29 Plot of inversion ratio and power output for cosine Q-switch when $t_s = 300$ nsec and $\eta_0 = 0.8$. After Midwinter, *Brit. J. Appl. Phys.* (1965).

Looking at the curves and considering the values of $\phi\gamma_0$, we note that the first pulse for $t_s = 300$ and 500 nsec is much larger than the second and occurs at a larger value of γ_0; the second pulse occurs near the minimum loss level and is much slower. The analysis of the multiple-pulse development can be explained by reference to the loss rate equations (5-12) and (5-16). For this discussion ignore the spontaneous loss term $w_s'(1+\eta)$

The following sequence occurs:

1. For $\gamma_s + \gamma_0 - w_i\eta > 0$ there is pumping; the threshold is not yet reached and $\eta = \eta_0$. A small photon density exists because of spontaneous emission.

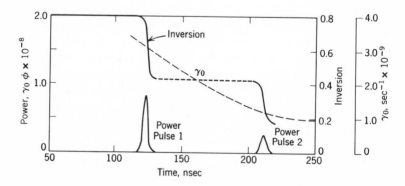

Figure 5-30 Plot of inversion ratio and power output for cosine Q-switch when $t_s = 500$ nsec and $\eta_0 = 0.8$. After Midwinter, *Brit. J. Appl. Phys.* (1965).

2. For $\gamma_s + \gamma_0 - w_i \eta_0 < 0$ the loss term is switched, the threshold is exceeded, and $d\phi/dt$ is positive. The photon density grows exponentially as η remains essentially unchanged. When $w_i \eta \phi$ becomes large as a result of large ϕ, then $d\eta/dt$ becomes large and negative, giving a pulse until $\gamma_s + \gamma_0 - w_i \eta \simeq 0$ again.

3. At this last point $\gamma_s + \gamma_0 - w_i \eta = 0$ the peak power is emitted, for $d\phi/dt = 0$ (ϕ is maximum); the $d\eta/dt$ is still large and negative, so that η falls below the threshold value η_t and finally reaches the value η_f.

4. Because $\eta = \eta_f$ is below threshold, the photon density ϕ is very small and a steady state is reached until the slowly changing loss rate term $\gamma_0(t)$ decreases enough so that the condition again obtains where $\gamma_s + \gamma_0(t) - w_i \eta_0' < 0$ results. The cycle then starts over, but because it now starts with a lower initial value of $\eta = \eta_0'$ a smaller, slower pulse is produced.

It should also be noted that for this multiple pulsing to occur the first pulse must be emitted at the point of a relatively high loss rate, so that another pulse can build up and be emitted when the output loss rate factor is lower and probably near its minimum.

5-7 PULSE SHAPING CONSIDERATIONS

From the preceding discussion it is apparent that altering the loss rate with time will change the shape of the output pulse. In principle, then, the ability to control the loss rate ($\gamma_s + \gamma_0$) permits us to shape the Q-switched pulse into a predetermined desired form.

For example, treat the case of attempting to achieve a square-topped pulse. This might be achieved by means of two different mechanisms. In the first method the cavity photon density might be held constant by varying some internal loss mechanism, $\gamma_s(t)$, and allowing a fixed proportion of the cavity photons to escape as output ($\gamma_0 = $ constant). In the second case the cavity photon density would be allowed to increase. Then, as the photon density decayed naturally, the output loss rate $\gamma_0(t)$ could be increased to compensate for the photon decay, thereby maintaining the product, $\phi \cdot \gamma_0(t)$, constant.

The region in which the flat-topped pulse occurs can be established in the first instance by reference to the photon rate equation (5-16):

$$\frac{d\phi}{dt} = -[\gamma_s + \gamma_0(t)]\phi + w_s'(1 + \eta) + w_i \phi \eta. \qquad (5\text{-}16)$$

We assume again that the spontaneous loss term is small during the laser action. For a square wave or flat-topped pulse the constant output power condition is established for $d\phi/dt = 0$, for $\gamma_0 = $ constant:

$$\frac{d\phi}{dt} = 0 = -(\gamma_s + \gamma_0)\phi + w_i\eta\phi$$

$$\gamma_s + \gamma_0 = w_i\eta$$

$$\gamma_s = w_i\eta - \gamma_0. \tag{5-71}$$

Thus the condition for a flat-topped pulse can be achieved by varying the internal loss factor γ_s linearly with the inversion ratio, for γ_0 is constant in this instance.

A computer solution for the square wave condition was achieved by Midwinter.[10] The results for the solution, assuming constant photon density, are shown in Figure 5-31. The variation of the internal loss rate factor is also shown here. It is indicated that about 40% of the energy is realized as useful output.

The output for the second case is not quite so quickly arrived at. The output is given by the product of photon density and the time-varying output rate factor and therefore the condition $d\phi/dt$ does not define constant power output. Thus in the second instance we are again concerned with keeping the product $\phi \cdot \gamma_0(t)$ constant in order to generate the square wave, but both terms now change with time:

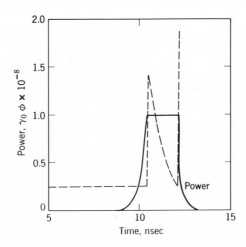

Figure 5-31 Square pulse generation by keeping photon density constant through varying internal laser loss rate. After Midwinter, *Brit. J. Appl. Phys.* (1965).

$$\frac{d}{dt}(\phi \cdot \gamma_0) = \gamma_0\frac{d\phi}{dt} + \phi\frac{d\gamma_0}{dt} = 0 \qquad (5\text{-}72)$$

and it follows that

$$\frac{d\gamma_0}{dt} = -\frac{\gamma_0}{\phi}\left(\frac{d\phi}{dt}\right) \qquad (5\text{-}73)$$

$$\frac{1}{\gamma_0}\frac{d\gamma_0}{dt} = (\gamma_s + \gamma_0) - w_i\eta. \qquad (5\text{-}74)$$

We see again that the output rate is related to the inversion ratio, although the governing factor is more complicated and not easily solved except by the application of a computer.

Even so, the variation in time of the loss rate factor can be achieved by an approximation in which the inversion ratio is assumed small; that is, the change in the output loss factor is most significant after the photon density has built up in the cavity because of the decay of the electron population inversion. Control is then exerted on the output pulse by varying the output rate term (γ_0) as the photon density decays.

Then we may approximate (5-74) as follows:

$$\frac{d\gamma_0}{dt} = (\gamma_s + \gamma_0)\gamma_0. \qquad (5\text{-}75)$$

The solution to this is given by

$$t = -\frac{1}{\gamma_s}\ln\left(\frac{\gamma_s + \gamma_0}{\gamma_0}\right) + \frac{1}{\gamma_s}\ln\left(\frac{\gamma_s + \gamma_0{}^*}{\gamma_0{}^*}\right), \qquad (5\text{-}76)$$

where $\gamma_0{}^*$ is the value of output rate term at $t = 0$ when the output change starts to become significant. This may be expressed in the form

$$\gamma_0(t) = \frac{\gamma_0{}^*\gamma_s}{(\gamma_0{}^* + \gamma_s)\,e^{-\gamma_s t} - \gamma_0{}^*}. \qquad (5\text{-}77)$$

This equation, for the realistic case in which $\gamma_s \gg \gamma_0{}^*$, reduces to

$$\gamma_0(t) \simeq \gamma_0{}^*\,e^{\gamma_s t}. \qquad (5\text{-}78)$$

It illustrates that the output loss rate factor must increase exponentially toward the end of the pulse in order to maintain the square top. The computer solution for this pulse-shaping condition of varying the output loss

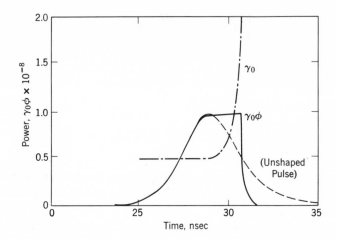

Figure 5-32 Square pulse generation by varying output loss rate as determined by decay of photon density in cavity. After Midwinter, *Brit. J. Appl. Phys.* (1965).

rate is given in Figure 5-32. Note here also the exponential growth of the loss rate term.

The variation of the output loss factor can be understood further from (5-75). As the pulse develops, the inversion ratio η is positive but decreasing; therefore the output loss rate changes in time as an exponential factor with an increasing exponent.

The calculation of this case indicates that approximately 70% of the photon flux becomes useful output.

In comparing the two techniques for generating square-topped pulses we should note that the first method of varying the internal loss mechanism is inherently less efficient than the second case because of the large proportion of energy lost in the artificial loss mechanism. The peak power output should then be lower in the first case for a given amount of stored energy than in the second.

The square pulse in the second case cannot be long maintained, for the population inversion is largely depleted when the photon pulse begins its decrease. In the first case the square pulse can be stabilized up to 10 nsec for the parameters considered.

It should also be noted that the pulse shape for the output loss factor, being exponential, could probably be achieved more easily than that of the variable internal loss factor. This is due to the complicated nature of the variation of internal loss term as noted in Figure 5-31.

It can be seen that some control, in principle, on the output pulse shape can be exerted on the giant pulse emission from a laser. The required elements are suitable devices for control that can be made part of the laser system.

REFERENCES

Daly, R., and S. D. Sims, "An Improved Method of Mechanical Q-Switching Using Total Internal Reflection," *Appl. Opt.*, **3**, 1063–1066 (September 1964).

Helfrich, J. L., "Faraday Effect as a Q-Switch for Ruby Laser," *J. Appl. Phys.*, **34**, 1000–1001 (April 1963).

Hercher, M., "Design and Analysis of Q-Switched Laser Systems," *NEREM Rec.* **6**, 168–169 (1964).

Hellwarth, R. W., "Control of Fluorescent Radiation," in *Advances in Quantum Electronics*, J. R. Singer (ed.), Columbia University Press, New York 1961, pp. 334–341.

Kay, R. B., and G. S. Waldman, "Complete Solutions to the Rate Equations Describing Q-Spoiled and PTM Laser Operation," *J. Appl. Phys.*, **36**, 1319 (April 1965).

McClung, F.J., and R. W. Hellwarth, "Characteristics of Giant Optical Pulsations from Ruby," *Proc. IEEE*, **51**, 46–53 (January 1963).

Menat, M., "Giant Pulses from a Laser," *J. Appl. Phys.*, **36**, 73–75 (January 1965).

Midwinter, J. E., "The Theory of Q-Switching Applied to Slow Switching and Pulse Shaping for Solid State Lasers," *Brit. J. Appl. Phys.*, **16**, 1125–1133 (August 1965).

Missio, V., and K. N. Seeber, "Performance Analysis of Giant-Pulse Ruby Lasers," *Microwaves*, **4**, 40 (July 1965).

Sanford, J. R., J. H. Wenzel, and G. J. Wolga, "Giant Pulse Laser Action and Pulse Width Narrowing in Nd-doped Borate Glass," *J. Appl. Phys.*, **35**, 3422–3423 (November 1964).

Skeen, C. H., and C. M. York, "The Operation of a Nd-Glass Laser Using a Saturable Liquid Q-Switch," *Appl. Opt.*, **5**, 1463–1464 (September 1966).

Sorokin, P. P., "Ruby Laser Q-Switching Elements Using Phthalocynanine Molecules in Solution," *IBM J. Res. Develop.*, **8**, 182–184 (April 1964).

Suproynowicz, V. A. "Giant Pulse Formation Using Ultrasonic Q-Spoiling," *J. Appl. Phys.*, **37**, 778–784 (February 1966).

Szabo, A., and R. A. Stein, "Theory of Laser Giant Pulsing by a Saturable Absorber," *J. Appl. Phys.*, **36**, 1562–1566 (May 1965).

Underwood, R.N., "A Survey of Laser Q-Switching Techniques," *EDN*, **11**, 44–49 (October 1966).

Vuylsteke, A. A. "Theory of Laser Regeneration Switching," *J. Appl. Phys.*, **34**, 1615–1622 (June 1963).

Wagner, W. G., and B. A. Lengyel, "Evaluation of the Giant Pulse in a Laser," *J. Appl. Phys.*, **34**, 2040–2046 (July 1963).

Wang, C. C., "Optical Giant Pulses from a Q-Switched Laser," *Proc. IEEE*, **51**, 1767 (December 1963).

Wayant, R. W., I. T. Basil, J. H. Collom, and G. D. Baldwin, "Measurement of Q-Switched Laser Beam Divergence," *J. Opt. Soc. Am.*, **54**, 1390 (November 1964).

Wenzel, J., "Q-Switched Laser Output," in *Symposium on Optical Masers*, **13**, Polytechnic Institute of Brooklyn, New York (1963), pp. 277–297.

6

Semiconductor Junction
Diode Injection Lasers

One of the most interesting devices that has been developed in the optical electronics field is the semiconductor junction diode laser; it is also referred to as the injection laser, for light is emitted as a consequence of the carrier injection action in a forward biased semiconductor p-n junction.

The most commonly used semiconductor material for fabricating injection diodes is gallium arsenide, the most common laser wavelength here being 8400 Å. The wavelength of the emitted radiation from injection diodes, however varies over the range from 6300 Å for the III–V mixed semiconductor gallium arsenide phosphide to 8.5 μ for the IV–VI semiconductor lead selenide. The semiconductor diode laser has the advantages that its size is small and that it converts d-c electric power directly into coherent light. Its output can be modulated simply by modulating the diode current because the output light intensity is extremely sensitive to the input current once laser action begins. Such a laser, when operated near liquid helium temperatures, has emitted several watts of continuous coherent radiation at close to 50% power efficiency. The radiation has been modulated at frequencies as high as 10 kMc. At room temperature such a laser can be used in pulsed operation to radiate coherent radiation in 50-nsec power pulses of the order of 20 W. When operated continuously at currents just above threshold GaAs lasers can operate stably in one mode of a Fabry-Perot cavity. This radiation is extremely monochromatic, the frequency width of such a cavity mode being of the order of 50 Mc/sec, or less than 15 parts in 10^6 of the output frequency.

Because of the advantages mentioned above injection lasers may be useful in radar, communications, and computer applications, in which the absorption of the laser radiation in the atmosphere is unimportant.

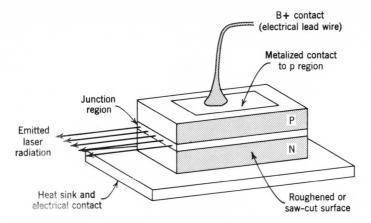

Figure 6-1   Diagram showing elements of a semiconductor diode structure, which is useful as a laser.

Before discussing the details of the mechanisms leading to laser action in a semiconductor diode, we will look at the structure of a typical unit. The basic elements are illustrated in Figure 6-1. Here a *p-n* junction has been formed in a rectangular semiconductor, electrical contacts have been made, and the sides of the rectangle have been abraded to be non-reflective. The end faces of that diode, in which emission occurs, are plane and parallel and form the end reflectors to provide feedback of the photon

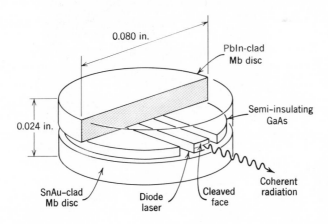

Figure 6-2   Gallium arsenide diode laser in a pill package. The diode laser is a small, rectangular parallelepiped of dimensions $0.010 \times 0.030 \times 0.003$ in. in thickness. The total package and structure is about the size of a pinhead. After R. H. Rediker, *Phys. Today* (1965).

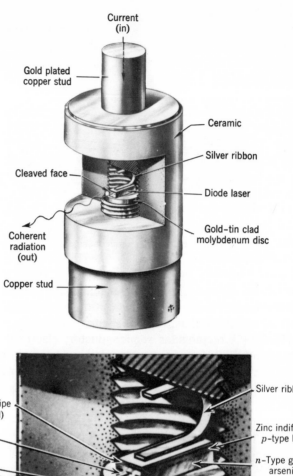

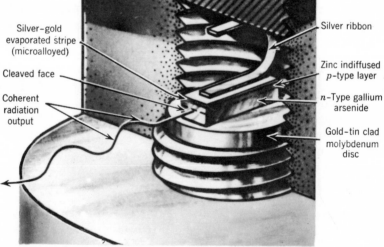

Figure 6-3 Conceptual design of a semiconductor laser in a microwave cartridge. This configuration permits improved cooling as well as impedance matching at microwave frequencies. The lower drawing shows an enlarged view of the actual diode structure and its mount. After B. Lax, *Solid State Design* (1963).

flux in the diode. These faces can be polished, but cleaving along the crystalline planes has proved most successful in obtaining the required flat, parallel surfaces. A large current is now supplied to the diode through the B+ contact and the heat sink; when the threshold current is exceeded laser emission occurs. The massive heat sink is necessary to control the temperature of the diode and stabilize the output intensity and wavelength. Both are sensitive to the temperature of the emitting p-n junction.

An example of a GaAs laser diode in a flat pill package is shown in Figure 6-2. The faces of the laser in this model are cleaved. The semi-insulating gallium arsenide accompanying the diode as filler between the package surfaces matches the thermal expansion, improves the package strength and provides insulation between electrical contacts. The voltage source to drive this current through the diode in this package would be connected between the top PbIn-clad molybdenum disk and the bottom SnAu-clad molybdenum. The top and bottom surfaces of the diode would be electrically attached to these two respective disks.

For higher frequency operation an alternative package must be used. An example of the laser diode package for operating at microwave frequencies is shown in Figure 6-3. Here the package modification is necessary to obtain improved cooling and impedance matching to the microwave circuitry. A detailed cutaway drawing is also shown here. The large top ribbon lead greatly improves the equivalent thermal coefficient of the device by reducing the thermal impedance and permitting heat to be conducted from the top as well as the bottom of the diode.

6-1 LASER DIODE PHYSICS

The injection laser diode is a semiconductor device with a p-n junction. For laser action to occur this junction is heavily biased in the forward, or conducting, direction. The current carriers, holes and electrons, are injected, or forced together, across the p-n junction and recombine. Thus recombination radiation is emitted; when the intensity is sufficiently high, or above the threshold value, laser action will occur and the laser beam will emerge. The emission line will narrow and the emerging beam will be coherent.

For orientation purposes, let us quickly review the properties of the p-n junction. The boundary in a semiconducting crystal between n-type and p-type material is called a p-n junction. This junction forms the basic building block of all semiconductor devices. We develop its properties in the following way.

A highly n-type piece of semiconductor material with a large electron density and a few holes is brought into intimate contact with a highly

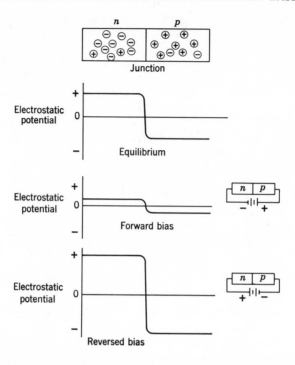

Figure 6-4 The effect of a voltage applied across a *p-n* junction bar under various conditions. After Steele, *Am. J. Phys.* (1957).

p-type specimen with a large hole density and a few electrons. Because of the large difference in electron concentrations in the two samples, the electrons on the *n*-type side will flood over into the *p*-type material, charging it negatively; the same action will occur for holes, which will flood over and charge the *n*-type side positively. Thus an electrostatic contact potential difference will soon be established between the two materials and the large flood of diffusing carriers will be stopped by the buildup of the potential difference between the two regions.

An equilibrium situation, schematically shown in Figure 6-4, will soon be established between the current flow due to diffusion from the region of high to low concentration and the current flow due to the contact potential difference; the total current will ultimately drop to zero.

At this point, in order for an electron to go from the *n*-type side to the *p*-type side, it is necessary for it to have sufficient energy to get up the potential hill. If an external battery is placed across the *p-n* bar, with the positive pole connected to the *p*-side, we see that both electrons and holes will be driven toward the junction and, with the potential hill

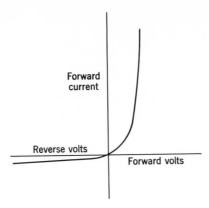

Figure 6-5 The voltage-current rectification characteristic for a *p-n* junction. After Steele, *Am. J. Phys.* (1957).

reduced by the battery voltage, a large current will flow; this is the forward conducting direction of the rectifying barrier.

If, on the other hand, the *p* side is made negative, the electrons and holes will be drawn away from the junction and the potential barrier made even higher. Fewer carriers will be able to rise up the potential hill, and the current will be very small; this is called the reverse conducting direction or bias of the junction and is also illustrated in Figure 6-4. A typical voltage-current characteristic for this rectifying barrier is shown in Figure 6-5 and is seen to be nonlinear as well as highly nonsymmetrical.

The actual *p-n* junction is usually a very narrow region compared with other physical dimensions of the semiconductor specimen. This means that the electrostatic field occurs over only a very short distance in the material, most of which is in a field-free region. Because the electric fields are very small in regions away from the junction, most of the current is carried by a diffusion process rather than the regular mechanism of driving by a field, as encountered in vacuum tubes. Once an electron gets up the potential barrier and into the *p* region it diffuses away. This rate of diffusion is very slow compared with field-controlled processes. For this reason the frequency limitation on these semiconductor devices can be severe; in general the only way to increase the frequency response is to reduce physical dimensions. Thus the rate at which a voltage change can modulate the current is strongly dependent on the diode geometry.

When the junction is biased in the reverse direction the only current, called the saturation current, arises from the few holes from the *n*-type side and small number of electrons on the *p*-type side being driven across the barrier; this reverse saturation current should be nearly constant for any reverse voltage applied. Use of semiconductor material that is highly *n*-type will greatly reduce the number of available holes in the *n*-type material and therefore immensely decrease this reverse saturation current. For example, if we desire to have most of the current across the junction carried by holes, we should use highly *p*-type material on one side of the junction and only lightly *n*-type material on the other side. This ensures that the reverse saturation current will be composed of few electrons from the *p*-type side and many holes from the *n*-type side.

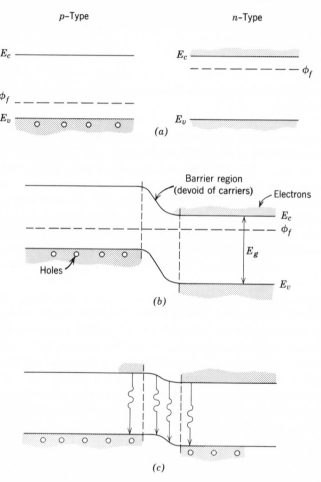

Figure 6-6 Band structure of (*a*) lightly doped semiconductor materials; (*b*) barrier region formed when *p*- and *n*-type materials are brought together and equilibrium is established; (*c*) forward-bias condition with reduction of barrier height. The injection of carriers results in increased recombination and radiation.

In the injection laser diode, however, we are less concerned about the reverse characteristics; we are interested in the forward current and the power dissipation. In order to achieve laser action, it is necessary to use very highly doped n- and p-type regions in the diode. In fact, they must be degenerate regions, which implies that these regions have extremely high conductivities; therefore the Fermi level, which determines equilibrium carrier concentrations, will be in the conduction band for electrons, or on the n side of the junction, and in the valence band for the holes, or the p side. The two regions have almost metallic electrical conduction characteristics because of the extremely high density of charge carriers.

Let us now examine the band structure of a semiconductor p-n junction. In lightly doped material, at low temperatures, the band structure of p- and n-types of material is illustrated by Figure 6-6a, in which the Fermi level (ϕ_f) is located in the band gap at different locations for the two materials.

When the n-type material is placed in contact with the p-type material to form a p-n junction, an equilibrium condition develops and the Fermi level must be the same throughout the complete composite block. This is shown in Figure 6-6b, and we note the existence of the potential hill or barrier separating the two regions. The holes represent an absence of electrons in the valence band in the p-type material. As previously discussed, when a forward bias is applied as in Figure 6-6c, this potential hill is diminished, electrons can drift up the hill, and some will then recombine with holes to emit radiation. In the lightly doped material considered here, however, the photon density arising from the radiation emitted will not be sufficient to cause *stimulated* emission. Only emission similar to the spontaneous process will occur; a higher density of carriers must occur for stimulated emission to become important.

When semiconductor regions with high doping densities are used in the diode structure the semiconductor regions are said to be degenerate. The Fermi level is then located in the conduction band for n-type material and in the valence band for p-type region, as shown in Figure 6-7.

The two separate regions have the Fermi levels and electron populations shown in Figure 6-7a. There is an absence of electron population at the top of the valence band in the p-type material and a high density of electrons above the bottom of the conduction band on the n-type side.

When the p-n junction is formed by using this degenerate material the band structure is in equilibrium, as illustrated in Figure 6-7b. Of course, no current flows under this equilibrium condition, for the flow due to the difference in electron density in the conduction band between the two regions is just canceled by the potential difference illustrated by the potential rise of the conduction band.

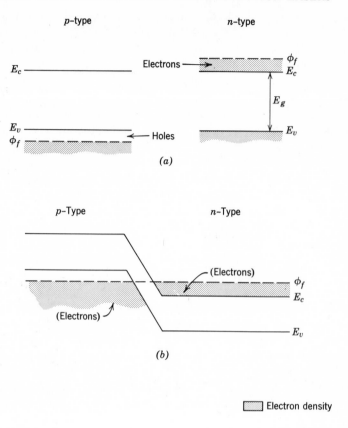

Figure 6-7 Band structure of heavily doped semiconductors and construction of a *p-n* junction. (*a*) Heavily doped semiconductors showing location of Fermi Level; (*b*) equilibrium band structure of *p-n* junction for degenerate material.

When a forward bias is applied to this degenerate diode, the potential hill is decreased and the band structure illustrated in Figure 6-8 occurs when the forward potential is applied; the Fermi level no longer is the same throughout the material. The voltage (V) applied between the p and n material displaces the Fermi level on the n side from that on the p side, and we find that

$$\phi_c - \phi_v = eV, \tag{6-1}$$

where ϕ_c is the Fermi level in the conduction band on the n side and ϕ_v is the Fermi level in the valence band on the p side. A detail of the *p-n* junction region is given in Figure 6-8*b* and illustrates that the excess

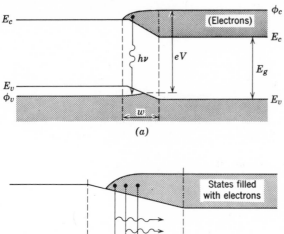

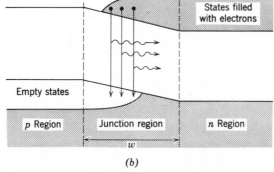

Figure 6-8 Band structure detail in junction region of heavily doped material suitable for laser diodes. (*a*) Forward-biased *p-n* junction with recombination occurring in junction region; (*b*) detail of electron density in junction region.

injected electron density recombines in the junction region of the diode. This process occurs because the electrons in the conduction band lose energy by dropping into a vacant state in the valence band; this energy shows up as a photon of energy $h\nu$. When a large photon density is built up by many of these transitions, the process is accelerated because of the *stimulated* emission, and, with reflection feedback occurring, laser action sets in.

The condition for laser action can be simply established. The rate of emission of photons due to electrons making the transition from the conduction band to the valence band must exceed the inverse absorption rates. Under this condition an excess photon density can build up and stimulated emission will result. Now the probability that a state in the conduction band at energy E_c on the *n* side will be occupied by an electron is given by the Fermi function (6-2),

$$f_c(E_c) = [1 + e^{(E_c - \phi_c)/kT}]^{-1}. \tag{6-2}$$

Similarly, for a state (E_v) being occupied by an electron in the valence band on the p side we have

$$f_v(E_v) = [1 + e^{(E_v - \phi_v)/kT}]^{-1}. \tag{6-3}$$

Define a stimulated emission coefficient, B_{cv}, as the probability per unit time that a transition will occur between a state in the conduction band to one in the valence band. The inverse process will have a probability per unit time of B_{vc}. The photon density is $\rho(\nu)$ for photons with an energy of $h\nu$.

The rate of generation of photons by transitions between the conduction band and valence band is given by

$$\left(\frac{d\rho}{dt}\right)_{emission} = AB_{cv}f_c(1 - f_v)\,\rho(\nu) \tag{6-4}$$

and similarly, for absorption,

$$\left(\frac{d\rho}{dt}\right)_{absorption} = AB_{vc}f_v(1 - f_c)\,\rho(\nu). \tag{6-5}$$

The constant A contains a factor concerning the density of state in the valence and conduction bands. Note that the product $f_c(1 - f_v)$ represents a composite probability that a state will be occupied in the conduction band and that a state will also be vacant in the valence band; thus a transition can occur.

The condition for a photon density increase, and therefore for laser light emission, is that the photon emission rate exceed the absorption rate.

$$\left(\frac{d\rho}{dt}\right)_{emission} > \left(\frac{d\rho}{dt}\right)_{absorption}. \tag{6-6}$$

Using (6-2) and (6-3) with the relations (6-4) through (6-6), we note for laser action that

$$AB_{cv}f_c(1 - f_v)\rho(\nu) > AB_{vc}f_v(1 - f_c)\rho(\nu) \tag{6-7}$$

$$f_c(1 - f_v) > f_v(1 - f_c) \tag{6-8}$$

$$f_c > f_v \tag{6-9}$$

$$[1 + e^{(E_c - \phi_c)/kT}]^{-1} > [1 + e^{(E_v - \phi_v)/kT}]^{-1} \tag{6-10}$$

$$e^{(E_v - \phi_v)/kT} > e^{(E_c - \phi_c)/kT} \tag{6-11}$$

$$\phi_c - \phi_v > E_c - E_v, \tag{6-12}$$

but we also note that

$$E_c - E_v = h\nu$$

and therefore

$$\phi_c - \phi_v > h\nu. \tag{6-13}$$

The difference in Fermi level must exceed the photon energy in order to have the photon emission rate exceed the absorption rate. When this condition occurs, it is said that population inversion occurs in the *p-n* junction diode. This condition also implies that the applied voltage is related to the photon energy by recalling (6-1) and

$$eV > h\nu. \tag{6-14}$$

To impart directionality to the emitted light and therefore achieve laser output rather than just light emission, it is necessary only to provide parallel reflecting mirrors on two opposite faces of the crystal. This can be done by polishing two faces of the crystal; the crystal-air boundary provides a natural reflecting surface. The natural cleavage faces of the crystal also make excellent mirrors. Only two opposite faces need be mirrorlike; the other faces are left roughly ground or are deliberately etched or roughened to eliminate reflections from the sides.

Because large numbers of excited electrons are produced in a junction diode when a current flows, only a small diode is needed to produce laser action; typically, the area of the junction is about 1mm². These junction diode lasers are efficient because nearly every electron injected across the junction contributes a useful photon, and the losses are mainly the electrical resistance losses in the rest of the diode.

One additional condition must be met to sustain the laser action. This can be stated by noting that the emitted photon rate has to exceed not only the absorption rate but also the photon loss rate from the junction region. This loss can occur by transmission of the light out of the diode because of partial reflection at the surface and by absorption in the *n* and *p* regions outside and adjacent to the junction volume.

The point at which the photon generation is just sufficient to overcome both the absorption and reflection losses is called the threshold. After the threshold is crossed the linewidth of the radiation emitted by the diode narrows and the intensity increases immensely. An example of this effect is shown in Figure 6-9 for an indium arsenide diode. The emission peak for the above threshold case is not to the same intensity scale as the case below threshold; the relative width is approximately to the proper scale. The laser line may actually be narrower than shown, but the determination is limited by the spectrometer accuracy.

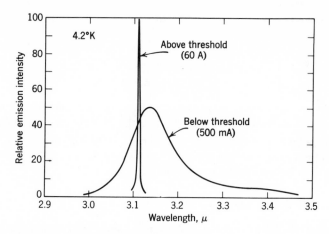

Figure 6-9   Emission spectra from an InAs diode with cleaved surfaces. The broad spontaneous spectrum line is not to the same intensity scale as the laser line above threshold. Notice that the peak of the emission shifts with current. The diode was at 4.2 K. After R. H. Rediker, *Phys. Today* (1965).

6-2   LASER THRESHOLD CONDITIONS

As previously noted, laser emission from a diode occurs only when certain conditions are met. The gain in the *p-n* junction region arising from stimulated emission must exceed the losses. As a corollary, the current density through the junction region must be high enough to bring together enough holes and electrons so that the photon density arising from their recombination radiation will cause stimulated emission in excess of the spontaneous processes.

As the current density is increased in a diode, a small amount of radiation will appear because of the spontaneous recombination. As the current is increased the intensity of this radiation will increase but will still not be coherent. On still further increase of current the stimulated emission will set in as the optical gain exceeds the losses in the junction, and the current density at this point will be the threshold value for this particular diode.

This threshold current density will depend on the absorption losses in the material near the junction region; it will also depend on the radiation losses due to transmission out of the diode where the junction region comes to the surface. Thus the reflectivity at the diode surface will play a role in determining the threshold. This reflectivity will vary depending on the basic semiconductor material; it can also be altered by plating or evaporating a reflective material, such as aluminum or gold, or a dielectric layer over the surface.

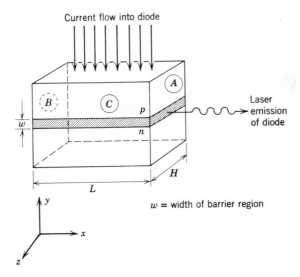

Figure 6-10 Diagram of laser diode showing direction of current flow and emitted radiation in a typical structure. Faces C would be roughened to discourage side reflections. The end faces (A and B) would be cleaved or polished.

The threshold current can be evaluated by the following procedure. Assume a current flowing into a semiconductor *p-n* junction diode as schematically illustrated in Figure 6-10. The junction region is of thickness *w* and the other diode dimensions indicate a length *L* and sample width *H*. The current thus flows into the diode over an area given by

$$\text{area} = HL. \tag{6-15}$$

Further, assume that the side of length *L* is rough so that standing waves will not exist between front and back, and therefore the laser cavity will be of length *L*; the laser emission will emerge from either end face A or B but not the side C.

The gain per unit length in the junction region due to stimulated emission is given by (6-16):

$$G = \frac{\mu}{c}\left(\frac{1}{\rho}\frac{d\rho}{dt}\right), \tag{6-16}$$

where ρ = photon density
μ = index of refraction
c = speed of light

and $d\rho/dt$ is the net rate of generation of photons. The gain per unit length for one mode is then given by

$$G_{\text{mode}} = \kappa G, \tag{6-17}$$

where κ is the fraction of photons going into the oscillating mode at the frequency (ν) where the spontaneous linewidth is $\Delta\nu$ and the cavity volume is V:

$$\kappa = \frac{c^3}{8\pi\nu^2\Delta\nu V} \tag{6-18}$$

$$G_{\text{mode}} = \kappa G$$

$$= \left(\frac{\lambda^2}{8\pi\mu^2}\right)\left(\frac{1}{\Delta\nu \cdot V}\right)\left(\frac{1}{\rho}\frac{d\rho}{dt}\right) \tag{6-19}$$

$$= \left(\frac{\lambda^2}{8\pi\mu^2}\right)P. \tag{6-20}$$

Note that P is the photon generation rate per unit volume per unit frequency interval.

This photon generation rate (P) can also be written in terms of the electric current density (J). Let ϵ be the efficiency of conversion of hole-electron pairs in the junction region into photons; it is the number of photons generated per hole-electron pair injected into the junction of thickness w. Then we write

$$P = (J\epsilon)\left(\frac{1}{e}\right)\left(\frac{1}{w}\right)\frac{1}{\Delta\nu}$$

$$= \left(\frac{1}{w}\right)\left(\frac{J\epsilon}{e}\right)\left(\frac{1}{\Delta\nu}\right). \tag{6.21}$$

Inserting this result into the gain equation (6-20), we see that

$$G_{\text{mode}} = \left(\frac{\lambda^2}{8\pi\mu^2}\right)\left(\frac{J\epsilon}{ew}\right)\left(\frac{1}{\Delta\nu}\right). \tag{6-22}$$

The losses from the junction can now be considered as composed of three elements:

1. Diffraction losses (α_D) at the aperture of the emitting region. This would occur at the aperture of size Hxw in Figure 6-10.

2. Losses due to transmission through the surface at face A or B.

3. Absorption (α_0) in the p and n regions on either side of the actual junction region.

The loss per unit length of the cavity can then be written

$$\text{loss/length} = \left(\alpha_0 + \alpha_D + \frac{T}{L}\right), \tag{6-23}$$

where T is the transmission across the end face of the diode. The threshold current J_t can be written by equating the losses (6-23) with the gain (6-22):

$$\left(\frac{\lambda^2}{8\pi\mu^2}\right)\left(\frac{1}{\Delta\nu}\right)\left(\frac{J_t\epsilon}{ew}\right) = \left(\alpha_0 + \alpha_D + \frac{T}{L}\right). \tag{6-24}$$

Thus

$$J_t = \frac{8\pi\mu^2 ew\Delta\nu}{\lambda^2\epsilon}\left(\alpha_0 + \alpha_D + \frac{T}{L}\right). \tag{6-25}$$

This can also be written in terms of the photon energy (E), where

$$E = h\nu. \tag{6-26}$$

Then

$$J_t = \frac{8\pi\mu^2 ew}{h^3\epsilon}E^2 \cdot \Delta E\left(\alpha_0 + \alpha_D + \frac{T}{L}\right). \tag{6-27}$$

By expressing the length measurements in centimeters, the energy in electron volts, and the current density in amperes per square centimeter, we evaluate the constant term and obtain

$$J_t = 6.3 \times 10^4\left(\frac{\mu^2 w}{\epsilon}\right)E^2 \cdot \Delta E\left(\alpha_0 + \alpha_D + \frac{T}{L}\right). \tag{6-28}$$

If the gain for a current density well above the threshold value is *considerably* greater than the losses for the lowest loss mode and the population inversion occurs well below threshold, we can let $\alpha_o = 0$ to a good approximation. In a normal laser diode, however the junction width (w) is very small, usually of the order of 10^{-4} cm, and therefore diffraction losses will be a major factor. Because of this diffraction effect all the light reflected from one end of the diode is not incident on the reflector at the other end. For the lowest order mode, assuming that the reflector width is the same as the junction width and plane-parallel, the diffraction loss factor (α_D) is given by

$$\alpha_D = 0.35(L)^{1/2}\left(\frac{\lambda}{\mu w^2}\right)^{3/2} \tag{6-29}$$

for the case in which

$$L\lambda/\mu w^2 \ll 1. \tag{6-30}$$

If we assume that the diode is coated with broad reflecting strips much greater in extent than the junction width (w), the loss of the lowest mode will be determined by absorption in the surrounding material and diffraction will occur over a larger aperture. Because of the absorption in the surrounding material in this case, the photon wave intensity will be reduced at the edge of the reflecting aperture and thus diffraction losses will be considerably changed. This evaluation is made by considering the light wave as being conducted down a waveguide with gain and of thickness (w) but surrounded by a lossy medium. The boundary condition

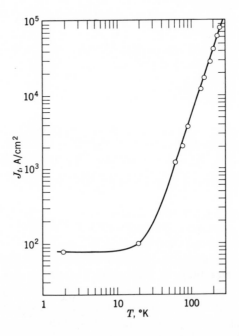

Figure 6-11 Threshold current for stimulated emission as a function of temperature for a gallium arsenide laser diode. After Burns et al., *Proc. IEEE* (1963).

on this solution requires that the wave and its derivative be continuous at the boundary between the junction region and the adjacent lossy material. The maximum diffraction loss factor is given by

$$\alpha_D = 0.42\left(\frac{\lambda}{\mu w^2}\right). \qquad (6\text{-}31)$$

A reflector material is not necessary for a semiconductor laser diode to operate as a laser. In gallium arsenide, for instance, the index of refraction is so high that the reflection at the air surface is approximately 35%, which is sufficient to provide feedback and obtain laser action. Of course, the threshold can be reduced by coating one end, but the diminished light output does not merit coating the output end also.

Finally, it should be noted that the threshold current density is also temperature-sensitive. This can be explained on the basis of increased loss by photon absorption due to free electrons, a variation illustrated in Figure 6-11. The theoretical explanation for this curve is given in terms of the increased reabsorption of radiation in the band-to-band transitions and the reduced effectiveness of stimulated emission. As the temperature increases, a higher density of empty states in the conduction band and valence band are permitted, for a greater deviation from total degeneracy occurs; reabsorption increases because more states are available. The variation of threshold current density with temperature after the knee of the curve is passed goes approximately as

$$J_t \sim T^3.$$

This curve, although given for gallium arsenide, is representative of indium phosphide as well.

6-3   LASER MATERIALS AND OUTPUT SPECTRA

Injection laser diodes have been successfully fabricated from many semiconductor materials. This allows the selection of various wavelengths by choosing the appropriate material. Table 6-1 lists the various semiconductors and the laser emission wavelengths that have been successfully obtained from them. The operating temperatures are also shown.

The original semiconductor diode lasers were fabricated from gallium arsenide, a material that has been investigated more extensively than others. The availability of GaAs in high quality crystals and high purity has led to its extensive use.

Figure 6-12 shows a plot of the output from a gallium arsenide laser for

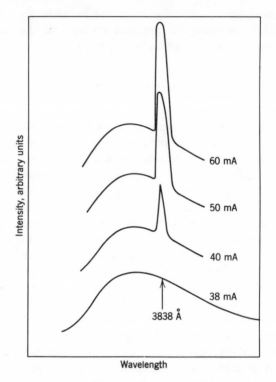

Figure 6-12   Emission spectra of a CW diode laser below threshold (38 mA) and at several values above threshold. The intensity of the emission increases dramatically at the laser wavelength. Note also the line narrowing. After Howard et al., *IBM J. Res.* (1963).

various current levels in the diode. A plot of output intensity versus wavelength is shown in Figure 6-13 for a diode fabricated from PbTe and operated at 12°K. The current through this diode is above threshold. The ends were cleaved to form the cavity.

The output wavelength can be changed or shifted by placing the diode in a magnetic field, exerting pressure on the material, or changing the temperature. The nature of these influences is discussed in the following sections.

6-4   EFFECT OF MAGNETIC FIELD ON LASER OUTPUT

The presence of a magnetic field affects the wavelength of emission and the threshold current in laser diodes. For instance, a magnetic field of the order of 15,000 gauss causes observable shifts in the spectral output of gallium arsenide diodes. This is attributed to a shift of output among

TABLE 6-1   SEMICONDUCTOR INJECTION
LASER MATERIALS

Material	Wavelength (μ)	Temperature (°C)
GaAs	0.84	20 (pulsed) −195 (continuous)
InAs	3.1	−196 (pulsed) −296 (continuous)
InP	0.91	−153 (pulsed) −253 (continuous)
Ga($As_x P_{1-x}$)	0.65–0.84	−175
PbTe	6.5	−285 (pulsed)
InSb	5.2	
Ga–InAs	0.84–3.1	−270 (pulsed)
PbSe	8.5	−270 (pulsed)

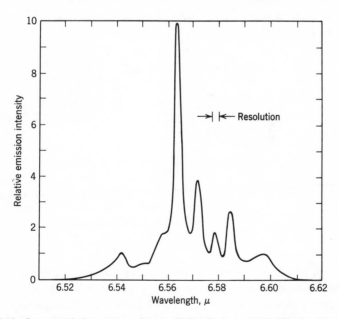

Figure 6-13   Laser emission spectra from a PbTe diode at 12°K. The mode structure is evident. The current through the diode is above the threshold value. After Butler et al., *Appl. Phys. Letters* (1964).

various modes that arise in different regions of the diode junction. The magnetic field causes a spatial redistribution of the laser filaments emitting the radiation.

The emission from gallium arsenide diodes, made with an initial doping density of 2×10^{17} per cm³, has been measured in very high magnetic fields. In a field of 90,000 gauss the emission frequency shifted *quadratically* with the applied field toward higher frequencies.

Because no linear magnetic shift of the emission line is expected if the initial state of the transition is the conduction band of pure material, it appears that the initial state cannot be the regular conduction band. The observed quadratic shift, however, is approximately equal to the shift for the ground state of a hydrogen atom–like donor. For this electron concentration range Hall effect measurements indicate that the donor level is probably merged with the conduction band. Thus it is possible that states near the bottom of this distorted conduction band would show the quadratic shift expected of the donor states.

In indium arsenide diodes, however, the emission line of incoherent radiation shifts to higher energy *linearly* with magnetic field. For lightly doped diodes the shift is equal to the expected energy band gap increase for the indium arsenide. This linear shift of energy with magnetic field can be explained in principle by the shift of the energy gap with magnetic field by the following relation:

$$\Delta E_g \approx \tfrac{1}{2}h(\omega_c + \omega_v), \qquad (6\text{-}32)$$

where ω_c and ω_v are the cyclotron frequencies of electrons and holes, respectively. These frequencies are related to the magnetic field (H) and the effective masses (m^*) as follows:

$$\omega_c = \frac{eH}{m_c^* c}$$

$$\omega_v = \frac{eH}{m_v^* c} \qquad (6\text{-}33)$$

Indeed, to a first approximation, the shift of the laser emission in both indium arsenide and indium antimonide can be explained on this basis. At very high fields of the order of 100 kilogauss, the frequency can be tuned by as much as 5–10%. Also, for InAs lasers there is a shift of the output from one spectral mode to another with the magnetic field. This shift is in the same direction as the shift of the spontaneous emission

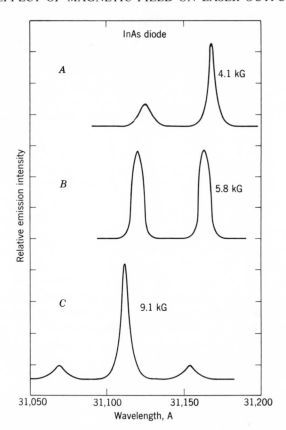

Figure 6-14 Laser line intensity versus wavelength with a magnetic field applied. Note the change in the preferred mode of operation as evidenced by the shift in wavelength for various values of magnetic field strength. With the shift in index of refraction the cavity resonant wavelength shifts. After Melngailis and Rediker, *Appl. Phys. Letters* (1963).

peak. In addition, the individual modes shift to higher energies with increasing field. This apparently is due to a decrease of the index of refraction with field (Figure 6-14).

Another striking effect of magnetic field on InAs lasers is a pronounced decrease of the threshold current density. A reduction by a factor of 4 was observed for about 8.6 kilogauss as illustrated in Figure 6-15. The effect tends to saturate with increasing field, and is largest for a transverse field. In Figure 6-15 the magnetic field is perpendicular to the direction of current flow.

This phenomenon of decreasing threshold can be explained in terms of the influence of the magnetic field on the diffusion coefficient of the

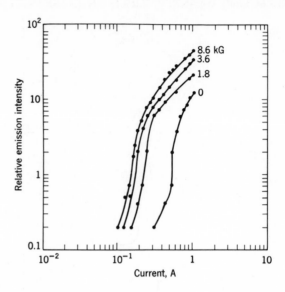

Figure 6-15 Laser emission intensity versus current for an InAs diode at 4.2°K. The threshold value of current shifts to considerably lower values with the application of a magnetic field. After Melngailis and Rediker, *Appl. Phys. Letters* (1963).

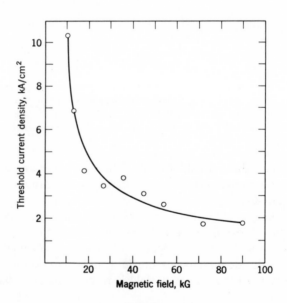

Figure 6-16 A graph showing the variation of threshold current with magnetic field in InSb laser diodes. Courtesy of Phelan et al., *Appl. Phys. Letters* (1963).

carriers moving into the junction region. The change is reflected by the relation

$$D_H = \frac{D_0}{\omega_c \tau},$$

where D_H is the diffusion constant in the presence of the field, ω_c is the cyclotron frequency, and τ is the collision time. At very high fields the transverse field might actually be disadvantageous for it could cut off the flow of current and inhibit injection. A curve showing the effect of the magnetic field on the actual threshold current density is given in Figure 6-16 for indium arsenide.

It should be noted that the appearance of mode structure, as illustrated in the three spectra of Figure 6-14, is a strong indication of laser action. The frequency separation between the adjacent modes of a Fabry-Perot cavity, modes that differ by a half-wavelength between the reflecting surfaces, is given by

$$\Delta\lambda = \frac{\lambda^2}{2L[\mu - \lambda(d\mu/d\lambda)]} \qquad (6\text{-}34)$$

and may be correlated with the length (L) of the cavity. It may also be used to determine accurately the refractive index and its dispersion in the host material and thus refine our technique of measurements.

It should be noted finally that still another effect of the magnetic field that reduces the threshold current is associated with the splitting of the energy levels into magnetic sub-bands. Here the energy relations are given by

$$E_n = \left(n + \frac{1}{2}\right)\hbar\omega_c + \frac{p^2}{2m^*}, \qquad (6\text{-}35)$$

where the magnetic field H is taken along the z-direction and n is the magnetic quantum number, p the momentum, and m^* the effective mass. The consequence is that the density of states is varied and causes a peaking of the emission therefore, also reduces the threshold. It can be separated from the diffusion effect by applying the magnetic field parallel to the current flow.

6-5 EFFECT OF TEMPERATURE AND PRESSURE ON LASER EMISSION

Just as the presence of a magnetic field will affect the injection diode light output, so will variations in temperature and pressure. The wavelength of the laser emission is altered by these two factors. The dependence of the threshold current on temperature has already been reviewed in the section on threshold conditions, and that discussion is not repeated here.

Let us note, however, that the exact wavelength (λ) of the laser output is determined by the effective length (L) of the laser cavity by the relation

$$n\lambda = 2\mu L, \qquad (6\text{-}36)$$

where μ is the index of refraction and n is the mode number. Thus the wavelength of a given cavity mode, corresponding to a given value of n, will vary as the index of refraction and the length of the cavity. For the laser radiation arising from transitions between the bottom of the conduction band and the top of the valence band, that is, photon energies near the band gap energy, the temperature or pressure changes will have a larger fractional effect on the index (μ) than on the length (L). Thus, besides measuring the separation between the modes at a given temperature, we can also measure the temperature dependence of the wavelength of the emission.

We note, too, that the broad spontaneous emission has nearly the same temperature dependence as the band gap. For GaAs the peak of the spontaneous emission shifts to longer wavelength as the temperature is raised at a rate of 1.2 Å/deg at 77°K, whereas the mode shift with temperature at 8400 Å is only 0.46 Å/deg.

Similar measurement on indium phosphide yield a spontaneous emission peak shift with temperature of 1.6 Å/deg and a mode shift of 0.55 Å/deg at a 9100 Å wavelength.

The conclusion to be drawn from this is that the individual modes have a smaller temperature coefficient than the spontaneous emission peak. Thus, as the temperature is raised, the modes at shorter wavelengths will cease to emit, whereas the ones at longer wavelengths will increase in intensity. This follows, for a cavity mode can be excited only if its wavelength is close to the emission peak and only here will the gain be high enough to maintain oscillations.

By examining (6-36) we can understand the temperature dependence of the modes. Let us differentiate the wavelength (λ) with respect to temperature and note that the index of refraction is a function of both temperature and wavelength. We then obtain

$$\frac{1}{\lambda}\frac{d\lambda}{dT} = \frac{1}{\mu}\left(\frac{\partial \mu}{\partial \lambda}\right)_T \frac{d\lambda}{dT} + \frac{1}{\mu}\left(\frac{\partial \mu}{\partial T}\right)_\lambda + \frac{1}{L}\frac{dL}{dT}. \qquad (6\text{-}37)$$

Because, as previously mentioned, the linear expansion term is negligible, the temperature dependence of the mode wavelength is determined only by the temperature and wavelength dependence of the index of refraction.

$$\frac{1}{\lambda}\frac{d\lambda}{dT} = \frac{1}{\mu}\left(\frac{\partial\mu}{\partial T}\right)_\lambda\left[1 - \frac{\lambda}{\mu}\left(\frac{d\mu}{d\lambda}\right)_T\right]^{-1}. \tag{6-38}$$

To put this in more easily measured terms we take (6-36) and differentiate to obtain the following:

$$n\lambda = 2\mu L \tag{6-36}$$

$$\lambda\frac{dn}{d\lambda} + n = 2L\frac{d\mu}{d\lambda}. \tag{6-39}$$

For single-mode separation and for large n we substitute

$$d\lambda \sim \Delta\lambda$$

$$dn = -1$$

$$n = \frac{2\mu L}{\lambda}; \tag{6-40}$$

the result is

$$\left[1 - \frac{\lambda}{\mu}\left(\frac{d\mu}{d\lambda}\right)\right] = \left(\frac{1}{2\mu L}\right)\left(\frac{\lambda^2}{\Delta\lambda}\right), \tag{6-41}$$

where $\Delta\lambda$ is the mode separation.

It makes more sense to rewrite (6-38) and combine the experimentally measured parameters to determine the temperature dependence of the index of refraction. Using (6-38) and (6-41) we obtain

$$\left(\frac{\partial\mu}{\partial T}\right)_\lambda = \left(\frac{1}{2L}\right)\left(\frac{\lambda^2}{\Delta\lambda}\right)\left(\frac{1}{\lambda}\frac{d\lambda}{dT}\right). \tag{6-42}$$

For gallium arsenide the variation of refractive index with temperature becomes

$$\frac{d\mu}{dT} = 2.9 \times 10^{-4}/\text{deg}.$$

The laser emission wavelength also changes with pressure just as it does with temperature. The pressure exerted on the semiconductor material changes the band gap. In gallium arsenide the pressure dependence of the energy of the broad spontaneous emission is 1.1×10^{-5} eV/atm, which agrees with the pressure coefficient of the energy gap. The pressure dependence of the modes is much smaller—about 3×10^{-6} eV/atm.

Again, considering (6-38) but differentiating with respect to pressure, we obtain an expression similiar to (6-43) except that pressure (P) replaces the temperature term:

$$\frac{d\mu}{dP} = \left(\frac{1}{2L}\right)\left(\frac{\lambda^2}{\Delta\lambda}\right)\left(\frac{1}{\lambda}\frac{d\lambda}{dP}\right). \tag{6-43}$$

The term dL/dP is still small compared with the other terms. In gallium arsenide the result is

$$\frac{1}{\mu}\left(\frac{d\mu}{dP}\right) = 3 \times 10^{-7}/\text{atm}.$$

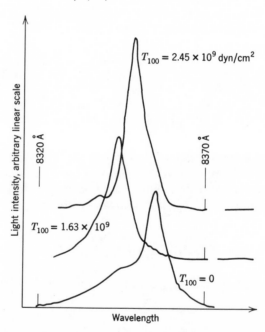

Figure 6-17 Recorder trace of the laser emission for a gallium arsenide diode for different values of stress applied along the 100 crystal direction. The curves are displaced vertically for clear presentation. The diode was at 77°K. After Meyerhofer and Braunstein, *Appl. Phys. Letters* (1963).

The application of uniaxial stress to semiconductors generally splits energy level that are degenerate in the absence of stress. Figure 6-17 shows the effect of uniaxial compression on the coherent emission of a typical lasing diode. Here the stress is applied perpendicularly to the junction in the (100) plane. The emission lines shown here are envelopes of a number of resonant modes.

The laser threshold current in gallium arsenide always decreases on the application of uniaxial pressure. A typical plot of threshold current as a function of pressure is shown in Figure 6–18. The threshold current is the current at which an emission spike begins to grow out of the narrow spontaneous curve.

The lowering of the laser threshold can be explained most simply by assuming that the application of a uniaxial strain normal to the plane of the junction increases the probability of spontaneous emission of photons in a direction parallel to the plane of the junction and decreases the probability in the direction perpendicular to the junction. This is feasible because the uniaxial strain destroys the cubic symmetry and causes an anisotropic spatial distribution of the spontaneously emitted photons. In the presence of strain more photons are emitted into the preferred modes, and thus the threshold will be lowered.

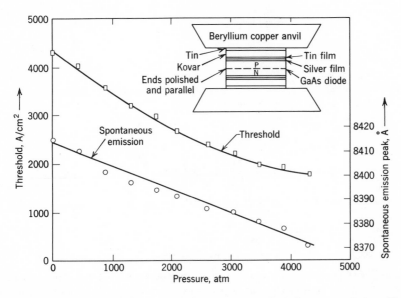

Figure 6-18 Shift of threshold current with pressure applied along one axis in gallium arsenide. The peak of sponteneous emission also shifts as predicted. After Ryan and Miller, *Appl. Phys. Letters* (1963).

Below threshold only those photons emitted parallel to the junction have a high probability of emerging from the diode. Because we assume that the number of these preferred photons would increase with uniaxial strain we expect an increase in the output of the diodes when a strain is applied.

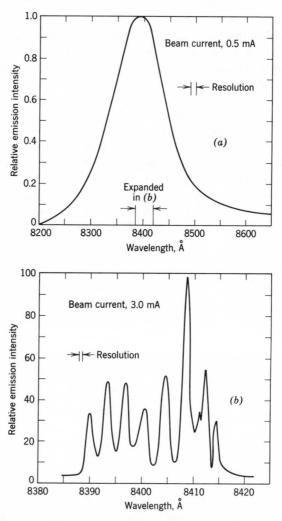

Figure 6-19 Emission spectra from a gallium arsenide sample pumped with an electron beam. The top curve (*a*) shows the spontaneous line below threshold while the bottom curve (*b*) shows the laser line and mode structure. Note that the wavelength scale for the lower curve is expanded. The intensity scale is similarly expanded. After Hurwitz and Keyes, *Appl Phys. Letters* (1964).

6-6 ALTERNATIVE SCHEMES FOR PUMPING
SEMICONDUCTOR LASERS

The pumping of injection lasers has most usually been accomplished by forward biasing the semiconductor diode and forcing a large current through it. Some other techniques successfully employed for generating laser emission in semiconductors include bombardment of the semiconductor with an intense electron beam and optically pumping with radiation from another laser.

Laser action in *p*-type gallium arsenide was excited by bombardment by a pulsed beam of 50-keV electrons. This beam was focused on a cleaved surface of the sample, and light emission occurred in a direction normal to the axis of the electron beam. The faces from which the laser radiation emerged were polished to form the optical cavity. The emission spectra of the sample below and above threshold are shown in Figure 6-19 for liquid helium temperatures. The line narrowing and the development of mode structure with the onset of laser action are immediately noticeable in this figure.

The intensity of the emitted radiation varies approximately linearly with the beam current at low currents below threshold. Above 2mA the intensity rises rapidly. This indicates the onset of laser action and corresponds to a threshold beam current density of about 1 A/cm^2. Assuming that the mean total energy required to produce a hole-electron pair in GaAs is 5 eV, this is equivalent to a threshold current density of 10^4 A/cm^2 in a diode injection laser.

The emission can also be viewed through an infrared snooperscope. The emission is intense at spots along the edge of the crystal, indicating

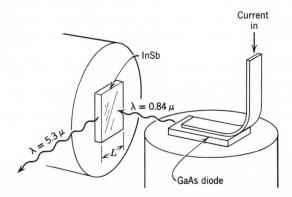

Figure 6-20 A suggested experimental configuration for pumping an InSb sample with a gallium arsenide laser diode. After Phelan and Rediker, *Appl. Phys. Letters* (1965).

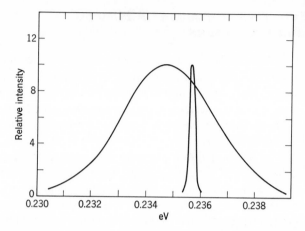

Figure 6-21   Plot of spectra for InSb when pumped using radiation from a gallium arsenide laser diode. Notice the linewidth narrowing when laser emission occurs. The intensity scales have been normalized for comparing the linewidth accurately. After Phelan and Rediker, *Appl. Phys. Letters* (1965).

that laser action takes place in filaments along the cleaved surface. In a similar manner laser action has been excited with electron beams in *n*-type GaAs, InAs, InSb, and GaSb.

Electron-beam pumping provides a means of obtaining laser action in semiconductors in which it is difficult to produce good *p-n* junctions.

The optical pumping of InSb and associated laser action has been successfully accomplished by using the intense beam from a GaAs laser diode. The experimental arrangement for achieving this is shown in Figure 6-20. The radiation from the GaAs diode is incident on an optically flat face of InSb. The two faces were cleaved perpendicular to the (100) axis to form a Fabry-Perot cavity. Laser emission from the InSb in the vertical direction was prevented by roughening the other two faces.

The radiation line shape below and above threshold is shown in Figure 6-21. Again, the line narrowing is evident as laser action begins.

The threshold of this optically pumped InSb compares favorably with the threshold value of 2000 A/cm² for a *p-n* junction injection laser diode fabricated from the same material.

REFERENCES

Bernard, M. G. A., and G. Duraffourg, "Laser Conditions in Semiconductors," *Phys. Stat. Solidi*, **1**, 699–703 (1961).

Burns, G., F. H. Dill, and M. I. Nathan, "The Effect of Temperature on the Properties of GaAs Lasers," *Proc. IEEE*, **51**, 947–948 (June 1963).

Burns, G., and M. I. Nathan, "P-N Junction Lasers," *Proc. IEEE*, **52,** 770–794 (July 1964).

Butler, J. F., A. R. Calawa, R.H. Rediker, R. J. Phelan, T. C. Harman, and A. J. Strauss, "PbTe Diode Laser," *Appl. Phys. Letters*, **5,** 75–77 (August 15, 1964).

Hall, R. N., "Coherent Light Emission from p-n Junctions," *Solid-State Electron.*, **6,** 405–416 (September–October 1963).

Howard, W. E., F. F. Fang, F. H. Dill, Jr., and M. I. Nathan. "CW Operation of a GaAs Injection Laser," *IBM J. Res. Develop.*, **7,** 74-75 (January 1963).

Hurwitz, C. E., and R. J. Keyes, "Electron Beam Pumped GaAs Laser," *Appl. Phys. Letters*, **5,** 139–141 (October 1, 1964).

Johnson, C. M., "Injection Laser Systems for Communications and Tracking," *Electronics*, **36,** 34–39 (December 13, 1963).

Lasher, G. J., "Threshold Conditions and Diffraction Loss for Injection Lasers," *IBM J. Res. Develop.*, **7,** 58–61 (January 1963).

Lax, B., "Semiconductor Diode Lasers," *Solid-St. Design*, **4,** 26–32 (November 1963).

Lax, B., "Progress in Semiconductor Lasers," *IEEE Spectrum*, **2,** 62–75 (July 1965).

McWhorter, A. L., "Electromagnetic Theory of the Semiconductor Injection Laser," *Solid-State. Electron.*, **6,** 417–423 (September 1963).

Melngailis, I., and R. H. Rediker, "Magnetically Tunable CW InAs Diode Maser," *Appl. Phys. Letters*, **2,** 202–204 (June 1, 1963).

Meyerhofer, D., and R. Braunstein, "Frequency Tuning of GaAs Laser Diode by Uniaxial Stress," *Appl. Phys. Letters*, **3,** 171–172 (November 15, 1963).

Phelan, R. J., A. R. Calawa, R. H. Rediker, R. J. Keyes, and B. Lax, "Infrared InSb Diode in High Magnetic Fields, " *Appl. Phys. Letters*, **3,** 143–145 (November 1, 1963).

Phelan, R. J., and R. H. Rediker, "Optically Pumped Semiconductor Lasers," *Appl. Phys. Letters*, **6,** 70–71 (February 15, 1965).

Rediker, R. H., "Semiconductor Lasers," *Phys. Today*, **18,** 42–50 (February 1965).

Ryan, F. M., and R. C. Miller, "The Effect of Uniaxial Strain on the Threshold Current and Output of GaAs Lasers," *Appl. Phys. Letters*, **3,** 162–163 (November 1, 1963).

Steele, E. L., "Descriptive Theory of Semiconductors," *Am. J. Phys.*, **25,** 174–179 (March 1957).

Definition of Symbols

CHAPTER 1

A_{21}	Einstein A coefficient (p. 6)
$B_{21}; B_{12}$	Einstein B coefficients (p. 6)
E_i	Energy level at state (i) (p. 5)
$n_1; n_2; n_3$	Electron densities in states at energy $E_1; E_2; E_3$ (p. 6)
$n_u; n_l$	Electron densities of upper (u) and lower (l) states in a two-level system (p. 33)
$B_s = B/\Delta\nu$	Einstein coefficient per unit frequency interval (p. 24)
$(\Delta n)_t = 1/B_s\tau_c$	Threshold value of electron inversion $(n_2 - n_1)_t$ (p. 27)
N	Total electron density in the laser system (p. 22)
κ	Fractional number of photons per mode in laser cavity (p. 23)
g_i	Degeneracy of states at E_i (p. 6)
λ	Wavelength (p. 7)
P_{out}	Power output (p. 31)
$\rho; \rho(\nu)$	Photon or quantum density at frequency (ν) (p. 7)
μ_m	Maximum dipole moment of linear oscillator (p. 4)
W	Energy of dipole oscillator (p. 4)
ν_{21}	Frequency of quantum emitted by transition between E_2 and E_1 (p. 5)
τ_s	Spontaneous radiative lifetime (p. 8)
τ_c	Decay or ringing time of optical cavity (p . 23)
τ_{ij}	Spontaneous lifetime or relaxation rate between states E_i and E_j (p. 22)
w_{ij}	Stimulated emission or absorption rate between E_i and E_j (p. 22)
w_p	Pump rate in a two-level system (p. 33)
w_i	Induced emission or absorption rate in a two-level system (p. 33)

CHAPTER 2

ϵ	Dielectric constant (p. 66)
$\phi_x; \phi_y; \phi_z$	Electro-optic phase shift for electric field in x, y, z direction (p. 60)
ϕ_0	Electro-optic phase shift with no applied field (p. 61)
$\Delta\phi$	Electro-optic phase shift due to addition of field (p. 61)
E, E_0	Electric field (p. 59)
V_0	Voltage for maximum transmission in an electro-optic modulator (p. 63)
ω_m	Modulating circular frequency (p. 64)

256

I, I_0	Intensity of electromagnetic wave in electro-optic modulator (p. 64)
Q	Quality factor of resonator (p. 71)
r	Linear electro-optic coefficient (p. 58)
P	Quadratic electro-optic coefficient (p. 58)
K_v	Verdet constant (p. 51)
λ	Wavelength (p. 74)
λ_c	Cutoff wavelength in an absorption modulator (p. 74)
d	Gap spacing in FTIR coupler (p. 79)
ω_S; ω_L	Angular frequency of signal (S) and local oscillator (L) for heterodyne mixing (p. 90)
R_s; T_s	Reflectivity and transmissivity of electromagnetic wave with propagation vector *normal* to plane of incidence (p. 80)
R_p; T_p	Reflectivity and transmissivity of electromagnetic wave with propagation vector *parallel* to plane of incidence (p. 80)

CHAPTER 3

a	Half-width of Lorentzian line (p. 102)
α	Gain coefficient per unit length in laser (p. 100)
α_D	Loss coefficient for diffraction losses (p. 120)
g_1; g_2	Degeneracy factor of states at E_1 and E_2 (p. 102)
$g(\nu)$	Probability of absorption or emission per unit frequency interval (p. 102)
Φ	Photon density (p. 100)
Φ_0	Steady-state photon density (p. 107)
q	Perturbation of photon density (p. 112)
$n = n_2 - n_1$	Inverted electron population density (p. 105)
n_0	Steady-state inverted electron density (p. 107)
η	Perturbation of population inversion density (p. 112)
$N_{\max}$	Integration constant equal to *maximum* population inversion (p. 110)
R_1; R_2	Mirror reflectivity on ends of laser cavity (p. 99)
W_p	Pumping rate into excited laser level (p. 105)
β	Energy loss per reflection in optical resonator (p. 120)
B	Einstein B coefficient per quantum (p. 105)
τ_c	Decay or ringing time of optical cavity (p. 101)
t_0	Time at which population inversion occurs (p. 109)
t_1	Time at which photon density and inversion population are equal (p. 110)
t_D	Decay time of spiking pulses (p. 112)
τ_s	Spontaneous radiative lifetime (p. 104)
$T = 2\pi/\omega_s$	Period between spiking pulses (p. 113)
ω_s	Angular spiking frequency (p. 113)
θ	Spot size (radius) of Gaussian laser beam (p. 122)
r	Radius of laser cavity (p. 121)
μ	Index of refraction (p. 125)
f	Number of modes in optical cavity (p. 106)

CHAPTER 4

| a | Half-width of Lorentzian line (p. 159) |
| D | Total number of photons in Lorentzian pulse (p. 154) |

α	Absorption constant (p. 151)
α_g	Laser gain factor in noise model (p. 162)
α_s	Laser loss coefficient in noise model (p. 162)
B	Amplifier bandwidth (p. 160)
$\beta(\tau)$	Convenient transformation of variables related to photon density at amplifier input (p. 137)
c	Speed of light (p. 132)
F	Noise figure of amplifier (p. 161)
G_0	Single-pass amplifier gain in reflective amplifier (p. 128)
G_E	Energy gain of amplifier (p. 147)
$K(x)$	Integration constant arising from time integral (p. 139)
$I_0 = c\Phi_0$	Incident photon intensity, constant at amplifier input (p. 141)
L	Length of laser amplifier (p. 135)
$L_g = 1/\sigma\eta_0 N$	Characteristic gain length of amplifier (p. 144)
$n_1; n_2$	Electron densities in states $E_1; E_2$ (p. 132)
N	Total density of electrons in system (p. 134)
$\eta = (n_2 - n_1)/N$	Excess relative population density (p. 135)
$\eta_0(x, t)$	Distribution of relative population inversion when signal enters the amplifier (p. 135)
Φ	Photon density (p. 132)
$\phi_0(x, t)$	Relative photon density per atom at amplifier input (p. 136)
$\phi = 2\Phi/N$	Relative photon density per atom in laser system (p. 135)
P	Noise power (p. 161)
P_{in}	Input power in noise model (p. 161)
P_w	Noise power from surrounding sources (p. 162)
r	Reflectivity in reflective amplifier (p. 129)
$\rho = 1/\phi$	Transformation variable for integration (p. 137)
P_a	Power flow in amplifier (p. 163)
$S_i; S_0$	Input and output signal amplitude in reflective amplifier (p. 129)
σ	Resonance absorption cross section per atom for photon-electron interaction (p. 132)
σ_0	Maximum absorption cross section for Lorentzian line (p. 159)
$t' = t - L/c$	Time delay for pulse to traverse amplifier (p. 144)
τ_0	Pulse length of square input photon pulse (p. 141)
T_0	Temperature at input of amplifier (p. 161)
T_w	Temperature of surrounding noise sources (p. 162)
$\tau = t - x/c$	Transformed time variable (p. 136)
μ	Feedback factor (p. 128)
$\xi = x/c$	Transformed spatial variable (p. 136)
Γ	Combination of constants (p. 148)
T_a	Negative temperature of amplifier attributable to the inverted population density in amplifier (p. 163)
T	Half-width of a photon pulse having a Lorentzian time distribution (p. 154)

CHAPTER 5

α	Absorption constant (p. 191)
α_s	Loss factor due to incidental losses (p. 193)

ϵ_u	Energy utilization factor (p. 200)
E_{out}	Energy emitted in Q-pulse (p. 202)
γ_s	Photon loss rate from incidental losses (p. 188)
$\gamma_0(t)$	Photon loss rate due to that portion of photon flux emerging from the output port of laser (p. 188)
L_a	Length of laser rod (p. 193)
$n_1; n_2$	Electron density in states 1, 2 (p. 186)
$n = n_2 - n_1$	Excess electron population inversion density (p. 186)
N	Total electron density (p. 186)
$\eta = n/N$	Inversion ratio (p. 187)
η_t	Threshold value of inversion ratio (p. 197)
η_0	Initial value of inversion ratio before Q-switch (p. 199)
η_f	Final value of inversion ratio after Q-switch (p. 199)
P_p	Peak power out of Q-pulse (p. 204)
R, T	Reflectivity and transmissivity of end mirrors (p. 194)
Φ	Photon density (p. 186)
$\phi = 2\Phi/N$	Normalized photon density per electron (p. 187)
ϕ_i	Initial value of normalized photon density before Q-switching (p. 199)
ϕ_f	Final value of normalized photon density after Q-switch (p. 199)
ϕ_p	Peak value of normalized photon density (p. 203)
ϕ_D	Normalized photon density at end of delay time (p. 209)
S_{32}	Nonradiative transition rate between levels at E_3 and E_2 (p. 185)
τ_c	Ringing time of optical cavity (p. 198)
τ_s	Spontaneous decay time (p. 193)
T_D	Delay time of laser pulse (p. 209)
τ_{rise}	Rise time of Q-pulse spike (p. 208)
t_p	Time at which photon density is a maximum in cavity (p. 190)
t_s	Period of cosine Q-switch (p. 215)
w_{ij}	Transition rate per particle between level E_i and E_j (p. 185)
w_i	Number of induced transitions per photon (p. 186)
$w_s = 1/\tau_s$	Spontaneous decay rate from excited level in two-level system (p. 186)
w'_s	Rate of energy added to laser beam from spontaneous emission into cone along laser axis (p. 188)
$W_1; W_2$	High and low loss rate from laser cavity before and after Q-switching, respectively (p. 196)
$\xi = -\ln(\eta/\eta_t)$	Normalized variable of integration (p. 206)
w_p	Pumping rate per photon (p. 186)

CHAPTER 6

B_{vc}	Probability of transition between valence (v) band and conduction (c) band (p. 234)
$\alpha_D; \alpha_0$	Respectively, the diffraction loss and incidental loss coefficients (p. 238)
E_g	Band gap energy in semiconductor (Fig. 6-6)
$E_c; E_v$	Energy at bottom of conduction band and top of valence band respectively (Fig. 6-6)
$f_0; f_v$	Fermi function for conduction and valence band (p. 234)
ϵ	Number of photons generated per injected electron (p. 238)
$G; G_{\text{mode}}$	Gain and gain per mode in injection laser per unit length (p. 238)

J	Current density driving the diode (p. 238)
J_t	Threshold value of current density (p. 239)
ϕ_c; ϕ_v	Fermi level in conduction and valence band on opposite sides of p-n junction (p. 232)
ϕ_f	Fermi level in semiconductor (p. 231)
$\rho(\nu)$	Photon density (p. 234)
w	Thickness of junction region in injection diode (Fig. 6-10)

Index

Absorption, coefficient, 191
  constant, 192
  cross section, 151, 152
    for Lorentzian line, 154
  edge, shift with applied field, 74
  spectra, Nd in CaWo$_4$, 14
    for ruby, 14
ADP (ammonium dihydrogen phosphate), 65
Aluminum oxide, 8, 191; *see also* Ruby
Amplification, at optical frequencies, 1
Amplifier, 127, 132, 135, 142
  action, 132
  image intensity, 47
  laser, 127, 128, 131, 132, 141, 153, 158, 167, 171
  measurements, 169
  multistage, 46
  one-stage, 46
  reflective, 128, 131
  regenerative, 49
  single-stage arrangement, 49
  traveling wave, 49

Bandwidth, 103
  equation, 160
    of amplifier, definition, 158
    of laser amplifier, 153, 158
Bernoulli equation, 213
Birefringence, 59
  induced, 77
Boltzmann relation, 166
Bragg reflection criteria, 76
Brewster angle, 47
  faces, 131
    on circulator, 56

Brewster angle, of optical surface, 128, 129

Cadmium selenide, 87
Cadmium sulfide, 87
Calcium fluoride, 8
Calcium tungstate, 14
  in ellipsoidal cavity, 45
Carrier, lifetime in germanium, 74
  transit time in detector, 90
Cavity, circular cylinder, 42
  decay time, 23, 109
  design, laser, 17, 39
  double cylinder, 42
  elliptical, 41
  loss rate, 109, 116
  modes, 118, 248
    condition for resonance, 118
    of injection laser, 224
  regeneration, 115
  resonant, 98, 106
  see also Fabry-Perot
Circulator, degree of isolation, 55
  insertion loss, 55
  optical, 52, 57
Coefficient, Einstein A, 8, 104, 106
  Einstein B, 8, 102, 104, 106, 163
  Einstein probability, 5
  induced emission, 7
  linear loss, 193
  radiation rate, 100
Contact potential difference, 228
Conversion efficiency, 32
Cooling measures for laser cavity, 43
Correlation time, electron-photon, 92
Critical angle, 181
  for internal reflection in prism, 79

Cross section, effective atom, 132
  per atom, 151
  resonance absorption, 132
Cuprous chloride, 68
Curie, constant, 69
  point, 69, 70
  temperature, 69
Curie-Weiss law, 69

Daly-Sims Q-switch, 180
Decay time, of spiking pulse train, 114
Degeneracy factors, 6, 7, 102, 105
Degenerate semiconductor regions, 231
Delay time, end of, 210
  in Q-pulse, 195, 207, 215
Delta function, 149
  Dirac, 101
Depopulation of lower state, 28
Detectivity, 90
Detector devices, 90
  laser, 83, 94
  photoconductive, 83
  photoemissive, 83, 90, 94
  photomixing, 83, 90
  photon effect, 83
  photovoltaic, 83, 87
  response time, 87
  thermal effect, 83, 90
Dielectric constant, in a modulator, 66
  versus temperature of ferroelectric, 69
Diffraction grating, from acoustic waves, 76
Diffraction losses, 188
  confocal arrangement, 123
  confocal resonator, 123
  factor, for junction, 240
  of junction, 238, 239, 240
Diode, gallium arsenide, 227
  laser, 227, 235, 241
  photoemissive, 84
Dipole moment, 4, 8
Divergence of beam, 11, 193
Doping, with Mn, 14
  with Nd, 14
Doppler shift from moving grating, 76
Double-lamp configuration, 42
Double pulsing, from Q-switching, 217
Dummy variable of integration, 138

Efficiency of conversion of hole-electron
  pairs, 238
Einstein radiation coefficients, 5

Einstein stimulated emission coefficient, 24
  see also Coefficient, Einstein
Electric field, driving, 3
  phase of, 1, 2, 5
Electroacoustic modulation, 76
Electron, classical, 2
  oscillating, 2
Electronic system, two-level, 6
Electron inversion, initial distribution, 139
  ratio, 189
Electron population excess, 186
Electron population inversion, 221
Electro-optical axis, 59, 61
Electro-optical effect, 58, 69, 70
Elements, FTIR, 77, 81
  nonreciprocal, 50
Ellipsoid of revolution, 43
Emission, fluorescent, 23
  induced, 2, 5
  rate, induced, 22
  spontaneous, 6, 9
  stimulated, 2, 5, 9, 98, 101, 105
  wavelength change with pressure, 249
Enclosure, double ellipse, 17
  elliptical, 17
  test for laser material, 16
Energy, transfer of, 4
  utilization factor, 200, 202, 203
Energy gain, 150
  of amplifier, 149
  for impulse function, 153
  in pulse, 147
Energy levels, 8
Energy state, discrete, 5

Fabry-Perot, cavity, 98, 121, 122, 123, 182,
  224, 247, 254
  resonator, 122
Faraday, effect, 50, 51, 52
  isolator, 53, 54
  rotator, 51, 56
  for Q-switching, 178
Feedback, 116
  amplifier, 131
  factor, 128, 131
  negative, 128
  optical, 2
  positive, 128, 131
  reflection, in p-n junction, 233
  signal, 128
Fermi, function, 233

Fermi, level, 231, 232, 233, 235
Ferroelectrics, 69
Four-level laser, 20, 24, 26, 29, 30, 32, 36
  laser system, 12, 104
  scheme, 23, 27
Four-port device, 52, 56
Frequency, response of photodiodes, 88
  of spiking oscillation, 113
Frustrated total internal reflection, 77
  dependence on spacing, 79

Gain, equation, 144, 148, 151, 152
  factor, 128, 162, 163
    for oscillator, 99
  optical, in p-n junction, 236
  power, 146, 156
  single-pass, 128, 132, 144, 159
  per unit length, 146
  see also Energy gain
Gallium arsenide, 241, 244, 249, 253, 254
  as absorption modulator, 74
  as detector, 87
  emission shift with temperature, 248
  in modulator, 66
Germanium, as absorption modulator, 74
  as detector, 86
  as FTIR cell, 82
Giant pulse, 151, 177, 185, 190, 200
Glan-Thompson prism, 50

Half-width, atomic line, 160
  of Lorentzian line, 159
Hall effect, 244
Helix slow wave structure, 94
Host material, 8, 12

Impurities, supplementary, 16
Incidental loss fraction, 194
Index of refraction, 77, 125, 241, 248, 249
  change with field, 60, 61, 72
  decrease with magnetic field, 245
  temperature dependence, 249
Indium antimonide, 244, 254
  as detector, 86
Indium arsenide, 235, 244, 254
Indium phosphide, 241, 248
Induced emission, 102, 105, 108, 189
  coefficient, 7, 8
  rate equation for, 103
  transition rate, 186
  see also Emission

Infrared spectrum, 90
Interferometer, cavity, 23, 29
  modulator, 77
  Twyman-Green, 77
Inversion, density, 139
  four-level, 30
  initial, 142
  ratio, 135, 141, 188, 189, 197, 205, 212, 213, 221, 222
    behavior with time, 190
    final value, 199
    initial, 146, 195, 199, 216
    rate equation, 188, 198, 210, 212
    rate of change, 187
    relative, 141
    threshold value, 198, 219
    see also Population inversion, ratio
  three-level, 30
  threshold, 27, 31, 203
  total, 31
Inverted electron population, 100, 108
Inverted population, 50, 127
  density, 109, 113
  during spiking, 114
  maximum, 110
Ions, supplementary, 15

KDP (potassium dihydrogen phosphate), 64
Kerr cell, for Q-switching, 178, 182
  liquid, 69
Kerr effect, 57, 58, 68, 69
  modulator, 68
KTN (potassium tantalum niobate), 70

Laser, configuration, 16
  emission wavelengths, semiconductors, 241
  linewidth, 104
  materials, 8
  oscillator, 45, 98, 105, 132, 169
  output port, 39
  resonator, 118
  schematic structure, 12
Laser action, 9, 11, 14, 17, 21, 24, 27, 28, 32, 104, 106, 107, 153, 185, 186
  buildup, 27
  in gallium arsenide, 253
  in semiconductor diode, 225, 227, 233, 234, 241
  spiking, 108
Laser amplifier, arrangements, 45

Laser amplifier, system, 46
  see also Amplifier
Laser cavity, 105, 117, 194
  see also Cavity
Lead selenide, 224
Lead sulfide detector, 86
Lead telluride, 242
Lifetime, of electron, 6
  of excited state, 105
  of photon in cavity, 101
    see also Ringing time, of cavity
  for spontaneous radiation, 8
Light wave, coherent, 2
Local oscillator, for photomixing, 93, 95
Lorentzian line, 102
  linewidth of, 103, 106
  shape, 192
  shaped pulse, amplifier solution, 154
Loss rate, coefficient, 192, 194
  factor, 194, 217, 221
    incidental, 193
    internal, 220
Lummer-Gehreke, interferometer, 181
  plate, 181

Manganese ions, 14
Material, *n*-type, 228
  p-type, 228
Mirrors, diffraction losses at, 120
  on ends of cavity, 39
  on ends of rod, 46
  high reflectivity, 79
  oscillator output, 99
  partially transparent, 98
  piezoelectrically driven, 77
  reflectivity of, in oscillator, 99, 100
  selectively reflecting, 77
  transmitting, 49
  vibrating, 57
Modes, allowed in laser, 117
  definition, 118
  diffraction losses, 121, 122
  field distribution, 123
  of laser cavity, 106
  in microwave cavities, 118
  number, 119
  number in cavity, 106
  oscillation, 125
  pattern, 120
  selector, 125
  separation between, 119

Modes, spacing, 125
  TEM, 123
  volume, 121, 123
Modulating frequency, 64
Modulation, cell, FTIR, 82
  transmission of, 81
  depth of, 64, 71
  of free carrier absorption, 74
  by optical absorption, 74
  phase, 65
  by variable absorption, 57
  by variable reactance, 57
Modulator, absorption, 72
  Debye-Sears, 57
  diffraction grating, 76
  driving power, 72
  electroacoustical, 57
  electro-optical, 57, 59, 61, 69, 70
  equivalent circuit of, 71
  impedance, 71
  mechanical, 57
  optical, 57, 63
  retardation type, 59
  schematic representation, 65
  transverse mode, 65
  traveling wave, 67

Nicol prism, 53
Nitrobenzene, 69
Noise, 160
  at amplifier input, 128
  equation, 164
  equivalent temperature, 161
  internal, in detectors, 90
  in laser amplifier, 161
  from spontaneous emission, 8
  thermal, at amplifier input, 161
    source, 161
Noise factor, 160, 165, 167
  definition, 160
  expression, 165
  for laser amplifier, 165, 167
Noise figure, definition, 161, 166
  of laser amplifier, 161
  for optically pumped laser, 166
Noise power, 161
  available, 161
  from spontaneous emission, 163
  thermal, 163
  from thermal sources, 162
Normal modes, 121

Optical, coupler, FTIR, 77
  coupling, 17
  feedback, 98
  isolator, 45, 49, 52
  modulator, FTIR, 77
  pumping, 5, 9
  resonator, 117
    regeneration of, 115
Optical absorption coefficient, 74
  characteristic wavelength, 74
Optical cavity, 98, 101, 170, 177, 204
  loss factor, 162
  Q, 77
Oscillation, threshold of, 99, 105
Oscillator, electronic, 2
  harmonic, 2
  loaded, 99
  optical, 98
  resonance, 118
  threshold, 104
Oscillator-amplifier, isolation section, 56
  system, 46
Output noise, 161

Period, pulse repetition, 114
  spiking pulse, 113
Phase angle, of successive reflections, 130
Phase of electric field, 1, 2, 3, 5
Phase retardation, 59, 62
  of polarized waves, 68, 69
Phase shift, in electro-optical crystal, 60
  of polarized components, 60
Photoconductivity, 86
Photoconductor response, 86
Photodiode detector, 87
Photoemissive, current in traveling-wave
    phototube, 94
  surface, 84
Photomixing optical system, 93
Photomultipliers, 84
Photon, beam intensity, definition, 141
  density per atom, definition, 135
  generation, rate of, 133
  lifetime in laser cavity, 198, 201
  relative density, definition, 136
Phototubes, 169, 171
  traveling wave, 94
Pill package, 227
p-i-n junction diode, 87
Planck's radiation law, 163

p-n junction, 225, 229
  for absorption modulator, 74
  band structure, 231
  depletion layer, 75
  detector, 89
  properties of, 227
  saturation current of, 229
Pockels cell, 72
  for Q-switching, 178
Pockels effect, modulator, 57, 58, 63, 64,
    68
Polarization, rotation of, 51
Population inversion, 9, 46, 104, 105, 109,
    110, 113, 127, 132, 163, 164, 165,
    167, 171, 172
  dependence on pump energy, 172
  in p-n junction, 235
  ratio, 135, 136, 203
    definition, 134, 135
  steady-state, 110
Power gain, for Lorentzian pulse, 157
  versus amplifier length, 146, 150
  versus input photon intensity, 146, 150
Prism, Glan-Thompson, 50
  polarizing, with amplifier, 49
Porro, 179, 184
  spinning, 196
Probability of emission, 102
Pulse, of photons, square-topped, 142,
    146
Pulsed oscillation, 105
Pulse reflection mode, 115, 117
  first, 116
  second, 116
Pulse shape, 136
  for exponential output loss factor, 222
Pulse shaping, 219
Pulse sharpening, 127, 144
Pulse spiking, 105
  oscillations, 111
Pulse transmission mode, 116, 117
Pump, band, 9, 12
  level, 20
  rate, 22
  reflectors, 40
Pumping, 5
  action, 9, 17
  coefficient, 172
  equivalent rate for four-level system, 37

Pumping, of injection lasers, 253
  by electron beam, 254

Q, definition of, 120
  of laser cavity, 117
Q-modulation, 184
Q-pulse, 183
Q-spoiling, 171, 177, 184
  of ruby, 170
Q-switch, 82
  action, 189
  pulse, 152
Q-switched mode of operation, 177
Q-switches, electro-optical, 178
  mechanical, 178
  photochemical, 178
  thin film, 178, 185
Q-switching, 115, 177, 178, 183, 188, 195,
  207
Quality factor, 177
  definition of, 101
  of electro-optical modulator, 71
  of resonant optical cavity, 100, 107
  of resonator, 120, 125
Quantum efficiency of photodetector, 84
Quarter-wave plate, 63

Radiation, black-body, 2, 7
Rate equation, 20, 136, 188, 191, 197,
  216
  for inverted population, 105
  for photon density, 103, 106, 189, 198,
  212, 219
Recombination radiation in p-n junction,
  227, 236
Reflecting mirrors, on amplifier, 49
Reflection, total internal, 68, 180
Reflectivity, of end mirrors, 194
  FTIR dependence on air gap spacing, 80,
  81
  FTIR dependence on polarization, 80, 81
  switching interval, 182
Reflector, cylindrical, 40
  elliptical, 41
  end of laser diode, 225
  selective, 53, 56
  side, 40
  spinning, 180, 181, 216
  surrounding flash lamps, 40
Refractive index, 58, 60, 68
  see also Index of refraction

Regeneration reflections, 169
Relaxation, from pump band, 172
  rate, 13
    for four-level system, 36
    from lower laser level, 28
  time, 23, 30
    due to output power, 31
    total of optical cavity, 31
Resonant cavity, optical, 17
Resonator, confocal, 123
Retardation, between polarized waves, 61
  modulator, 77
Ringing time, of cavity, 101, 104, 106, 107,
  114
  of optical cavity, 198, 204
Rotating mirror, 215
Ruby, 9, 108, 134, 151, 152, 153, 169,
  194
  in ellipsoidal cavity, 45
  laser, 47, 184, 208
    configuration, 17
    oscillator, 47
  R-lines, 12
  radiation, FTIR transmission, 79, 80
  spectrum, 14
  spiking pulses in, 115
  system, 153, 157
  two-level approximation, 35

Saturable dye, 178, 183
Secondary electrons, 85
Semiconductor laser materials, 243
Silicon as absorption modulator, 74
Solid state devices, detectors, 89
Spacing, of FTIR elements, 79
Spiking, frequency, 112
  period, 114
  pulses, 108, 109, 110, 113
    decay constant, 112, 114
Spontaneous, decay rate, 186
  emission, 105, 161, 178, 188, 193, 212,
  218, 248
    coefficient, 6, 8
    lifetime, 104, 163
    losses for two-level approximation, 33
    noise power, 164
    rate, 132, 193
  lifetime, 12
  linewidth, 238
  radiation trigger for oscillator, 99
  recombination, 236

Spontaneous, relaxation time, 22
Square pulse, 142, 143, 147
Square-topped pulse, 219, 222
  input, 148
State, discrete energy, 5
Stimulated emission, 22, 109, 127, 132,
    133, 162, 177, 207, 212
  coefficient, 6, 23, 24, 234
  in *p-n* junction, 231, 233, 236, 241
  probability rate, 192, 198
Strip transmission line, 67
Structure, three-level, 8
Superheterodyne detection, mixing of
    light beams, 90
  with traveling-wave phototube, 95
Switching speed, of rotating prism, 180
Switching time of *Q*-switch, 178, 180
Synchronized flash lamps, 46

TEM, mode, 123
  wave, 67
Temperature, definition of equivalent
    atomic, 162
  dependence of modes on, 248
  effective, 162
  negative, 163
Three-level, diagram, 12
  laser, 9, 20, 24, 26, 30, 33, 104
  model, 132
  system, 13, 27, 29
Threshold, 14, 172, 219
  current, 236, 247, 251
    affected by magnetic field, 242, 245
    density, variation with temperature, 241

Threshold, current, diode, 227, 235, 236,
    237, 239, 241
  laser, 43, 99, 104, 183, 197
  for laser action, 15
  relationship, 104
Transition, laser, 12
Transmission, atmospheric bands, 90
  of FTIR gap, 79
  versus voltage for electro-optical system,
    63
Transport equation, for photons, 132, 135
Two-level, equations, 35
  pumping rate, 33
  system, 102, 105
Two-level approximations, 34, 37
  to four-level system, 35, 36
  to three-level model, 34, 132, 185

Ultrasonic waves, 76

Variable FTIR cell, piezoelectrically driven,
    82
Variable FTIR coupler, 81
Velocity synchronization, in modulator, 67
Verdet constant, 52
Voltage, modulator driving, 72

Wavelength, affected by magnetic field, 242
  of emission, temperature dependence, 248

YAG (Yttrium-aluminum-garnet), 8, 15

Zinc sulfide, 68